AMERICA'S
CHANGING
ENVIRONMENT

THE DAEDALUS LIBRARY

Published by Houghton Mifflin Company and
The American Academy of Arts and Sciences

A New Europe?, edited by Stephen R. Graubard
The Professions in America, edited by Kenneth S. Lynn
The Woman in America, edited by Robert Jay Lifton
Science and Culture, edited by Gerald Holton
Utopias and Utopian Thought, edited by Frank E. Manuel
The Contemporary University: U.S.A., edited by Robert S.
Morison
The Negro American, edited by Talcott Parsons and Kenneth B.
Clark
Creativity and Learning, edited by Jerome Kagan
Fiction in Several Languages, edited by Henri Peyre
Conditions of World Order, edited by Stanley Hoffmann
Toward the Year 2000: Work in Progress, edited by Daniel Bell
Religion in America, edited by William G. McLoughlin and
Robert N. Bellah
Color and Race, edited by John Hope Franklin
Students in Revolt, edited by Seymour Martin Lipset and
Philip G. Altbach
America's Changing Environment, edited by Roger Revelle and
Hans H. Landsberg

AMERICA'S CHANGING ENVIRONMENT

EDITED BY ROGER REVELLE
AND HANS H. LANDSBERG

With illustrations

HOUGHTON MIFFLIN COMPANY   BOSTON   1970

Library of Congress
Catalog Card Number: 69-15028

The Introduction by Roger Revelle and Hans H. Landsberg,
"The Several Contexts of Water" by Joseph L. Fisher, "New
Towns?" by Frederick Gutheim, "Crisis Mentality and the
Deteriorating Environment" by Ann Louise Strong, and "Landscape
and Aesthetic Quality" by R. Burton Litton, Jr., are
published here for the first time. The other essays in the
book appeared originally, some of them in slightly different
form, in the Fall 1967 issue of *Daedalus*, the Journal of the American
Academy of Arts and Sciences.

Printed in the United States of America

ACKNOWLEDGMENTS

THE IDEA for this book and the previous *Dædalus* study originated with Jerome Wiesner and Carl Kaysen, arising from their experience as members of President Kennedy's administration. Upon their return from Washington, they felt that a certain kind of planning effort is rarely undertaken by the federal government; the task force reports that frequently emerge from Washington are too short-range in their ambitions and too dominated by a concern with calling for programs that are modest and, hence, politically inoffensive.

In the summer of 1966, a group of some twenty people met for a week in Woods Hole to discuss the issues here raised. Thanks are due to Chester Brown, John Buckley, John C. Calhoun, Jr., Howard Eckles, Dean F. Frasche, Roy W. Hann, Jr., Walter Hibbard, Ian McHarg, Dan Ogden, Roland Renne, Ann Satterthwaite, Paul B. Sears, Andrew Scheffey, Charles Schweighauser, Robert L. Teeters, Philip Thompson, Eugene W. Weber, and Adele Wilson. They contributed many ideas which helped to sharpen and focus the issues discussed herein.

CONTENTS

ix ROGER REVELLE AND HANS H. LANDSBERG
Introduction

I. *Ecology as an Ethical Science*

3 F. FRASER DARLING
A Wider Environment of Ecology and Conservation

20 S. DILLON RIPLEY AND HELMUT K. BUECHNER
Ecosystem Science as a Point of Synthesis

II. *Water, Air, and Land*

31 JOSEPH L. FISHER
The Several Contexts of Water

39 AZRIEL TELLER
Air-Pollution Abatement:
    Economic Rationality and Reality

56 DAVID ALLEE
American Agriculture—
    Its Resource Issues for the Coming Years

67 HAROLD GILLIAM
The Fallacy of Single-Purpose Planning

83 ANN LOUISE STRONG
Crisis Mentality and the Deteriorating Environment

91 R. BURTON LITTON, JR.
Landscape and Aesthetic Quality

III. *Economics and Politics*

107 HANS H. LANDSBERG
The U.S. Resource Outlook: Quantity and Quality

131 NATHANIEL WOLLMAN
The New Economics of Resources

147 AARON WILDAVSKY
Aesthetic Power or the Triumph of
the Sensitive Minority Over the Vulgar Mass:
A Political Analysis of the New Economics

161 JOHN V. KRUTILLA
Some Environmental Effects of Economic Development

174 ROBERT W. PATTERSON
The Art of the Impossible

IV. *The Humane City*

191 FREDERICK GUTHEIM
New Towns?

219 ATHELSTAN SPILHAUS
The Experimental City

V. *Playgrounds for People*

235 ALEXIS PAPAGEORGIOU
Architectural Schemata for
Outdoor Recreation Areas of Tomorrow

253 ROGER REVELLE
Outdoor Recreation in a Hyper-Productive Society

VI. *The Roles of Education*

275 GEORGE J. MASLACH
The Reorganization of Educational Resources

285 ROBERT S. MORISON
Education for Environmental Concerns

299 Notes on Contributors

303 Index

ROGER REVELLE AND HANS H. LANDSBERG

Introduction

> When Daniel Boone goes by, at night,
> The phantom deer arise
> And all lost, wild America
> Is burning in their eyes.
> *Stephen Vincent Benét*

RELENTLESS TRANSFORMATION of the natural world was a central theme for eighteenth-century Americans. Forests should be cleared, rivers harnessed, the Indians scattered, earth put under the plow. The land must be changed, not cherished. Benjamin Franklin thought the population of the Colonies was doubling every twenty years and would grow to a hundred million people. To him this increase meant that a nation of farmers would spread across the continent, displacing the savages, conquering the wilderness, and building a new kind of civilization. Daniel Boone, wandering "through the wilderness of America in quest of Kentucke," was happiest in the wild forests. But he believed he was "an instrument ordained to settle the wilderness," even though he himself had a tendency to move on when too many settlers' wagons came over the horizon.

Malthus' dark forebodings that the resources of the earth were limited, and that, because of this limitation, there must be a positive check on human numbers, did not enter into American thinking for another century, when Schurz, Powell, and Pinchot began the conservation movement, and tried to estimate realistically the natural resources available for the nation's growth. To both Boone and Franklin, the land was endless, its riches inexhaustible and ripe for the taking. They had no doubt it was the duty of white Anglo-Saxon Americans to increase and multiply so that they might take dominion over the continent.

Our dominion has been a harsh one for our fellow creatures. While our own numbers have risen from less than four million in 1790 to more than two hundred million today, many other species have been extinguished or drastically reduced. John Krutilla has called the roll of destruction: The wood bison and woodland caribou are gone; American elk and gray wolves roam no more through the eastern forests, nor do the giant herds of bison graze on the prairies; Guadalupe petrels, masked bobwhites, heath hens, passenger pigeons, and sand-shoal ducks have all followed the great auks to extinction. Swallow-tail kites, whooping cranes, prairie chickens, California condors, even our national symbols, the bald eagles, are struggling to survive, as are moose and red wolves, lynx, bobcats, cougars, and more than a hundred other species. Overgrazing has transformed some western ranges into deserts, and overcutting has changed forested hills to wastelands. Gullied slopes and naked ridges are the remainders of abandoned farms in Appalachia. Mining and smelting have left behind choked streams, blighted vegetation, and defaced landscapes. In Hawaii, the vulnerable native species of the lowlands are gone, replaced by crops, foreign weeds, and animals introduced from the mainland.

A sad and cautionary tale, but perhaps an inevitable part of a unique event in history—the creation, within a scant three hundred years by a nation of egalitarian Puritans, of a continent-spanning, world-bestriding colossus of a country.

The New Problem of Environmental Quality

As our technology has advanced, our ability to reuse materials and to substitute abundant materials for scarce ones has grown. We have learned how to mine ores that were once thought too lean, to draw upon the rest of the world for some of our needs, and to add altogether new items to our bag of materials. Though concern for natural resources still ran high in the years immediately following World War II, the scarcities forecast by Pinchot and his men have not appeared, nor are they likely to. In our lifetimes and those of our children, the availability of energy and raw materials will not put any serious limits on our prosperity.

But we have learned during the last few decades that we must think not only about natural resources as material utilities, but also about the whole environment as a resource that can be depleted or worsened by misuse. Our happiness and our health are jeopardized, and our fulfillment as human beings limited, by destructive changes in our environment. Unless we can find remedies, the quality of life for our own and future generations will be dulled and diminished.

Pollution and environmental deterioration certainly existed before World War II, but their greater, more pervasive prevalence today may indicate that a quantum jump has occurred. The capacity of air, water, and land to absorb abuse without much visible change is very large, yet if enough pressure is exerted, the system may break down. Accelerating, ever more obvious change may then spread rapidly through the environment. An alternative explanation is that our destructive capacities have grown exponentially to a level where they are now on the same scale as many natural processes in the environment. We do not have enough evidence to decide which of these explanations is correct, or whether both are true.

What are the causes of the degradation of our surroundings that has become so evident during the past twenty-five years? One is undoubtedly rapid population growth, but a good case can be made that two other important villains are the increase in Gross National Product and the changing patterns of our lives. Our growing affluence has had several effects: Each of us uses a larger quantity of materials, and thus there is more to throw away. We can afford to discard many objects we once saved and reused. Our habits of consumption have changed toward using materials and doing things which are especially destructive to our environment. As the primary wants of the great majority have become satiated, we have become more concerned with the quality of life and the effects of our own actions in demeaning it. (Like beauty, the degradation of the environment lies in the eye of the beholder; we now see ugliness and destruction where formerly we saw progress through increasing production.) By clumping ourselves together in cities we have become more effective at fouling our living space. We must now dispose of more and more trash in the air, the waters, and the soil of a relatively small area, less than 2 percent of the land of the United States.

During the twenty-five years from 1940 to 1965 the population of the United States increased by 47 percent, but the Gross National Product almost tripled. The number of passenger automobiles and the amount of gasoline burned in their engines kept pace with prosperity. There was one private automobile in use for about five Americans in 1940. By 1965 there were almost two automobiles for every five people. Each automobile burned a little more gasoline with the passage of time—590 gallons per year in 1940 and 650 gallons in 1965. By the same token it contributed more to air pollution. The average man, woman, or child in the United States accounted for 750 pounds of gasoline in 1940 and over 1500 pounds or more than ten times his own weight in 1965. About half of this gasoline ended up in the atmosphere as carbon monoxide and unburned hydrocarbons, and the heat of its burning resulted in the injection of two ounces of nitrogen oxides into the air for every gallon of gasoline consumed (see Tables 1–4).

As our affluence grew, our use of polluting materials grew even faster. The average American used about 250 pounds of paper in 1940. By 1965 his paper consumption had more than doubled, rising to 510 pounds a year.

Electric utilities consumed 54 million tons of coal and fuel oil, containing more than a million tons of sulphur in 1940. By 1965, this industry was using 263 million tons of coal and oil, and releasing over 10 million tons of sulphur oxides into the air. It took almost twice as much fuel—not counting natural gas—to make our electricity as to drive our automobiles. From four tenths of a ton per person in 1940, consumption of coal and oil to produce electricity jumped to one-and-a-third tons per person in 1965. If the sulphur oxides injected into the air had been spread evenly across the country, they would hardly have been noticed, but the electric power companies, by concentrating their plants in cities, managed to produce about 500 pounds per acre of sulphur oxides over densely populated areas in 1965.

The amount of nitrogen used in chemical fertilizers increased even more rapidly than the sulphur oxides from electric power generators, though the total quantity was less. In 1940, American farmers used 420 thousand tons of nitrogen. In 1965, they used thirteen times as much, 5.3 million tons. A good deal of this washed off the fields and polluted ground waters, lakes, and rivers.

Production of plastics nearly doubled between 1960 and 1965, from 34 pounds to 60 pounds per person, while the population was growing by 8 percent. Plastic materials were used increasingly as containers which, like our enormous production of paper, quickly became waste products. Unlike paper, large numbers were virtually indestructible and simply accumulated in our surroundings.

Longer vacations, rising incomes, and shorter travel times were clearly the major causes of the slumlike crowding of our national parks. Between 1940 and 1965, the number of visitor days in the national park system went from 19 million to 121 million, an increase of 550 percent, and the per-capita visits rose by nearly 350 percent.

The lack of utility of any simple correlation between environmental deterioration and population growth can be demonstrated by calculating the size of population in the United States which,

TABLE 1. Increase of Population and Gross National Product
in the United States, 1940-1965

Year	Population		Gross National Product		Gross National Product Per Capita	
	Millions of People	% Increase Over 1940	Billions of 1958 Dollars	% Increase Over 1940	1958 Dollars	% Increase Over 1940
1940	133		227		1,720	
1945	140	5	355	56	2,540	48
1950	152	14	355	56	2,340	36
1955	166	25	438	93	2,650	54
1960	181	36	488	115	2,700	57
1965	195	47	614	170	3,160	84

Source: Long Term Economic Growth 1860-1965,
U.S. Department of Commerce, Bureau of the Census, October 1966.

TABLE 2. Use of Some Commodities and Services in the United States, 1940-1965

Year	Registered Automobiles	Gasoline Consumption	Paper Consumption	Coal and Oil Used by Utilities in Generating Electricity	Production of Plastics and Resin Materials	Nitrogen in Chemical Fertilizer Consumption	Visits in National Park System
	Millions	*Gallons per Automobile*	*Millions of Short Tons*	*Millions of Short Tons of Coal Equivalents*	*Millions of Short Tons*	*Millions of Short Tons*	*Millions*
1940	27.5	594	16.8	54.1	N. A.²	.42	18.7¹
1945	25.8	517	19.7	77.9	N. A.	N. A.	13.1¹
1950	40.3	603	29.0	103.7	N. A.	1.24	37.2
1955	52.1	644	34.8	155.5	N. A.	1.92	56.6
1960	61.7	661	39.2	189.9	3.07	3.02	79.2
1965	75.3	649	49.7	262.8	5.85	5.32	121.3

Sources: 1. Statistical Abstract of the United States, 1967.
2. Historical Statistics of the United States, Colonial Times to 1957,
U.S. Department of Commerce, Bureau of the Census.

Note: ¹ Estimated. ² N. A. = data not available.

TABLE 3. Per Capita Use of Some Commodities and Services in the United States, 1940-1965

(Pounds per year per capita)

Year	Automobiles (No. per capita)	Gasoline for Automobiles	Paper	Coal & Oil for Utility Electricity	Plastics	Nitrogen in Chemical Fertilizers	National Park System (Visits per capita)
1940	.21	750	250	810	N. A.	7	.14
1945	.18	580	280	1110	N. A.	N. A.	.09
1950	.27	980	380	1360	N. A.	16	.24
1955	.31	1230	420	1880	N. A.	23	.34
1960	.34	1380	430	2100	34	33	.44
1965	.39	1530	510	2690	60	55	.62

Source: Computed from Tables 1 and 2.

TABLE 4. Percentage Increase in Per Capita Use of Commodities in the United States, Compared with the Percentage Change in Per Capita Gross National Products, 1940-1965

Percent Increase Over 1940, Per Capita

Year	Automobiles	Gasoline for Automobiles	Paper	Coal and Oil for Utility Electricity	Plastics	Nitrogen in Chemical Fertilizers	Visits in National Park System	Gross National Product
1945	−14	−22	12	36			−36	48
1950	29	31	51	67		30	71	36
1955	48	64	67	130		230	143	54
1960	62	85	71	158		370	214	57
1965	86	104	102	230	77[1]	680	340	84

Source: Compiled from Tables 1 and 3.

Note: [1] Percentage increase over 1960.

with the same per-capita income and dirty habits as the average U.S. citizen in 1965, would have produced no more pollution than the country experienced in 1940. Other things being equal, the number of automobiles and the amounts of gasoline and paper consumed would have remained about constant over the quarter century if the population had declined from 133 million to 67 million. To maintain a constant flow of sulphur dioxide into the air from electric power plants, the population should have decreased to 40 million. Presumably the amount of nitrogen fertilizers would not have increased if all but 17 million Americans had reemigrated to the homes of their ancestors. The national parks would have remained as uncrowded in 1965 as they were in 1940 if our population during the interval had gone down to 30 million souls.

The chief merit of these speculations is that they emphasize the uncertainties of the relationship between population, Gross National Product, and the quality of life, of which environmental deterioration is one aspect. Almost surely our national productivity would not have risen, and indeed the country would be in the grip of a horrendous depression, if any such declines in population had occurred. Conversely, it is widely believed, at least by many businessmen, that a growing population is a strong stimulus to economic growth. Indeed, this is a well-known hypothesis in economics, associated especially with the name of Alvin Hansen in the late 1930's. If this belief is correct, then the increase in Gross National Product per person and the accompanying changes in patterns of consumption, which we have indicted as the principal factors in the destruction of environmental values during the past twenty-five years, may reflect the growth of our population over the quarter century, at least to the extent that population growth is a necessary, if not a sufficient, condition for continuing prosperity.

That this proposition is highly doubtful is suggested by a comparison of rates of economic growth and population increase in the developed countries of Europe, North America, Japan, and Australia during the period 1958–1965 (see Table 5). Thirteen countries with an average per-capita annual economic growth rate of 7.2 percent had an average annual increase in population of 0.8 percent. The remaining thirteen countries had average rates of economic growth and population increase of 3.4 percent and 1.1 percent, respectively. Evidently, there was little correlation between economic and population growth in these twenty-six countries. If we omit the Soviet Union and the Eastern European countries, for which the yardstick

TABLE 5.   Economic Growth and Population Increase
in Twenty-six Relatively Developed Countries, 1958-1965

Country	Average Annual Increase in per capita Gross Domestic Product at constant prices *percent*	Average Annual Increase in Population *percent*
Japan[1]	12.95	1.0
Yugoslavia[2]	(9.90)	(1.1)
Rumania[2]	(9.56)	(0.8)
USSR[2]	(8.10)	(1.6)
East Germany[2]	(7.75)	(−0.2)
Greece	6.80	0.6
Hungary[2]	(6.50)	(0.4)
Poland[2]	(6.20)	(1.3)
Portugal	5.65	0.8
Italy	5.35	0.7
Austria	5.30	0.5
West Germany	5.15	1.3
Denmark	4.50	0.8
Mean of above thirteen	7.21	0.82
Mean, omitting Eastern European Countries	6.54	0.81
France	4.45	1.3
Czechoslovakia[2]	(4.40)	(0.7)
Norway	4.33	0.8
Finland	4.24	0.8
Sweden	4.10	0.6
Belgium	3.98	0.6
Netherlands	3.81	1.4
Ireland	3.30	0.1
Switzerland	3.09	1.9
Canada	2.30	2.0
Australia	2.20	2.1

Notes: [1] Per capita Gross National Product at constant market prices.
[2] Per Capita net material product at constant market prices.

United Kingdom	2.22	0.7
U S A	1.94	1.5
Mean of above thirteen	3.41	1.12
Mean, omitting Czechoslovakia	3.33	1.15

Sources: Statistical Abstract of the United States, 1967, Tables 1257 and 1262. Except where noted, per-capita gross domestic product at constant factor costs or constant market prices is given.

of economic growth is not directly comparable with that for the developed capitalist countries, the results are essentially unchanged. Within the United States itself, the periods of most rapid economic increase over the past quarter century were from 1940 to 1945 and from 1960 to 1965. These were the periods of lowest rate of population rise. Of course, the overwhelming fact of 1940–1945 was World War II, which makes any comparison with later periods highly uncertain.

One must not go too far in discounting the effects of population growth. Even conceding the important roles of per-capita economic growth and changes in consumption, it is still clear from the data in Tables 2 and 3 that population changes have also been significant factors in the degradation of our environment. About half the increase in Gross National Product, numbers of automobiles, and gasoline and paper consumption can be accounted for by our increasing numbers.

Changes in population density and distribution have been even more destructive of environmental values. For one who lived in and loved California in the 1920's and 1930's, the fourfold growth of the state's population since 1930 can be thought of only as a disaster. Instead of the brilliantly clear air, vivid blue skies, and sharp-edged mountains of those days, there is now a brownish, opaque, and acrid veil of smog over vast areas. Gently rolling wheat fields and orange groves have been replaced by an endless monotony of tract houses, shopping centers, and "roadside businesses" of such an ugliness that they dull the eyes and cannot be perceived in detail, but only as a blur. Through the wonders of modern earth-moving machinery, the soft brown and green oak-covered hills have been "recontoured" into flat building sites and badlands slopes, and cut and filled for the straight scars of freeways more deeply than one would have believed possible.

Elsewhere in the country, the effects of the great migration to the cities and the coasts have been equally destructive. In the countryside, these effects are revealed by rotting farmhouses, decaying towns, dismal second-growth brush, and untended piles of trash; in the cities, by the boarded-up windows and rat-infested buildings, the dirt and despair, of the ghettos.

Nor can one view with much complacency the future increase in numbers of Americans. We live in a generous land, and by comparison with many European countries it is still a sparsely filled one. Of its nearly 2300 million acres, almost 2000 million are forests, open range, pasturelands, and farmlands. Cities, towns, highways, and airports cover less than 60 million acres. But the semiarid western half of our country has a delicate ecology that is highly vulnerable to the destructive actions of man. Even in the eastern half, the difficulties of maintaining a quiet harmony with the world of nature will increase with increasing numbers of people.

The demonstration that our environmental problems are caused by our behavior as well as by our growing numbers is nevertheless of fundamental importance. It points strongly to the conclusion that preservation of the quality of life requires changes of values and priorities, from private goods and individual consumption, which in the aggregate destroy the environment, to public goods and cooperative action aimed at its preservation and improvement, from short-range concerns for the production of material things to longer-range and broader concerns for the effects of these things on our surroundings and for the health and integrity of our national heritage.

In the past, our growing affluence has led to environmental destruction. In the future, it can give us far greater opportunities, both to perceive and to protect the quality of life and the diversity, beauty, and wonder of our land. As long as we were preoccupied with the struggle for existence, we could give little thought and less energy to cherishing our surroundings. Now the situation has radically changed. For the good of our own bodies and souls we need to assume new responsibilities and take up new causes, both to serve our fellow men and to become faithful stewards of our planet Earth. The question then becomes: What tools do we have at hand to help us achieve our new goals? In the case of the environment they are of five kinds: scientific, economic, political, technical, and educational.

Roles in Environmental Improvement

The scientific task is to measure, understand, and predict environmental changes. In considering air pollution, for example, we need to measure how much carbon dioxide is being added to the air from the burning of coal, oil, and gas, and the proportions being absorbed by the ocean or locked up in dead organic matter. How rapidly is the dust content of the atmosphere increasing, what are the sizes and shapes of the particles, and how do they act as nuclei for ice crystals or water droplets and as reflectors of sunlight? What is the sequence of chemical reactions, under the action of sunlight, between atmospheric oxygen and the unburned gasoline and nitrogen oxides emitted in automobile exhausts? What are the long-term effects of different air pollutants on healthy human beings and on asthmatics or sufferers from emphysema? What do the levels of carbon monoxide on a crowded freeway do to the sensory acuity and response times of automobile drivers? The list of needed measurements is long, and the difficulties of making them are great. For many measurements ingenious new instruments must be developed, and for others meaningful experiments must be devised.

But measurement is not enough; we also need to understand environmental processes, and this requires sophisticated analysis. Flood control dams have been built across many rivers in Southern California, and the river channels have been lined with concrete. As a result, the larger streams have almost ceased to carry coarse sediment to the sea. How will this affect California beaches from which sand appears to be intermittently sluiced away down the steep submarine canyons that have their heads just beyond the breaker zone? The answer depends on understanding the sources and movement of sand on the beaches, and on interpreting measurements of changing depths in the canyon heads.

Farther offshore, the harvest of California sardines declined from 800,000 tons in the late 1930's to a few thousand tons during the last several years. Over this thirty-year period, the population of anchovies off California increased perhaps threefold. Did this shift in population result from heavy fishing pressure on the sardines while the anchovies were hardly fished at all, or were there changes in ocean currents, temperatures, or fish food supplies that favored the anchovies at the expense of the sardines? To answer convincingly, we need to understand not only the behavior and environmental tolerance of the two species, but also the ways in which they compete with each other.

If our purpose is to act to preserve or improve the environment, one objective of measurement and understanding must be prediction. Would the chemical reactions between atmospheric oxygen and unburned hydrocarbons be more or less obnoxious if a new kind of automobile engine that did not produce nitrogen oxides came into widespread use? What will happen to California beaches if we build undersea barriers at the submarine canyon heads? Will the sardines come back if we start heavily fishing the anchovies? And how many anchovies can be caught without seriously depleting their population?

Prediction is the most difficult of the scientist's tasks in helping to solve practical environmental problems. The economist or the politician wants to know not only what he predicts, but also how sure he is that his prediction will come true, and this is a traumatic question.

Science has another, deeper significance for our environmental concerns than serving as a basis for predicting the consequences of environmental actions. This is the building of the structure of concepts and natural laws that will enable man to understand his place in nature. Such understanding must be one basis of the moral values that should guide each human generation in exercising its stewardship over the earth. For this purpose, ecology—the science of interactions among living things and their environment—is central. Fraser Darling and Dillon Ripley and Helmut Buechner discuss the character and promise of ecology in two of the chapters of this book. They point out that it is an integrative and synthesizing science, both in dealing with different levels of biological organization, where the whole is greater than the sum of its parts, and in point of view. Human societies and their total environment form the highest and most complex level of biological integration. Advances in the still rudimentary science of human ecology depend in part on mutual understanding and cooperation among social and natural scientists and humanists, and in part on the development of new methods for studying interacting processes in complex systems—systems which are in fact so complex that they cannot be thought through in the unaided brain. The development of large, high-speed computers may have come just in time to extend our intellectual capacities so that these systems can be at least partially understood.

Economic Analysis and Political Action. Environmental problems usually involve conflicts of interest among different individuals or groups. For example, a paper manufacturer can lower his costs of production by using a river as a costless sewer to dispose of sulfite liquors and waste lignins. His customers benefit by being able to buy paper at a lower price, and the whole society gains something because the increased productivity of the paper industry releases resources to be used elsewhere and contributes to the growth of the Gross National Product. But people who live near the river are offended by its stench, and others who would like to fish or swim in it cannot do so because it is polluted. The whole society loses something because the sum total of non-material satisfactions of its members is lessened. One role of the economist is to introduce as much rationality as possible into striking a balance between these gains and losses.

In principle, if the economist knows the preferences and tastes of different groups within society, he can order and balance these in a reasonable scheme for making decisions. His difficulty in dealing with environmental problems is that his most effective means for discovering preferences and tastes, and the intensity with which they are held by different groups, have been the signals exchanged in the "market"—that is, the sum of money transactions entered into between buyers and sellers.

As a result, the economist's preferred device for measuring social values has been to quantify benefits and costs in terms of dollars and cents. As Nathaniel Wollman points out, quoting some of his colleagues, economists like to think about money because this neutral substance helps them achieve "exactness, precision, and rational calculations . . . a matter-of-fact attitude in dealing with men and with things." In consequence, the economist's ability to measure social utility is most highly developed in one dimension—the production and productivity of goods and services. The invention of tools for economic measurement of human sensory or emotional delight and deprivation is at an early stage.

Whenever he is able to cast the losses from environmental deterioration in dollars and cents or, what is almost as satisfactory, to estimate the monetary prices of other things people want but are willing to forgo in order to maintain or improve environmental quality, the economist can provide essential information for decisions about environmental actions. In particular he may be able to analyze the relationship between different levels of costs and degrees of benefit.

Azriel Teller gives an illustration in his discussion of air-pollution abatement. The benefits from additional abatement diminish as the degree of abatement increases, while the costs of control rise steeply as higher and higher levels of purity are sought. The maximum economic gains to society from expenditures on pollution control will be reached at that level where the difference between the benefits from abatement and the costs of control is greatest; in other words, when the sum of the losses from pollution damage and the costs of pollution control is least. Of course, even greater benefits may be obtained from an expenditure of the same funds on some other social problem, and this consideration should also enter the economist's calculus.

It is relatively easy for the economist to deal with half the problem; for example, the economic benefits of pollution to the polluter and his customers and the economic costs of pollution control to these parties or to the general public through government. The other half—the costs of pollution and the benefits of pollution control—is hard to state in ordinary economic terms because these quantities can be dealt with only partially or not at all in the marketplace.

Clearly, some pollution effects can be priced: for example the costs of soot removal and sand blasting of Paris buildings, extra laundry and dry cleaning bills in a smoky city, or the accelerated deterioration of rubber tires and nylon stockings caused by sulphur oxides where high-sulphur coal is the principal fuel. But how much is it worth to have a beautiful view of the city from a high building? If we attempt to gauge this by counting the number and price of tickets sold for admission to the Eiffel Tower, we learn only what people are willing to pay when they take it for granted that the view exists and may be seen at almost any time. We do not learn how much more they would pay to restore the view if it were obscured by smog, or to prevent its destruction. The problem is logically similar to that of the price of bread. When bread is plentiful, people may be willing to pay twenty-five cents a pound loaf for a certain number of loaves a week. But presumably they would be willing to pay a good deal more than twenty-five cents to avoid getting along without any bread at all.

The value of the improvements in health and physical well-being that would result from abatement of air pollution is hard to put in dollars, first, because the health effects for the average person are small and uncertain, though they may be severe for some people, and, second, because the value to the individual of improved respiratory comfort and less eye irritation is much greater than simply a reduction of days lost from work or an increase of productivity on the job. Health values, like survival itself, tend to be both absolute and incommensurable. People will pay whatever they can for some kinds of improvement in health, just as they will pay to stay alive, and different kinds of improvement are not usually weighed against one another or against other goods in terms of relative costs and benefits.

Other difficulties with attempts to solve environmental problems in a conventional economic framework arise:

The costs of environmental deterioration and the benefits of environmental improvement are widely dispersed—relatively small for any individual, but large in the aggregate.

The environment has different uses for different people, and political conflicts between these users frequently arise which economic rationalism can at best clarify but not solve.

An environmental change often has effects at a distance from the location where the change is made. Excess chemical fertilizers washed off farms may result in eutrophication of a downstream lake a hundred miles away.

Some parts of the environment are unique and nonreproducible; they cannot be substituted for by something else, hence their value cannot be stated in terms of price. They are literally "priceless."

Other parts of the environment are common property resources and hence cannot be bought or sold by individuals. The intrinsic worth of clean outside air to society is obvious. But no one can buy or sell an exclusionary stake in any part of it, and hence no market can emerge and no values, in the economic sense, can be established.

As Joseph Fisher shows, an environmental change—for example, the building of a dam—must be considered in several incommensurable contexts, including engineering efficiency, economic development, ecological disturbances, and aesthetic satisfaction.

Maintenance and improvement of environmental quality generally have a long time horizon, hence at normal interest rates the calculated "present value" will be small. Only the use of a very low discount rate will raise the present value. Yet if actions are not taken today, it may be impossible to make improvements in the future, no matter how large the future expenditure. This is one reason why the cost of environmental improvements must usually be paid in the public sector.

One may conclude from the above considerations that environmental problems should be handled politically rather than by the usual economic mechanisms, but there are also several difficulties with political actions and procedures, at least of the kind we are used to:

Pollution ignores political boundaries. One must think of airsheds and watersheds instead of the areas of cities, counties, or even nations.

Political action must be carried out over a large area, otherwise polluting industries will simply move to a location where regulations are lax. But balances and choices for action depend on regional environmental conditions. For example, the choice between burning solid wastes and dumping them in a sanitary fill may depend on the frequency and extent of atmospheric inversions.

Questions of environmental quality are broadly pervasive, entering into many areas of public action, including highway and airport locations; regulation of electric power generation; testing of military weapons; water resource development and flood control; use of public lands, forests, and recreational areas; land-use planning and control of privately held lands; urban redevelopment; governmental subsidies for new technological development, such as supersonic aircraft; agricultural policies; fisheries management; public health activities; and regulation of foods, drugs, and new chemicals. Each of these activities has its own pressures and pressure groups.

Any political solution should involve definition of goals and balancing alternative uses of resources. How clean should a stream be, at what cost, for what purpose, at what future time? What proportion of public resources should be spent on environmental maintenance or improvement in competition with the demands of other long-term payoff activities such as education, welfare, housing, or mental health, let alone national security and economic well-being, which, being short-term, usually take overriding priority?

At least in the United States, most of the easily used political tools for environmental control are firmly attached to the lowest levels of government because they involve the ownership and use of land. These tools include zoning and restrictions on use. Yet only the highest government levels can do the necessary broad planning. The tools available to the national government for implementation of plans are subsidies, tax incentives, condemnation, and publicity, all expensive or difficult to use effectively.

A political solution should depend on finding out what people really want, rather than assuming what they ought to want. But as several authors in this volume emphasize, most people do not know what they would want if they had enough experience of several possibilities. In outdoor recreation, for example, most people are incapable of inventing uses for their own leisure. Moreover, because political questions involve traditions, habits, emotions, unspoken desires, and conscious or unconscious remembrance of things past, the political reactions of people are often irrational and unpredictable. "Passions spin the plot."

A related difficulty is that many people have little or no ability to perceive their environment, and hence are indifferent to the political problems of environmental maintenance or improvement.

Simply counting heads is not enough. One must also consider the intensity of desires and feelings of the individuals on each side of an issue, and the apathy, indifference, or uncertainty of those in the middle. Furthermore, most environmental questions are highly complicated, involving numerous interactions and requiring expert knowledge for a satisfactory solution. It is often impossible to formulate the issues in such a way that they can be resolved by a yes or no vote.

Political problems are usually conflict problems. A *decision* may be reached by a majority vote, but this seldom represents a *solution*. The minority remains dissatisfied, and often lies in wait until it can become the majority and reverse the decision.

To overcome these difficulties of political action, it may be necessary to invent new political institutions and modify old ones and to devise new procedures. Robert Patterson, Harold Gilliam, Aaron Wildavsky, and Ann Strong are among the authors in this book who have addressed these problems.

Governmental agencies with jurisdiction over entire watersheds or airsheds are clearly needed, and, indeed, some exist, both in the United States and in Europe. The Ruhr River Associations in Germany and the Delaware River Basin Commission and the Ohio River Sanitary Commission in the United States are notable examples. The latter two derive their authority from states which provide their members. The legal powers of all three agencies are limited, and they must depend on cooperation with local governmental jurisdictions which exercise land-use controls, in addition to wise engineering and partly voluntary sanctions based on publicity and public opinion. Nevertheless, they have shown that impressive progress toward basin-wide planning and management can be obtained. The work of the River Basin Commissions is supported by voluntary associations which form an effective political constituency.

In the face of the complexity of many environmental problems and the technical expertise needed to solve them, how can we obtain adequate public participation in the decision-making process?

Consider, for example, the development of a commercial supersonic aircraft in the United States. The decision to support this development with federal funds was largely based on the recommendations of a government agency whose task is to help the aircraft industry. Little attempt was made to determine how many people would find intolerable or unacceptable the five to fifty sonic booms a day that would occur along the flight paths of these aircraft throughout much of the interior of the United States. How can we ensure that these people have a chance to be heard? And how can their interests be weighed against those of the busy, highly paid people who will be the majority of the passengers? Most of these passengers will be residents of the East and West Coasts and, consequently, they may never hear a sonic boom, while the people subjected to the booms will be those who live more than a hundred miles inland and have little opportunity or need for supersonic flight.

Public hearings in which interested groups and individuals can record their views and confront one another with their reasons for holding them have been used by the U.S. Public Health Service, the River Basin Commissions, and many state agencies. Increasing their effectiveness depends upon greater public education concerning the issues, and on the willingness and skill of public officials to respond openly and convincingly to the expressions of public opinion. Patterson points out that a network of knowledgeable voluntary associations and private technical organizations can be a useful link between the public and the governmental agencies in both these areas. Official decisions should take full account of the records of public hearings and should be presented not as arbitrary findings, but as reasonable conclusions from persuasive arguments.

Various devices can be thought of to ensure that considerations of environmental quality and wise use are taken into account in public activities which affect the environment. An "ombudsman" for the environment might be appointed to each public agency with authority to delay or stop actions that would destroy environmental values. Harold Gilliam proposes that "multiple-purpose planning agencies" with a mandate to consider the highest and best use of all lands should be established within state governments. Nathaniel Wollman suggests that boards of experts with authority equal to that of military officials may be necessary to prevent critical environmental destruction which threatens human health or welfare.

In the present state of understanding of political mechanisms, as Wildavsky emphasizes, a good deal of experimentation is needed to determine which types of government agencies and kinds of action are most effective in preserving environmental quality. It is not clear whether agencies with broad mandates or narrow ones are better, nor whether automatic incentives and penalties—carrots and sticks—are more useful than regulatory agencies with discretionary powers.

Technological "Fixes." Obviously both politics and economics must enter into our ways of dealing with environmental questions. But sometimes a *solution* rather than a *decision* can be attained by a technological "fix"—that is, a technological innovation which removes or ameliorates the problem. For example, if a method could be devised for profitably using the sulphur in coal, the electric power companies would extract it from their fuel or from the stack gases, and air pollution by sulphur oxides would disappear.

Until a few years ago, detergents in municipal sewage were an obnoxious source of pollution in many rivers, lakes, and estuaries. Unsightly windrows of foam accumulated in backwaters and on shorelines, and considerable damage was done to aquatic animals. The detergents used in those days were highly resistant to bacterial decomposition and could not be broken down in ordinary sewage disposal plants. The problem was solved by a technological fix. The soap manufacturers developed a new generation of "bio-degradable" detergents that disappear by bacterial activity as other garbage does.

Visual pollution caused by the beer cans, glass bottles, and plastic containers that litter every well-traveled country road and public place is greatly worsened because this trash is virtually indestructible and, consequently, accumulates from year to year. A most welcome technological innovation would be a "bio-degradable beer can," a container with satisfactory storage properties and adequate shelf life that would be attacked and disintegrated by bacteria as soon as it was discarded. The beer can problem illustrates another aspect of the relation between technology and environmental quality. In our wasteful economy, the specifications for new products need to include either profitable reuse or easy disposal. From this point of view, the large-scale replacement of steel by aluminum containers is a technical step backward. Steel cans have the virtue that they disappear relatively quickly after they are thrown away, while aluminum cans seem to last forever. Both, of course, would cease to clutter up the landscape if it paid the user to return them to the producer or distributor. Here we have a possible choice between a technological and an economic "fix."

Usually a technological innovation will not remove the problem as did the development of bio-degradable detergents. But it may bring the costs of environmental improvement within a politically and economically acceptable range, or it may reduce the level of conflict between interest groups enough to make a satisfactory political solution possible.

As an example, consider remedial action to restore a lake which has suffered eutrophication—that is, an overfertilization with plant nutrients from municipal sewage, industrial wastes, and drainage of highly fertilized farm fields. In such a lake, a rank growth of noxious, inedible blue-green algae occurs, forming a canopy near the surface so dense that deeper plants die from lack of sunlight. The dead plants decompose, using up the dissolved oxygen in the water, and fish and other aquatic animals suffocate. The phenomenon is at least partly the result of the imbalance among different nutrients flowing into the lake. The blue-green algae do not need all the nutrients that other, more desirable, microscopic plants require. Research on the nutrient requirements of different kinds of lake plants would probably show that the addition of certain micro-nutrients to sewage effluent, or changing the balance between nitrogen and phosphate compounds, would stimulate the growth of desirable plants that would fit into the food chain for fish and useful invertebrates. The lake could then be transformed from a toxic cesspool to the source of a productive fishery.

The cost of supplying the additional nutrients would not be negligible, but it would be much less than that of the tertiary sewage treatment plants required to remove all nutrients from the waters flowing into the lake, and it would probably be within an economically acceptable range.

Poisonous pesticides and herbicides are being used on a rapidly increasing scale in agriculture throughout the world. These substances are dreadfully persistent in the environment, and they tend to accumulate in relatively high concentrations in fishes, and especially in fish-eating birds. Their increasing concentrations present a largely unknown, but probably dangerous, threat to human beings. They are the source of a serious conflict between farmers and their supporters, who claim that the use of these chemicals is essential for high-yielding agriculture, and many nonfarmers, who worry about the destruction of wildlife and the hazards to public health. The development of other methods of insect control—for example, through the use of juvenile hormones which would not affect other living organisms—could lower the level of conflict. Even if these newer methods were more expensive than the old ones, the difference in cost could be recovered through higher prices, or if this were socially or politically infeasible, it might well be subsidized by governments on the ground that where society benefits as a whole, it should pay as a whole, via government.

Much of our environmental deterioration is the direct or indirect result of advances in technology, and it is ironic, therefore, that remedies should be found in further technical developments. In effect, we are using technology to climb out of a technological trap of our own devising. But the new technology may, in fact, create a new technological trap from which we will be able to extricate ourselves only with further technology, and so on indefinitely. The problem is as old as the Garden of Eden. Once man has eaten of the fruit of the tree of knowledge, there can be no return to innocence.

An example of the probable substitution of a new technological trap for an old one is the unfolding development of nuclear electric power. This will reduce sulphur dioxide pollution in the atmosphere, but will introduce two new hazards—the danger of radioactive contamination and the hazard to aquatic life from the larger quantities of waste heat produced by nuclear reactors, compared to fossil fuel plants, that may be injected into streams, lakes, and inshore marine waters. Correspondingly two new technical problems will arise: the discovery of safe means for disposal of radioactive wastes, and either beneficial use or nondestructive dispersion of the waste heat.

Athelstan Spilhaus has suggested that we need to conduct a large-scale environmental experiment at the limits of new technology. In his proposed experimental city, new methods of waste disposal, urban transportation, communication, climatic control, electric power production and distribution, industrial design, and building construction would all be tested and modified on the basis of experience. Even more fundamental, the optimum population size and geometric pattern of the city, and social, psychological, and behavioral factors related to the physical environment would be studied experimentally.

The Roles of Education. The functions of education in the maintenance and improvement of environmental quality are three-fold: production of the many kinds of specialists who will be required to deal professionally with the problems, formulation and inculcation of the moral and intellectual values on which environmental improvement must rest, and creation of a heightened sensitivity among young people to the world around them—the ability to use their senses and to respond to what they perceive. Robert Morison and George Maslach have written specifically about the role of universities. Both emphasize that the entire university must be involved in the enterprise. "Nothing is alien to our environment, and thus nothing can be alien to the environmental manager," says Morison. Maslach argues persuasively that the professional schools of the university, with their emphasis on the relevance of teaching to the problems of the real world, the synthesis of science and art in professionalism, and the importance of action as well as thought, can contribute greatly to the general education of all university students, and that the professional schools can also cooperate with one another in training for environmental concerns.

The small number of students who are being recruited for the environmental professions presents a serious difficulty. The remedies are by no means clear, but Morison makes three suggestions: New and more intellectually stimulating ways of studying complex ecological systems and presenting the results to students must be found, faculty members who are involved with the attack on environmental problems in the world of government and industry outside the university should be encouraged to relate this work more closely to teaching and cooperative research with students, and the status of the environmental professions should be improved. Possibly a new higher degree should be established which emphasizes professionalism and broad technical and scientific competence, rather than research contributions.

A more fundamental difficulty arises when we consider moral and intellectual values. For a variety of reasons, our universities have been more concerned with means than with ends. But in a world in which we have the means to do almost anything we want, the choice of what to do becomes crucial. In our society, only the universities have the intellectual breadth and humanistic depth to give young people the basis for the development of tastes and the choice of goals. In the new world of science and technology "the ultimate basis of choice is aesthetic," says Morison. "We must have faith that the soundest basis for aesthetic judgment is the cultivation of the best that has been known and thought."

Four Areas of Action

What are the principal kinds of action that need to be taken to create a better future environment for the United States? We suggest four major areas: getting rid of poisons, adopting a new land ethic, re-creating urban environments, and balancing our population and our resources.

"Ours is the age of poisons," said Rachel Carson in her book *Silent Spring*, which first made many of us aware of the murderous man-made substances that have spread throughout the world during the last few decades. Since the publication of her book, many of the substances she warned us against have continued to accumulate in living creatures, the birds of the air, the fishes of the sea, and our own bodies, wreaking more and more obvious havoc.

What are these poisons? The list is long; it includes DDT and other chlorinated hydrocarbons; mercury, chromium, lead, and other heavy metals; beryllium, arsenic, fluorides, and nitrates; radioactive isotopes; and the various kinds of air pollutants, sulphur and nitrogen oxides, ozone, hydrocarbon reaction products, carbon monoxide, and asbestos. Each one presents a separate problem, and many have politically or economically powerful defenders. Yet we are slowly realizing that our health, the survival of our fellow creatures, and perhaps even the fate of our own species depends on keeping these substances out of our environment. In many cases, such as DDT, this means a prompt abandonment of production and use, the latter now a reality in this and several other countries, in favor of substitutes which will kill harmful organisms without affecting harmless ones. In others, it means the development of better ways of containing the byproducts and wastes of the worldwide industrial civilization, and rigorous control of the use of such compounds as nitrates, which are valuable when properly employed as crop fertilizers, but dangerous in well water, and destructive when large quantities are allowed to enter lakes and estuaries.

For all potentially dangerous substances, we should learn more about their effects on man and other creatures, and the pathways of concentration in shellfish, fish, birds, and mammals. We need to monitor the amounts present in the soil, fresh waters, the ocean, and organisms, including ourselves, and how these amounts are changing with time.

The costs of getting rid of poisons will be high, but the stakes are higher, and the urgency of radical action becomes continually greater.

To create a new land ethic, we need to return to the sense of awe and kinship for the natural world that characterized both primitive man and our intellectual ancestors, the Greeks. Our aim should be not to control nature, but to live in harmony with it. We must learn to think of ourselves as loving and careful stewards whose purpose is to pass on our natural heritage to future generations with its beauty undiminished and its usefulness enhanced. Our concepts of highest and best use must be modified from a concern with immediate commercial value to take into account the properties of soil, underground water, surface drainage, topography, micro-climate, and aesthetic quality that fit different areas for distinctive uses. We need especially to conserve for the greatest public good such limited resources as the coastal shoreline, estuaries, and wetlands. Above all, we need to preserve diversity.

In the use of land, the public good should be paramount, but private rights must be respected. A new land ethic must be accompanied by practical devices to compensate property owners for the constraints imposed on their free use of their own land. Systems must be established to enable all property owners to share in the monetary benefits of planned development, even though their own property is retained as open space or confined to a relatively unprofitable use.

We are among the most urbanized of peoples, yet ever since the days of Jefferson we have had a love-hate relationship with cities. We have never fully accepted them as the centers of our culture, and as a result most of our cities have grown without much form or plan into the monstrous life-destroying aggregations that some of them are today.

The revolutions of our time have not lessened the need for cities, but they have changed their reasons for existence. In recreating the urban environment, we must first consider the new purposes of the city. With the growth of automation and other new industrial processes, and changes in modes of transportation, cities are no longer necessary as entrepôts for transshipment of goods or centers for industrial production. They are becoming, more and more, simply places where people can meet face to face in business and social contact; centers of learning, research, information-handling, entertainment, sport, and art; places where people provide services for one another; above all, places where a great variety of ecological niches exist for individual human beings, a diversity of occupations, avocations, and life styles that provides maximum opportunities for each individual to develop his own uniqueness.

To fulfill their new functions and to provide a more humane environment for their citizens, our existing cities should be redesigned and in large part rebuilt. But in addition we need new cities, perhaps as many as fifty during the next three of four decades. These new cities must not be satellites of the old ones. Instead, they can be located at the most attractive and unique sites throughout the fifty states. Like giant passenger ships, they should be carefully planned to be self-contained and of a definite size, set in an inviting countryside as a ship is surrounded by the sea. They must be large enough to offer a diversity of choices to all their citizens and to provide the full intensity and variety of city life, yet not so large that the quality of life is degraded by the sheer mechanics of living in congestion and noise or that individual citizens lose their sense of responsibility for one another and for their community.

Massive investments, perhaps as much as 50 billion dollars a year for the next thirty years, will be needed to rebuild our present cities and to create new ones, but even more important will be a recognition of the needs and a dedication to the tasks by many of our most imaginative, energetic, and highly trained citizens.

In thinking about the future size of the population of the United States, two basic premises are clear: Quality is inescapably related to quantity, and we must balance our numbers against our ability to provide human services and a humane environment for all our citizens. No one can say today what the optimum size of the United States population should be, but we know that we already have human resources in excess of our present ability to use them fully as human beings. The growth of our numbers exacerbates every environmental problem: the dull ugliness of our cities, the deterioration of natural areas, the increase of ecological imbalances, the depletion of natural resources, the growth of urban pathology, and the proliferation of noxious wastes.

Though man is the most adaptable of animals, we need to remember that our physiological character, sensory capacities, and behavior patterns evolved in a sparsely populated world. Our continually growing numbers demand an ever-increasing complexity of interactions and produce a multiplication of stimuli that could overwhelm our inherited capacities.

At least until we learn more about ourselves and can use our knowledge to ensure lives of happiness and fulfillment for all our fellow citizens, control of population growth must be a high-priority national goal.

Some Common Themes

In essence, this is a book about decision-making in environmental problems. The authors of the different chapters have approached the question in different ways. Fraser Darling and Dillon Ripley and Helmut Buechner have presented the scientific viewpoint of the ecologist, and Burton Litton has attempted an aesthetic rationale for the landscape planner. Hans Landsberg, John Krutilla, Nathaniel Wollman, and Aaron Wildavsky have indicated the ways in which economists can help provide an intellectual basis for decision-making. Harold Gilliam, Ann Strong, and Robert Patterson have described the successes and failures of political action. George Maslach and Robert Morison have discussed the potential contributions of higher education. Joseph Fisher, Azriel Teller, and David Allee have explored the application of economics to the problems of specific resources. The remaining authors have taken a more general view. Frederick Gutheim and Athelstan Spilhaus have discussed the complex problems of environmental betterment in cities, while Alexis Papageorgiou and Roger Revelle have concerned themselves with the whole environment as it affects outdoor recreation.

One is always tempted to look for common strands that give a sense of unity to a collection of essays as are here assembled. We have just named one, decision-making, and this much-abused term must be understood to embrace the entire chain from the formation and identification of societal values to the consequences, in the marketplace and outside it, of private as well as of governmental actions.

But several other common themes run through the book. One is our appalling ignorance of physical interactions in the environment. Much of the time we go on no more than hunches and guesses, cry for more research, though we are barely able to formulate the relevant questions for such research, while, on the other hand, we cannot delay committing increasingly large resources to remedial or preventive action that, we hope, moves in the right direction.

Equally pervasive is the theme of our deficient knowledge of what society as a whole really wants, and what we are to do about it when we find out; how it perceives the environment; and, most importantly, what costs it is prepared to assume in order to preserve, improve, beautify. Here the Brandywine story serves as a grim reminder of the clash between theory and practice. When the chips are down, it is just possible that environmental improvement ranks low in the average citizen's priority, and especially so when it becomes a budget line. Perhaps the educator and the politician are the ones least troubled by the implications of this dilemma, though the conclusions they reach are likely to move in opposite directions.

One final theme is worthy of mention, especially as it is a negative one—namely, the absence of writing on a purely or largely technological plane. Even the "experimental city" has technology only as one of many inputs. Nor is this accidental. What we are facing is less a lack of appropriate science and technology than a lack of new managerial principles, institutions, new attitudes, new administrative devices—or old ones shaped to new purposes. We tell developing countries that if they shed old habits and traditions and move into a world of new institutions, laws, incentives, and so forth, half their battle will be won. Yet we are only beginning to realize that the shoe pinches us at just the same spot.

We groan about the abandoned beer can or Coke bottle, but instead of making it worthwhile not to throw it away (and we do not even have to develop the profit motive first), we are much more likely to look for a new type of can: R & D to the rescue! Our eyes may smart from exhaust fumes in the city streets, but instead of making city driving and parking so expensive that the demand for mass transportation, subsidized or even free if necessary, will become overwhelming, we look for a new type of propulsion system, attended by as yet unknown environmental problems.

In the handling of commonly owned resources—be these parks, or watercourses, or air—so wedded are we to traditional ways of doing things, to time-honored orders of magnitudes in costs and prices, that we allow them to be ruined for all in the name of free access for all. It is in questioning the validity of these traditions, pointing to their grim consequences even to this day, and indicting not neutral technology but our inability to organize intelligently for its beneficial use that perhaps the major common theme of the book lies.

ECOLOGY AS AN ETHICAL SCIENCE

F. FRASER DARLING

A Wider Environment of Ecology and Conservation

PIERRE DANSEREAU's first of twenty-seven propositions or laws of ecology has the shattering simplicity of great thoughts. His Law of the Inoptimum says, "No species encounters in any given habitat the optimum conditions for all of its functions." Few ecologists give sufficient heed to this dictum when studying the life history of any single species, though it glimmers through when a whole community or biome is being considered. Most earnest workers for the supposed welfare of man have never heard of the Law of the Inoptimum and would scarcely be ready to believe it anyway. Yet Dansereau has given us the perfect text for that desirable state of being for all those who delve into the ground of living things and their environment—namely, the state of unembittered disillusion.

Ecology, as the science of the organism in relation to its environment and of the relations between communities of organisms of like or different kinds, was a bigger idea than the initiators grasped. The beauty of the idea was in its bigness and readiness to cross boundaries, looking into less well understood fields than one's own and finding links, correlations, comparisons, contrasts, and differences of exquisitely fine scale and subtlety.

The botanists did the first critical work that set a standard. Animal ecology followed rather hesitantly. In 1927, at the age of twenty-seven, Charles Elton published *Animal Ecology*, a landmark in this field because it expresses, almost without saying so, a philosophy, a vision of complexity in which the behavior of animals is itself a factor in the environment of others. He asked that botanists and other scientists co-operate in coming to an understanding of how communities coexist. "The movement of the moon or of a dog's tail or the psychology of starlings" was a matter of significance; answers were not in books. Julian Huxley's introduction to

3

the volume saw clearly the social implications that ecology would have; that all applied biology would need to shed its *ad hoc* approach, such as thinking of the elimination of a "pest," and seek guiding principles in pure and applied ecology. We now under-stand that a "pest" is an indicator of environmental imbalance.

Elton's contribution to ecological theory has been progressive and massive. His latest book, *The Pattern of Animal Communities,* gives us guidelines for the future. This book represents twenty years of research by Elton and his graduate students on a small wooded landscape at Whytham Hill, near his university and home. Our mo-bile academic world is producing too few of such studies, when they are so much needed. We may hope that Elton's work will in-spire someone else of his quality to further exploration, just as Victor Shelford's studies stimulated him. Despite Shelford's pri-marily physiological approach to each animal's life history, Elton's schoolboy leanings were enormously supported by Shelford's whole-ness of approach.

Wholeness in approach has been carried through in Elton's book in beautiful detail, but with a leisured, philosophical quietness and literary quality that can be deceptive. The key has been the handling of large amounts of data without losing track of their validity or meaning. In this larger field, the early American contri-butions of Homer Shantz, primarily a botanist, and Aldo Leopold, the philosophic founder of the study of wildlife management, were very great indeed and redound to the credit of a hardheaded but imaginative governmental agency, the U. S. Forest Service, and its first head, Gifford Pinchot.

Shantz, in my mind, was the exponent of the biotic factor, for he saw examples of the interaction of vegetational cover and animal life wherever he went and found youthful enjoyment in each facet he discovered. In 1923, he journeyed from Cairo to the Cape with C. F. Marbut and produced a vegetational atlas that stood for thirty years. As an indefatigable photographer, he took a series of photographs of all he saw. This proved its value spectacularly in 1956 when he repeated the journey and took a new series of photographs from as near the same points as possible. The before-and-after pictures were published by the University of Arizona and backed up Shantz's scrupulous observations. (Shantz showed me the link between the antelope ground squirrel and that important desert browse plant, bitterbush: Single seeds do not germinate and survive in nature, whereas the forgotten caches of seeds of these

4

little rodents do germinate as a group, though only one plant will survive the shortage of water.) Shantz enjoyed the dynamic interacting world of natural history; he saw that it made sense. Leopold was deeply influenced by the deserts of New Mexico and Arizona and what people were doing to the land. I suppose there is no philosopher who does not suffer, and Leopold reflected, "One of the penalties of an ecological education is that one lives alone in a world of wounds. Much of the damage inflicted on land is invisible to laymen."

He, too, saw wholes and grappled with them, as his book *Game Management*, published in 1933, shows. His greatest contribution, however, was his struggle for a land ethic of conservation based on impeccable scientific principles:

When we see land as a community to which we belong, we may begin to use it with love and respect. There is no other way for land to survive the impact of mechanized man, nor for us to reap from it the aesthetic harvest it is capable, under science, of contributing to culture.

That land is a community is the basic concept of ecology, but that land is to be loved and respected is an extension of ethics. That land yields a cultural harvest is a fact long known, but latterly often forgotten.

If this attitude of mind is held at all, I would say it is an ecological factor affecting the world environment and a proper stage in our own development of awareness.

There are obvious limits to the breadth and depth of any man's science. Thus, early ecology, which looked far and wide, drew pursed lips from the purists and those to whom research meant learning more and more about less and less. The ecologists made mistakes, but they could be faultless and fearless in the scientific principles—old truths really—they were unearthing like archaeological treasures. Ecology was stimulating, without being particularly rewarding of ambition in the profession of science.

Ecologists certainly wished to be respectable and acceptable in the profession of science. Indeed, I think, papers in today's ecological journals are less generally interesting than those of thirty or fifty years ago. Elton says:

Ecologists have to some extent been dazzled by the technical and mathematical triumphs of physics and chemistry, and have embarked on various quantitative investigations without fully taking into account the whole context in which their populations live in nature.

[Despite the numbers of species and problems of taxonomy], one has to

5

make a considerable effort to break through from one level of study to another above it, and while doing so to forge through the apparent complexities to a higher level of integration and arrive at simple ideas applicable to that higher level but invisible from the jungle below.

Inevitably, specialization has taken place. It was necessary to have such fine analysis for the larger synthesis, but to what extent are we prepared now to step forth into the world of men and its psychological dimension? Ecologists have resisted the notion of human ecology, in much the same way that earlier plant ecologists neglected biotic influences on plant communities. Shantz and Leopold cut right through this sophistry in their studies of the over-grazed western ranges. The geographer Carl Sauer always saw ecology in the larger terms of human activity, as his early study of the Ozark region shows. This was also my own approach in *West Highland Survey*. There is only one ecology.

Nevertheless, there has been a further tendency on the part of ecologists to turn inward and to exclude, when their science demands outward vision. The governmental and administrative world, even the commercial world, has heard of ecology. The idea—or at least the word—is liked, for we hear it generally bandied about, but are ecologists demonstrating that their science has a continuing stream from the academic watershed to the complexity of the estuary with its people and its pollution? Physicists, chemists, and mathematicians are conscious of their streams of permeation. Ecology as a profession arrived belatedly and has not yet devised its means of communication.

A recent conference drew together a small group of ecologists, economists, architects, planners, lawyers, publicists, and a physician to discuss the subject of the future environments of North America. As one of the ecologists present, I felt our science seemed unable to rise to its opportunity. Some of us expressed the need for much deeper research before anything definite could be said; others put forward as proposals for study space and material that the group thought unrealistic. The ecologists were fine idealists, and their philosophy was unexceptionable. Finally, they came out with truths which the company warmly accepted, but before then that ecologically sympathetic economist Kenneth Boulding had said, "You do not have any sophisticated knowledge in ecology. Ecology, as far as I can see, has been one of the most unsophisticated of the sciences. You are a bunch of bird-watchers. You really are."

Boulding spoke surer than he knew, for out of the nest of bird-

6

watchers have come some of those ecologists who have essayed the furthest forward. At the risk of being invidious, I would mention William Vogt, who did more to shock the world into consciousness of the human-population problem than anyone else; and Max Nicholson, who at twenty-one wrote a book on avian economics, *How Birds Live,* and who, since then, has founded the research organization, Political and Economic Planning, and has been Director-General of the Nature Conservancy, a British government agency.

What Boulding was thinking and what made me uncomfortable that day was the ecologists' apparent inability to make constructive proposals in the face of specific and urgent problems. I have often heard in high places the complaint that our discussion is very interesting but not concrete enough in the immediate context. Just as ecologists see an immensely complex world of nature, a governmental administration sees the complex world of men and their opinions and habits of thinking. It must compromise all the time and think quickly, whereas ecologists abhor snap judgments. Nevertheless, there is much we do know, and we must be prepared to use this knowledge. The auditor of a balance sheet has a form of statement that safeguards his signature; the ecologist should be no more fearful nor diffident.

Such a meticulous worker as Derrick Ovington cautions that we know too little and that ecology cannot answer with authority the questions asked of it. He pleads for more time in research. By concentrating his work on the breakdown and recycling of detritus in woodlands, he is building some accurate notion of primary and secondary productivity in this kind of ecosystem. Edward Deevey has been doing the same sort of work in fresh-water systems; the Odum brothers and Larry Slobodkin have almost produced a revolution in ecology by their quantitative work in recycling of nutrients, while C. Overgaard Nielson and H. Ellenberg have been doing similar work in Europe. All these workers are either bound up with the International Biological Program or its study of the productivity of biological systems. From the academic side of ecology, they employ difficult technical methods and imaginatively adapt techniques from other sciences to their work. These scholars are representative of the fundamental research we can hope will be supported and enlarged to give us the basic reasoning for ultimate social application.

The concept of the ecosystem or biome as the unit is quite clear, but it would remain philosophical and speculative unless the in-

7

volved laboratory work on the detailed nature of conversion cycles is developed further. The long-term program of the Nature Conservancy, one of the largest in this field in the world, recognizes this quite clearly. It has been reckoned that over two thousand man-years have already gone into fundamental research and that management of nature reserves and land-use ecology in general are now having some meaning. These scholars are not bird-watchers but bricklayers.

The preservation of samples of the planet's natural areas is no supine task of designation, acquisition, and thereafter letting be. Rather, it requires having such an understanding of the dynamic nature of the plant and animal communities and of the physical and social interaction of environmental factors that knowledgeable regulatory action can be taken before irrevocable change impinges. When Elton discussed his concept of *niche* in ecology in 1927, he stressed the functional quality of an organism in its habitat. The wolverine in the Arctic and the hyena in the tropical environment were filling the same niche, being the bone-grinding kind of scavenger. This is a graphic expression of a principle now comprehended more fully in the study of ecosystems: In short, organisms exploit their environment to their best advantage and contribute unconsciously to the ideal of non-loss of energy from the ecosystem as a whole and, at the same time, to the maintenance of the maximum active flow of energy through the ecosystem.

The government of the United States is considering the establishment of an ecological survey as an agency within the Department of the Interior. If this should come about, there would be a concomitant designation or acquisition of "natural areas" thought representative of their kind. Some of these would already be owned publicly, falling within national parks, national forests, or national wildlife refuges, but their value to the new agency would be different from that which might be placed upon them as a national park or forest. Only the wildlife refuge would approximate the same value in conservation of habitat. Moreover, the potential ecological survey would go much deeper in its research. Many new areas are needed, but, insofar as they are already in public ownership, they would have greater expectation of being maintained in their native condition and of yielding a new and deeper dimension of knowledge. Even though many users would be excluded, their designation by the proposed ecological survey would represent a new aspect of multiple use. Such a program would yield the datum lines we so badly need for future thought and action. A government agency of ecological survey would greatly expand environmental understanding, for it would ramify through the universities, influencing many disciplines—biology, the social sciences, psychology, and medicine. This has happened already in the United Kingdom, where the Nature Conservancy has become an integral part of a new National Environmental Research Council.

The aim to acquire natural areas in the United States is a most desirable one for ecology; it is exceeded only by the need to do this for the planet as a whole. The British Nature Conservancy is giving advice to less-developed countries, and the International Union for Conservation of Nature and Natural Resources is poised by its expertise to make world conservancy a reality were it adequately supported by the nations. A.I.D. money could move in these directions with advantage. Not only should the human-population problem not be ignored, but overseas aid should be aimed at direct ecological research in the field of human population as a long-term policy for human survival.

Ecology no longer has to bother about academic respectability, and it should face firmly its social destiny. To some extent, conservation has been applied ecology or ecology in action, but, in general, the ecologist is nervous in the company of the devotee of conservation. The idea of conservation is easy and emotionally satisfying, and the half-bake finds himself in a mutual-admiration society. Without much difficulty, this kind of conservationist can believe he is a superior sort of person, which boosts his ego. It is all very trying, yet our greatest ecologists are in the front ranks of the Conservation Movement with all its shortcomings; they rise above academic diffidence and are ready to accept the social destiny of their science. Moreover, they are helping us to think of many administrative and political problems in ecological terms. The supreme example has been the appointment of Stanley Cain, former head of the Michigan School of Conservation Studies, as an Assistant Secretary in the Department of the Interior. Paul Sears, Fairfield Osborn, Marston Bates, and Raymond Dasmann have all written books with direct social impact. Sears's *Deserts on the March* and Osborn's *Our Plundered Planet* were early classics that made some world-wide difference, but I have an uncomfortable feeling that several good books published since then have been treated as "scare" literature. It behooves every writer of these necessary pieces to prune his English. The facts do not need the big drum.

Politics, let us admit, is an immensely important ecological factor on this planet. Perhaps howler monkeys show the rudiments of political tribalism, but otherwise man is the unique political animal. To this unique characteristic is linked man's ability to lie to himself and be believed. These aspects of animal behavior influence the ecology of our planet and have done so throughout history. The notion of biopolitics, while not new, is capable of immense development even in one's own mind before it reaches action. Nations, like ecosystems, tend toward complexity, which, at its best, means efficiency in energy flow. As each organism evolves, it must find its own niche and survive by natural selection. If we liken a nation to an ecosystem, have we an interlocking community of institutions furthering energy flow within itself or an agglomeration of almost random organizations (that is, organisms) operating without natural selection, without a definite trend toward integration and establishment of a niche structure? Both nation and ecosystem are in a state of process: Losses are suffered and can be adjusted by adaptation and, in the same way, introductions can be taken into the system. Occasionally, either loss or introduction might wreck the ecosystem or the civilization.

Our proliferations of institutions have not yet become integrated as an ecosystem. Our communication is imperfect, and we must deal with loyalties and egos. G. F. Gause's axiom states that if two species occupy the same niche-function in the same habitat, one will eventually become dominant and replace the other. This kind of thinking is necessary as an ecological attitude in our management of bear gardens. Political economy needs the ecologist who can apply himself without becoming a politician.

I look upon Lynton Caldwell as the leading thinker in biopolitics. He is a political economist who has realized the possible fruitfulness of the borderline areas between sciences. Leopold used to talk about "edge effects," the richness of natural history on the borders of habitats. The academic ecologist speaks of the *ecotone,* and Caldwell is examining one of these areas in administrative possibilities for environmental control. His book, *Biopolitics: Science, Ethics and Public Policy,* was published in 1964, but has taken too long to get through to general comprehension. The White House Conference on Natural Beauty, held in 1965, was perhaps a turning point, because it clarified an enlarged concept of public responsibility and administrative innovation, the keynote of Caldwell's biopolitics. The President, in his Message on Natural Beauty, said:

Our conservation must not be just the classic conservation of protection and development, but a creative conservation of restoration and innovation. Its concern is not with nature alone but with the total relation between man and the world around him.

Caldwell writes:

Politics in the broad sense operates through the administrative process as well as outside of it, and is one of the fibers that tie together the internal and external aspects of public administration, giving it functional coherence. The character of administrative action often reveals the extent to which this coherence has been achieved in politics, and can be expressed in public policy.

In short, public policy has to be ahead of popular consensus, which is often confused, even when informed action is crucial.

Two books by one author, Richard Cooley, have had Alaska as their common subject. One, *Politics and Conservation,* deals with the natural resource of the salmon and its treatment through a century, and the other, *Alaska: A Challenge in Conservation,* with land-use policy. These books bear out Caldwell's ecological approach to administration and politics. The first shows the futility of any notion of a single panacea to sustain the Alaska fishery. The forces and pressures are biological, economic, political, and social. The biological side calls not only for patient research, but for "wise judgment based on intimate experience in the interpretation of partial information," which unfortunately is the only kind available. The institution of a free and common fishery complicates the economics of salmon conservation. The individual is powerless to conserve either in the public interest or in his own by listening to counsels of moderation. Economics of salmon fishing involves ratios of men and gear to the total available resource and the final price of a tin of fish, and these ratios are a complicated study in themselves. The political side has been bitter, badly informed, and, of course, highly vocal. Little has been done toward developing a well-rounded, permanent settlement for stability of society. The federal agency established for this purpose bred resentment, mistrust, and flagrant disregard of regulatory measures. As Cooley points out, a man-made institution can be modified by man. There is nothing immutable in the free fishery, which evolved without thought of a public policy in resource management.

Cooley's second book stands on the concept of the relevance of the total environment to each individual. Statehood has given opportunity for a new constitutional framework and resource code; the earthquake of 1964 gave an edge to the new planning and ordered approach of a growing society integrating its ecological relationship to the resource base. To quote Caldwell once more:

In the absence of an ecological perception of the environment in its interrelated totality, neither electorates nor party leaders nor public administrators give serious attention to the over-all effect of government action on environmental change.

Alaska is a simpler problem than the United States as a whole or the United Nations. Nevertheless, Cooley's work demonstrates that ecology and conservation can move surely into the hurly-burly without losing scholarly integrity, a course more of us must be prepared to follow in rougher areas.

Conservation as ecology in action is indeed looking outward from its traditional field of nature. Recent speeches by Russell Train and Raymond Dasmann have spelled out conservation's concern with planning and the phenomenon of urbanism. Urbanism is one facet of the increase of human population with which ecology is already involved. But advancing urbanism also implies rural regression, an area in which conservation can offer special help. The mobility provided by the internal-combustion engine has made possible the leaping urban sprawl so different from the medieval, intensely urban city with its sharply defined country of fields and woods. More, however, is involved than the mere nonbeauty of urban sprawl. Rural life has many disciplines that have survival value for the community and its land. The fracture these undergo as they fall increasingly within the penumbra of modern semi- and sub-urbanism can have sharp ecological consequences that may be apparent even in psychosomatic manifestations in the population.

We know little about the human environment, and its complexity does not lend itself to full analysis because subjective values of widely varying character are concerned. Indeed, many human environments are speciated by their subjective values. Social anthropology and sociology are directly concerned with such analysis, but ecology can fill a very obvious gap. The ecology of stress in human communities and environments immediately demonstrates the truth of Dansereau's first law. The unembittered *désillusioné*, who finds no place for rose-colored spectacles, does not foster the impulse to create the perfect environment nor to bring the human being to the encapsulated state of homeostasis that can only be imaginary and never real. But analysis of the environment is worth trying, and the ecologist should not avoid considering subjective values ecological factors. Early construction of super-highways naturally favored the straight line, but drivers tended to fall asleep on them; some curving and landscaping are now normal at some extra engineering cost. Diversity, be it ever so little, has value in relieving stress. As we urbanize, the green leaf is becoming increasingly important to our content and well-being. The eastern forest of the United States, which has little or no timber value and a rapidly declining significance for fuel supplies, is approaching its zenith of service to mankind as the suburban forest, the pleasance of the people.

Psychosomatic diseases are a manifestation of varied patterns of environmental conditions bearing on persons of different habitus types. These diseases may be alleviated by drugs or surgery, but their radical cure depends on removing stress conditions. Habitus type may well determine whether the expression of the psychosomatic ill is a duodenal ulcer, asthma, migraine, lumbago, or cardiac disease. It is imperative that physicians inclined toward ecology take part in the investigation of the human environment. Pure water and pure air are accepted as being desirable, but the nature of the environment is too little considered. Uncontrolled "development" instigated largely by economic motives is prodigal and destructive of what could be desirable human habitat. Tactile and visual repose should be considered by engineers and builders, and the ecologist could help if he devoted some research time now. Curving lines, trees and their textures, masses and seasonal variation, the place of water still and in motion—these things may be impractical, but so much of human pleasure is impractical. Municipalities must deal with impractical things without thinking them impracticable. An art gallery is most impractical except for those who earn their living running it; the realtor must often think of Central Park and Hyde Park as prodigal impracticality. If we subscribe to the idea that the National Gallery or the Palisades contribute materially to human health, these enjoyments become practical, but still somewhat intangible under analysis. Thus, they might well tend to suffer under economic pressures that the increase of population will only strengthen. The so-called rise in the standard of living is being attended by a definite lowering of the standard of living in environmental terms. Silence or absence of cacophony is a scarce commodity; the simple peasant fare of home-baked brown bread and freshly made butter

13

can be enjoyed only by the very rich in Western society.

We find these factors difficult to analyze, yet the ecologist can join with the physician and the psychologist in helping the planner and the landscape architect. Ian McHarg, of the University of Pennsylvania, has emphasized the place of ecology in landscape architecture and practiced the idea in the Delaware River project. Unfortunately, expression and practice of this kind of ecology and continuing research demand a present prosperity of high order in a society that has neglected public beauty and amenity for so long. Wars cut very deep into the surplus that could be applied to environmental research and experimentation. The tendency then is to make do in an environment that is steadily deteriorating ecologically.

Ecology has, as yet, too little to offer in definite terms. The ecologist's understanding of the "physiology of community" is much needed to retain in urban, suburban, and rural landscapes those dispositions of nature that are apprehended, often subconsciously, by the human being. The connoisseur may enjoy in fuller fashion by knowledge, but subconscious, environmentally induced joy must not be treated with indifference.

All of us are aware of the rapid change in our environment, and how projected changes can be brought to the stage of "starting on Monday morning" before the citizen is aware of them. The public hearing is precipitated, and any ecological evidence offered is hurried in its preparation and unimpressive. At rather less short notice, come the announcements of intended dams, about which the public can have its say. The Wilderness Society, the Sierra Club, and the National Parks Association in the United States do a splendid job in guarding the nation's heritage, often using sound ecological arguments, but the ecologists themselves might well maintain through their societies an intelligence center, making them more ready to serve the public. An excellent example of good ecological reconnaissance and subsequent presentation of a report of immense strength was the effort by Dean Spurr's team which examined the Rampart Dam proposal on the Yukon. The deduced consequences of the dam were worked through with the utmost scientific integrity, completely devoid of bias or special pleading. (Several societies had asked for this survey and collectively paid for it.)

Another example of scholarly overlook of a large region, of value both to an administrator and an enquiring public, is the symposium volume *Man's Place in the Island Ecosystem,* edited by Ray Fosberg. The idea of the symposium was conceived by UNESCO, and

14

a sense of social involvement of ecology pervades the book. Fosberg writes of the approach to land use in terms of the whole ecosystem:

The practical importance . . . is enormous. Such matters as the determination of the degree of stability or instability of existing ecosystems, the determination of causes of instability, and the prediction of courses of change in unstable ecosystems should be fundamental to all economic and community planning, as well as to the planning of most other public and private enterprises. This should be equally so whether planning is on a local or national, or perhaps especially, on a world level.

Instability, especially induced instability, in ecosystems seems to be at the root of most of the economic loss, political disturbance, and social unrest in the world. With adequate understanding of the nature of the ecosystems concerned, disturbance of inherently unstable but satisfactorily functioning systems may be avoided. Then it might be more likely that the blundering pattern of exploitation and "development" . . . would be replaced by intelligent manipulation of ecosystems.

Ecologists might conduct surveys methodologically similar to the "scenarios" of the Hudson Institute. There, imaginary military debacles are set forth, including the hypothetical dropping of atomic bombs of certain weights on certain places. The consequences are followed through in considerable ecological detail by the time the scenario is presented. Ecologists could learn much from this technique, and the cases they could work on would not be nearly so imaginary. This would not only be excellent training, but a line of research to be developed. The subject of recreation needs ecological inquiry of the "scenario" type if the face of the country is not to suffer from skin disease.

In the same line of thought, ecological reconnaissance can be developed further to give a fairly accurate, reasonably quick answer to specific problems. The ecologist cannot expect to be taken seriously in public affairs if he constantly takes refuge behind the need for more research. If he has kept himself aware of the width of his subject and used the ecologist's special aptitude, natural and developed, for comparative observation, he will have gained a shrewd notion of indicators that may themselves be single species of plants or animals, types of growth, or combinations of these. One of the pioneers of "short cuts" in ecological reconnaissance has been Thane Riney, now with the Food and Agriculture Organization. The Sierras of California were his nursery when he worked on the mule deer; he then spent seven years in the steep country of South Island in New Zealand, and he traveled extensively throughout most of Africa. Even the press of the heel into the ground can indicate much to the trained observer. The art and science of rapid, accurate reconnaissance must surely be one of the developments in academic ecology in the future, though in my opinion not enough attention is being paid to it in training curricula. The need is great in all countries. Immense areas of the so-called developed countries (I prefer the truer word, *overdeveloped*), as well as the developing countries, need the scrutiny of an ecological survey. Such reconnaissance gives us a notion of carrying capacity, to use the agronomist's phrase. The ecologist would use it in a wider sense, perhaps the weight and incidence of flat feet in national parks, the year to year density of snowy owls on an Arctic tundra, or the balance of the wide spectrum of grazing and browsing animals on an African savannah. Riney has brought the word *syndrome* into ecological use in recognizing the composite ills of land in nature.

The airplane has proved to be a boon for the ecologist. Other sciences quickly took advantage of this tool, and two world wars provided breakthroughs in the interpretation of aerial photographs that have been immensely useful to the ecologist since 1945. The first ecologist employed by a commercial firm in the United Kingdom was concerned with ground checking an aerial survey in the Middle East, and fortunately he developed the techniques to a high level of accuracy, speed, and application. Aerial survey in Scotland and Ireland shows remarkably undisturbed results of glaciation and soil drift for study. As a corollary to this, the much changed vegetation picture of England makes aerial photography of national nature reserves in that country a necessity for ecological study of process.

Nothing equals the value of carefully slanted aerial photographs in census work on certain birds and mammals. The method is suspect, however, for some creatures that do not make themselves evident even though they are above ground. Excellent combined plant and animal ecological studies have been done for the wilder lands, such as Alaska and Africa, but what has gone before seems elementary to what is hoped for in the future. Remote sensors and photogrammetry promise extraordinary detail and accuracy; satellite and radar photographs can be used for estimating environmental change and land-use patterns in places we cannot reach.

These special techniques borrowed from other sciences will make possible much deeper intellectual penetration of study areas and provide quickly a mass of data. Mathematics has already served ecology well through the work of Lotka, Bodenheimer, Solomon, Nicholson, Leslie, and, more recently, Martin Holgate, who is also an ecologist. Mathematics will now play a larger role in testing and interpreting data, for the plain descriptive ecologist will increasingly seek the specialist aid of the mathematician.

Ecology has also borrowed from gas chromatography its means of selective detection of pesticide residues and metabolites. The use of pesticides has been a subject of heated public controversy, and some rather uncritical work has been done on these compounds in relation to wildlife conservation. Pesticides have damaged the environment, but the extent and nature of this damage have not yet been satisfactorily determined. The practices used by commercial firms in determining effects and safety factors are very deficient. Commerce cannot afford the time to get the results the ecologist would consider adequate. The ecologist, on the other hand, is called upon to be accurate for field conditions, rather than for laboratory experimentation. The answer is an anticlimax if the endangered species is by then extinct. The new selective-detection techniques may save the ecologist's face in this field as well as precious time.

The practice of using pesticidal compounds in the last quarter of a century has certainly brought the ecologist nearer to his social role. Robert Rudd's book *Pesticides and the Living Landscape* is a scientific successor to Rachel Carson's *Silent Spring* and should have had equal public attention. I would emphasize that the interdisciplinary approach to ecological problems is now essential. The ecologist is less likely to be the lone naturalist who observes and contemplates than a member of a team that is able to draw on diverse disciplines.

The pesticide problem has also triggered much fundamental ecological research on population dynamics, whether of soil fauna or American robins. Thus, monitoring systems on indicator organisms —man, bird, and mollusk—are being made possible. Monitoring itself is in line with the "scenario" technique. It attempts to supply us not only with contemporary knowledge but with forecasts of future trends—both of which ecology needs for prompt, active, and effective social participation.

Pollution of the environment is a product of our age, resulting from increase of human population, from technological activity, and from the linked phenomenon of urbanization. At the moment we are losing the battle for man's sense of well-being. Ecology and conservation have much to offer and discover. By their future concern and involvement with the human species and its environment, they will serve no less well the field of nature where they have worked heretofore.

The burden of this essay has been the breadth of concern of ecology and conservation. Is the field of endeavor to become so diffuse that we become all-embracing, utterly superficial, and lightweight? There is this danger, but I do not think Caldwell, Cooley, and Fosberg will fall into it. They are men of different skills, expressing similar ideas. Proponents of the ecological approach with this breadth of skills can talk the same language, and such communication produces the rich dynamism of "edge effects." This interaction may be the ecologist's salvation. If specialists can be outward-looking as well and ecologists can communicate with them quickly, breadth of front can be deep also. Then ecologists will be able to take their place at the council table as socially conscious people capable of adjustment and compromise in a complex world where politics is a major ecological factor in the total environment.

REFERENCES

Kenneth E. Boulding, "Economics and Ecology," *Future Environments of North America*, eds. F. Fraser Darling and J. Milton (New York, 1966).

Lynton K. Caldwell, *Biopolitics: Science, Ethics, and Public Policy* (New Haven, 1964), and "Administrative Possibilities for Environmental Control," *Future Environments of North America.*

Rachel Carson, *The Silent Spring* (Boston, 1962).

Richard A. Cooley, *Politics and Conservation* (New York, 1963), and *Alaska: A Challenge in Conservation* (Madison, Wis., 1966).

Pierre Dansereau, "Ecological Impact and Human Ecology," *Future Environments of North America.*

Raymond F. Dasmann, *The Last Horizon* (New York, 1963); *The Destruction of California* (New York, 1965); "Aesthetics and the Natural Environment," Address to the Bureau of Sport Fisheries and Wildlife (Washington, D. C., 1966); "Wildlife and Outdoor Recreation," Address to Outdoor Recreation Resources Review Commission (St. Paul, Minn., 1966).

Charles S. Elton, *Animal Ecology* (London, 1927), and *The Pattern of Animal Communities* (London, 1966).

F. R. Fosberg (ed.), *Man's Place in the Island Ecosystem* (Honolulu, 1963).

F. Fraser Darling, *West Highland Survey* (Oxford, 1955); "The Unity of Ecology," Presidential Address to Section D, British Association for the Advancement of Science (Aberdeen, 1963); "Conservation and Ecological Theory," *Journal of Ecology* (Jubilee Supplement), pp. 39-45; ed., *Future Environments of North America.*

Aldo Leopold, *Game Management* (New York, 1933), and *A Sand County Almanac* (New York, 1948).

Ian McHarg, "Ecological Determinism," *Future Environments of North America.*

J. Milton and F. Fraser Darling, "Air Photography in Zoological Studies," *The Uses of Air Photography: Nature and Man in a New Perspective,* ed. J. K. S. St. Joseph (Cambridge, 1966).

E. M. Nicholson, *How Birds Live* (London, 1927).

H. T. Odum, "Ecological Tools and Their Use: Man and the Ecosystem," *Lockwood Conference on the Suburban Forest and Ecology* (held by the Connecticut Experimental Station), pp. 57-75, and "Ecological Potential and Analogue Circuits for the Ecosystem," *American Science,* Vol. 48, pp. 1-8.

P. E. Odum, *Fundamentals of Ecology* (Philadelphia, 1955).

Fairfield Osborn, *Our Plundered Planet* (Boston, 1948).

J. D. Ovington, "Quantitative Ecology and the Woodland Ecosystem Concept," *Advances in Ecological Research* (New York, 1962), pp. 103-92, and "Experimental Ecology and Habitat," *Future Environments of North America.*

Thane Riney, "Influence of Land Use on Large Mammal Problems in New Zealand," *New Zealand Science Review,* Vol. 16, pp. 33-36; also, "The Impact of Introductions of Large Herbivores on the Tropical Environment," *The Ecology of Man in the Tropical Environment,* Proceedings of the International Union for the Conservation of Nature Conference held in 1963 in Nairobi (Morges, 1964).

R. L. Rudd, *Pesticides and the Living Landscape* (Madison, Wis., 1964).

J. K. S. St. Joseph (ed.), *The Uses of Air Photography: Nature and Man in a New Perspective.*

Carl Sauer, *The Geography of the Ozark Region* (Chicago, 1920) and *Land and Life* (Berkeley and Los Angeles, 1963).

Paul B. Sears, *Deserts on the March* (Oklahoma, 1947).

Homer Shantz, with C. F. Marbut, *Vegetation and Soils of Africa* (New York, 1923), and, with B. L. Taylor, *Photographic Documentation of Vegetational Changes in Africa Over a Third of a Century,* University of Arizona Report #169.

Victor Shelford, "Animal Communities in Temperate America," *Bulletin of the Geographical Society of Chicago,* Vol. 1, pp. 1-368, and *The Ecology of North America* (Urbana, Ill., 1963).

Larry B. Slobodkin, "Energy in Animal Ecology," *Advances in Ecological Research* (New York, 1962), pp. 69-101.

Hon. Russell E. Train, "Air, Water and Action," Address to the Consumer Assembly (1966), and "New Perspectives in Conservation," Address to the Garden Club of America (1967).

William Vogt, *Road to Survival* (New York, 1948), and *People* (New York, 1961).

19

S. DILLON RIPLEY AND HELMUT K. BUECHNER

Ecosystem Science as a Point of Synthesis

THE MOST critical problem facing humanity today is an ecological one of relating human societies harmoniously to their environments. Before conditions caused by radioactive fallout, pollution, exploding populations, the greenhouse effect of increased atmospheric carbon dioxide, and intersocietal aggression can be treated, the knowledge of the humanities and the behavioral sciences, as well as the natural sciences, must be integrated. Our recent awareness of critical environmental problems has created a favorable climate of thought for an intellectual orientation of knowledge relevant to contemporary world problems. But the task of orienting knowledge in a contemporary ecological context seems overwhelming. Knowledge has become so complex that depth of understanding requires specialization. Appreciable understanding of other disciplines is often necessary to a satisfying performance in a given specialty, but comprehension of the unity of knowledge appears difficult to achieve.

An idea for orienting knowledge on an ecological theme in a context of today's world problems is suggested by the concepts of "levels of biological integration" and "points of view," and their philosophic basis, formulated by Frank E. Egler twenty-five years ago.[1] The levels of integration are now so widely accepted that this approach has been incorporated into the BSCS series of high-school textbooks. The points of view, however, have not had a comparable impact. Although this system for organizing knowledge was already established in Europe during the nineteenth century, its use in American research and education has been casual and seemingly without full awareness of its value. Our purpose in the present paper is to present a two-dimensional conceptual model, based on levels of integration and points of view, as an aid in orienting knowledge with relevance to the ecological crisis.

The first dimension of the model considers levels of biological integration in terms of ecosystems. Biological entities, such as cells, organisms, populations, and communities, represent levels of integration in which the whole is more than a mere sum of the parts. A population of an African antelope, for example, has a birth rate, a death rate, a social behavior, an intrinsic rate of population increase, and a pool of genetic variation—all attributes that emerge at the population level of integration through the interactions of the individual members. By integrating the population of antelopes with all other kinds of living organisms and the nonliving, or physical, components (such as earth, water, and air), a more complex level of organization emerges, to which the term *ecosystem* has been applied. An ecosystem, or ecological system, functions as an interacting whole in nature. It is an open-energy system in which solar energy is incorporated into organic compounds through the photosynthetic process in green plants. Energy circulates within the plant, from plant to animal, from animal to animal, and finally through decomposing organisms, such as fungi and bacteria. In this process, the original potential energy in plants is degraded from concentrated form to greater and greater dispersion as unavailable heat energy, until all of it is lost to the living systems. An ecosystem is somewhat analogous to an open reservoir, with energy in place of water flowing through the system. Maintaining the ecosystem requires a constant input of energy, which moves through the system and is eventually lost to the system. Through feedback mechanisms, the system maintains a certain degree of stability in what is known as a steady state, or homeostasis. A single cell and its microenvironment, whether free-living or part of a tissue system, may be conceptualized as an ecosystem. If viruses and rickettsiae are accepted as living systems, one can go to biological levels below that of the cell. Tissues, organs, organisms, populations of organisms of a single kind, interspecific populations of plants or animals, and biocommunities constitute biological entities at levels of increasing complexity; each can be considered an ecosystem if the total environment is added as an integral part of the system.

Populations of human beings are uniquely characterized by their highly complex social behavior, which emerges as human society. The societies of man, together with their total environments, form the highest level of biological integration, the emergent attributes of which are incomparably more complex than those of a population of an African antelope. Man's societies dominate all ecosystems on earth. The current ecological crisis arises out of this dominance, since man has allowed his populations to increase excessively and to degrade his environmental systems.

We need to concentrate our orientation of knowledge on the human-society-plus-environment level of integration because of its relevance to the central world problem of achieving a reasonably steady state between human societies and the finite resources of our planet. We are as much concerned with human society itself as with the environments in which men live; both are parts of an interacting whole that evolves as a unit through time.

The second dimension in our conceptual model concerns the points of view suggested in 1910 by S. Tschulok, and slightly modified by Egler, for studying any subject matter. Although the interfaces between points of view are increasingly recognized as significant areas of study, the separate points of view provide the basic framework for organizing knowledge. Any entity—be it a purely physical system, a biological organism, or a complex of any kind— may be studied from the following points of view:

1. The components of the system—sub-atomic particles, cells, living organisms, physical components (such as air and water) or planets of a solar system

2. Structure or morphology—the organization of the parts, including the social organization within and between species of animals, the structural relationships of plants in the physiognomy of vegetation, or the cells and organs of higher plants and animals

3. Functions and processes—the physiology of the system, including regulatory mechanisms that control homeostasis in living systems at any level of organization

4. Distribution in time—changes in the system through time, whether ontogenetic or phylogenetic

5. Distribution in space—zoogeography, phytogeography, or human geography, for example

6. Relationships to environment—the influence of the entity on the environment as well as the environmental effects on the entity

7. Classification—for example, the taxonomy of plants or animals, the classification of vegetation, or the classification of whole ecosystems

These points of view can be applied to the human-society-plus-environment level of integration. At this level, as at any other, there are unique attributes for the system as a whole. The movement of radioactive particles or DDT through plants and non-human animals into man—who released these contaminants in the first place—is an ecosystem phenomenon. It involves decisions in the minds of men as well as the physical movement of the particles through the air, water, and soil. Through the past five thousand years, man has been altering his environments to his own disadvantage—as in the salinization of the soils of Mesopotamia, the deforestation of Iran and Greece, the overgrazing by sheep in Spain, the destruction of the Great Lakes fisheries by the sea lamprey, the drying-up of the Everglades National Park, the expansion of the arid lands of the world, pollution of rivers, the eutrophication of lakes and estuaries, the excessive erosion of topsoil from our most valuable arable lands, and the atmospheric pollution in Los Angeles. Modern technology provides the capacity for macroenvironmental manipulations unimagined a few years ago. Man's alterations of planet earth are phenomena of ecosystems at the level of human-society-plus-environment. They involve new processes, resulting from the behavior of man, that were not part of the physiology of the earth's ecosystems five thousand years ago.

It is important to recognize that human societies are an integral component of the highest level of biological integration. Man is in nature; he is a part of nature, not a separate and divine creation acting as an outside influence on the earth's ecosystems. The impact of man on natural systems is mediated through human societies. Societies themselves are complex, integrated wholes with unique characteristics that emerge from the interactions of individual human beings. Mob violence or peaceful civil rights demonstrations exhibit characteristics not expressed by man as an individual. Similarly, the making of decisions that affect society is normally a phenomenon of group action. The U. S. Congress represents something more than a mere summation of the individual thoughts of congressmen. The quality of the individuals that constitute society and the groups within societies naturally determines the behavior of society as a whole. One person can have a significant influence on society, as in the case of Rachel Carson through her book *The Silent Spring*.

Society can be conceptually segregated from the natural ecosystem for the purpose of studying its unique attributes, although society is, in fact, a component of a larger whole and the segregation is an artificial one. The study of society from the seven points of view mentioned earlier provides a perspective on the role of the social scientist and humanist in reaching an understanding of the total system of human-society-plus-environment.

Man's image of the world in which he lives and his understanding of man's place in the universe are critical in achieving ecological homeostasis. Science can contribute basic facts and ideas about ecosystems. But man's concerns and values also determine the behavior of societies. His conceptual environment has changed through time, a transformation expressed in literature, poetry, music, architecture, and modifications of the landscape. The natural scientist will most probably have less influence in the evolution of a conceptual environment relevant to today's ecological crisis than the humanist. Man's conceptual environment, not science, will determine the future of humanity.

The humanist now has the responsibility of developing our understanding of values with relevance to the central ecological problems of our times. Seemingly, an ecological theme in which one studies the history of man in the context of his environmental relationships can be as fundamental and intellectually rewarding as a traditional approach through the cultural evolution of man with emphasis on political systems. Instead of studying society isolated in a historical context, one should study the whole ecosystem of human-society-plus-environment and the interrelationships between these systems on a global basis. By segregating society from the rest of the natural system, the behavioral scientist and humanist can perhaps more readily identify his role in helping to achieve a steady state, but ultimately they must integrate society and man's total environment into an ecosystem concept.

Ecosystems at the highest level of biological integration are not only more complex than we think they are, but more complex than we *can* think. Thus, we can never achieve a total understanding of the human-society-plus-environment system. Nevertheless, the two-dimensional conceptual model suggested here does provide an approach through which interdisciplinary efforts can be organ-

24

ized to evolve unifying principles and concepts leading to a better understanding of man's place in the universe. In this model, the human-society-plus-environment ecosystem represents a point of synthesis for the focus of research and education on the contemporary problems of adapting human societies harmoniously to their environments. The orientation of knowledge necessary to achieve a self-sustaining homeostasis of human societies within the ecosystems of the world is the responsibility not only of university scientists and educators, but also of scientists in private corporations and government agencies, congressmen, city planners, musicians, landscape architects—indeed, all individuals and groups that can contribute effectively in a common effort ranging from the pure theory of ecosystem-oriented science to its application.

How can we come to grips with the formidable task of achieving an ecological orientation before irreversible alterations in our ecosystems preclude the evolution of higher levels of human life? Our universities are at the heart of the advancement of knowledge in the separate disciplines, but their administrative structure tends to militate against the interdisciplinary programs. Students and higher administrators may be ready for a contemporary ecological orientation for education and research, but many university scholars were programmed before the space age, and for some, reprogramming is impossible. Many government agencies are filled with mission-oriented bureaucrats and scientists who fight for their projects like department heads at universities. Fortunately, the educated public is becoming more and more concerned with the problems of the atomic bomb and pollutants. There is a gnawing feeling that we cannot know the safe levels of DDT and Strontium 90 without more basic research over a significant period of time. Many congressmen, expressing concern over the quality of our environment, are ready to tackle such fundamental problems—problems left untouched in the past.

The task involves research, education, and communication of information to society. The solution of our problems in agriculture resulted in large part from the remarkable feedback system at our land-grant colleges, in which all three of these components were present. Compared with agriculture, the problem of bringing the world's exploding populations into homeostasis within the limited natural resources is infinitely more challenging. Perhaps we can develop the organizational structure we need at regional centers for ecosystem science, which would emphasize interdisciplinary approaches and use the human-society-plus-environment ecosystem as a point of synthesis. Such centers for ecosystem science are needed not only in the United States, but in other strategic regions of the world. Initially, the body of basic knowledge required for ecological homeostasis must be accumulated. But subsequently, education and the flow of sound information to the general public will be vital to rapid progress and ultimate success. In research, the guidance of our best scholars in science, technology, social science, and the humanities is needed so that knowledge meaningful in the context of time and relevant to our ecological crisis will evolve. Our critical shortage of professional ecologists and the urgency of orienting general education to an ecological theme define the problem in education. Since society will ultimately determine the future of our ecosystems, the decisions of society require an ecological basis that can be developed only through communication of sound knowledge to the general public. Special centers for advanced studies focusing attention on the critical problems of man's ecological behavior can enhance the programs at regional centers in the major ecosystems of the world.

Regional centers must involve universities, but because the centers are new and organized on an integrative theme, they will provide opportunities for developing interdisciplinary programs without being hampered by the conventional departmental structure of universities. Strong financial support from Congress would preclude the struggle for survival among departments or disciplines. The co-operation of universities, governmental laboratories, federal agencies, industry, and private foundations is essential to such regional centers. Each organization will have clearly identified roles and indispensable functions. The value of the Smithsonian Institution as a basically private organization with strong governmental relationships should not be overlooked by society.

By recognizing that human societies and their total environments form the highest level of biological integration, one can direct thought and research to the unique phenomena that emerge at this level in nature. By approaching the human-society-plus-environment ecosystem as a whole, the special disciplines of knowledge are more precisely revealed in their relationship to one another and to the entire scope of man's knowledge. A more profound ecological knowledge of man-in-nature, developed through the two-dimensional model suggested here and others, is fundamental to higher levels of human life and meaning—both in respect to the quality of human individuals and human societies and to the symbolic expression of these values in the external landscape.

REFERENCES

1. Frank E. Egler, "Vegetation as an Object of Study," *Philosophy of Science*, Vol. 9, No. 3 (1942), pp. 245-60.

2. S. Tschulok, "Das System der Biologie," ed., Forschung and Lehr, *Eine historisch kritische Studie* (Jena, 1910).

WATER, AIR, AND LAND

JOSEPH L. FISHER

The Several Contexts of Water

THE FASHION nowadays is to call magazines by such names as
Scope, Focus, Dimension, Horizon, and Situation, not to mention
Time, Life, and Fortune.[1] The word for the following discussion is
context, because water is of no particular importance apart from its
relationship with other resources, geographical areas, programs of
development, jobs and incomes, legal and institutional forms, and
the perceptions people have regarding its present and possible future
uses. Despite the obvious importance of water not only in the desert
regions of the country but everywhere, water is not the lifeblood of
the nation. It is not the single foundation of the western economy
nor a thing to be worshiped. Water is not any of these things by
and of itself.

Water has to be placed in an appropriate setting, surrounded by
and related to other elements in the natural and social environment,
before it has meaning for individuals and relevance for regional and
national policy. To alter slightly the catchphrase of Marshall Mc-
Luhan, the *context* is the message.

This is the day of systems research, computer programming, and
matrices. Accordingly, I ask the reader to picture a simple two-way
matrix or table. Listed up and down in the left-hand column are what
I shall call the principal social purposes of water conservation and
use: engineering efficiency, economic development, ecological balance, and aesthetic satisfaction. Across the top of the table or matrix,
and forming the heading of a series of columns, are regions or geographic areas of increasing size: first the river itself narrowly conceived, next the basin or drainage area of the river, then the multi-
basin region, then the whole country, and finally an appropriate
international region, or perhaps the whole world. I shall examine
water resources in terms of this matrix, this set of contexts, and indi-

cate how efficiency, economic, ecological, and aesthetic purposes for water development take on different meanings and dimensions depending on the size and the natural and social characteristics of the geographical area under consideration.

I shall not come down in favor of planning, developing, conserving, using, or even looking at water in any one context. Rather, I shall argue that each relevant context should be considered and that choices for water-development activities should be made through carefully structured, professionally sound, democratically based processes. No one approach and no one formula will do the job. Different kinds of evidence and argument must be brought to the table for consideration by those in government and industry who ultimately are responsible for the decisions.

In a sense, the easiest of the four major social purposes to deal with is the one labeled engineering efficiency, but even this is quite complicated. Taking the narrowest of my regions, the river itself, one is faced with certain questions: What is the most efficient set of dams, reservoirs, power generating facilities, canals, and the rest to store some specified amount of water, to regulate flow within specified ranges and probabilities, or to produce a given amount of electric power to meet loads with specified characteristics? How can the carefully defined job be done at the lowest cost? What is the most sensible sequence in which to construct the various elements in the engineering plan? Difficult though these questions may be in terms of the data and analytical techniques available for answering them, they are compounded if one moves back from the riverbanks to include the agricultural land, the forests, and the other resources in the river basin. The problem becomes more difficult still if other adjoining river systems and basins are brought within the ambit of concern. Ultimately one can conceive of continental water development and management systems for which the relatively simple notion of engineering efficiency becomes exceedingly difficult to apply.

But, of course, the engineering-efficiency context is limited, as engineers would be among the first to point out. One quickly moves on to the social purpose I have labeled economic development. In many respects, economic development is a logical and inevitable extension of considerations of engineering efficiency. As soon as one begins to think of the wider consequences of whatever engineering plan is being considered, he comes quickly to such matters as markets for the goods and services that may be produced as a result of the river development, jobs that may arise from construction of projects or later from new agricultural and industrial activities, various indirect economic results, such as the creation of new cities, and the loss of certain opportunities that are foregone when dams and reservoirs are put in place. Beyond this level are the problems of securing the investment funds for the water development, not to mention the raw materials and labor skills necessary for construction and operation. The economic consequences that follow from river development may extend well beyond the region concerned—to the country and perhaps to the whole world. Furthermore, they extend in time for decades and perhaps for centuries into the future. The development of a river is like the development of a railroad system or a great city: One gets a sure sense of the profound and lasting effects that will follow without being able to assess them accurately and in some cases even to imagine them. Try, for instance, to imagine the Pacific Southwest without Hoover, Davis, Parker, and Imperial dams. Look into the future and try to imagine this region with large importations of water from the Northwest and with numerous desalinization plants probably powered by nuclear energy.

Frequently the cost-benefit estimate is the merit test applied to a water-development undertaking. The idea here is to reckon in dollars the benefits and costs that are expected to be associated with a particular project as its effects move out like ripples on a pond. The notion is straightforward and sensible and bears comparison with the profit calculation of a private enterprise. But a number of partially hidden difficulties make estimating the cost-benefit ratio uncertain in its fundamental meaning and difficult to apply in concrete situations. For example, there is the problem of deciding exactly which benefits and which costs should be included in the calculation. This is not so bad for those goods and services produced as a result of the project for which there is a market and a clear indication of monetary value, such as hydroelectric power. But as one moves away from what can be gauged in the market, the problems of estimating the costs and benefits increase. Recreational benefits can be indicated, for example, by adding up the expenditures that a family makes in going to a reservoir for recreation or by arbitrarily assigning a value to such recreation of five dollars a day per person, or one dollar and sixty cents as the U.S. Corps of Engineers does, or some other figure. But few would argue that recreation values can be measured in dollars with much precision. Fortunately the cost of providing recreational experiences can be measured more accurately than the benefits, but even here the difficulties are formidable. For example, what portion of the cost of forest protection, land acquisition, or general management should be allocated to recreation as compared to timber production?

Other shortcomings of cost-benefit estimates as a way of evaluating water-development projects abound. One difficulty is the selection of a rate of discount by means of which one can compare benefits and costs that accrue over time. The rate of discount can be all-important for long-term investments like multiple-purpose dams and reservoirs. In a long-term house mortgage, 4 percent over twenty years adds up to as much in interest charges as the cost of the house, and 6 percent is half again as much. Forest conservationists will typically advocate a low discount rate, thus favoring projects whose benefits are expected to be received further in the future. A study of 178 Army Engineer projects authorized by Congress in 1962 and involving about three billion dollars showed that 9, 64, and 80 percent, respectively, of the dollar amounts of these projects would fail the cost-benefit test if rates of discount of 4, 6, and 8 percent were used instead of the lower rates actually applied.[2]

Benefits from multiple-purpose projects also tend to be overstated whenever each single purpose is marked up against the cost of achieving it separately by a single-purpose project. And costs are frequently understated by failing to take into account the more remote damages and losses that inevitably result from most large water developments. Thus, the diversion of some 1.2 million acre-feet of water from the Colorado River by the Central Arizona project would force a reduction of income (or fail to permit an increase) from irrigation and other activities downstream, but this effect is not reflected in the stated costs of the project.[3] Beyond this is the effect of water and irrigation development in one part of the country on farm income and on employment in other parts. One estimate indicated that by 1957 federal irrigation programs in the West had displaced about 480 million dollars in annual farm production in the South, representing 5 percent of the total southern farm production, or about one farm worker out of twenty.[4]

In water-poor regions there is serious question as to whether the scarce water supply is being used wisely from the economic viewpoint. For example, a recent study of new water supply from the San Juan River in New Mexico indicated that, in terms of effects on incomes within that state, using the water for industry would yield benefits some forty times greater than would accrue from using the water for irrigation agriculture. For recreation, the benefits thus measured might be five or six times as large.[5] In the arid West, a reduction in irrigation use of water by 5 percent would make possible a doubling of industrial water use.

On the other hand, cost-benefit estimating procedures tend to be biased against further off, indirect, hard-to-see benefits, such as the opening up of whole regions. There is truth in the statement that much of the West might never have been settled had the narrow-minded economic analysts and the strict engineering efficiency experts called the shots. A sense of history and a flair for seeing hidden possibilities are essential in these matters. However great the difficulties of measurement, some rating of expected benefits and costs, or net returns, on water projects is necessary to make intelligent decisions. These benefits and costs have to be seen in alternative contexts of regions of different size.

I come now to my third social purpose, which I have termed ecological balance. This is primarily a constraint on the first two —engineering efficiency and economic development. It cautions against those water-development projects that will so seriously disrupt the natural environment over time that they ultimately defeat the purposes they were intended to advance. One thinks of the rapid siltation of reservoirs, the salting of the soil, the flooding or drainage of wildlife habitat, and the spoiling of scenery by reservoirs of fluctuating depth. In the wake of water programs come agricultural, industrial, municipal, and recreational development as well as many more people. Water and air pollution increase; the rural and back-country environment becomes disfigured. The inevitable result is the disruption of important natural balances—involving land, water, forests, grass, and the atmosphere—that form the basis for man's livelihood and social activities. These disruptions are more visible and dramatic in the fragile environment of arid lands than elsewhere. In other places, such as tidewater, Virginia, lush vegetation quickly covers up most of the egregious insults that people can inflict on the land, and the rivers flush themselves out in a short time. But in arid zones, nature's balances are more delicate, and points of no return are reached much sooner. The exercise of greater care must become ingrained in the habits of the people as well as the plans of government if a viable ecology is to be sustained—whether in the Arizona desert, the Florida Everglades, the Chesapeake marshes, or the Dakota potholes.

Ecological balance should be conceived of in the dynamic sense; it has a time dimension as well as a spatial one. But the notion, when greatly extended, raises profound issues. What can be said, if any-thing, about whole communities of people, or whole regions, com-ing into flower and then being allowed to decline—either to pass out of existence altogether or perhaps to resume an evolution along a different and more modest pathway?

Many mining communities in the West have passed through such an evolution into ghost-town oblivion from which only the curiosity of tourists can rescue them. Should whole sections of the Southwest desert region be permitted to mine out the ground water (and to an extent the soil because of salinization or erosion), make their con-tribution to the nation's food and fiber supply for two or three gen-erations of time, and then pass from the scene? This process has happened before, unplanned, in earlier Indian times. Similarly, should a water area like Lake Erie be allowed to lose all its fish and much of its recreational potential because of eutrophication (the using up of oxygen by excessive algae growth caused by drainage of phosphates and discharge of other pollutants into the lake)?

The regional dimension is important for ecology also and can vary all the way from the microbiology of the lower Colorada basin, San Francisco Bay, and the dunes of Cape Cod and Lake Michigan. Activities to reduce water losses from evaporation, transpiration, and seepage can have effects that range in scope from the minutely local to the regional and national.

Somewhere out beyond the economic and the ecologic, but in certain ways more important nowadays than either, are aesthetic considerations. The mounting problems of pollution constitute an aesthetic threat as well as a danger to health and a drain on the econ-omy. In both their design and function, water developments can delight the eye and satisfy one's sense of order and purpose, or they can offend both. Similarly, the related works of man that are erected and put into operation as a result of water programs can please or displease. People probably know better what they dislike in land-scapes and water scenes than what they like—although, of course, one can get 100 percent agreement that the Grand Canyon is beau-tiful and inspiring.

A few psychologists and anthropologists have recently become interested in ferreting out the ingredients of what we call natural beauty. Does it inhere in nature and things or is it solely in the eye of the beholder? How much of it can be reduced to form, color, sequence, and association? How may one classify the types of scen-ery along a highway in terms of the motorist's visual impressions and emotional or sentimental associations? To rate the various elements of natural beauty on some kind of value scale and thus allow the aesthetic appeal of a dam, a trout stream, a recreational lake, or even an irrigation canal to be taken systematically into account in deciding upon water projects is an objective worth striving for.

The size of the region under consideration makes a difference too—whether it is the river alone, the basin with its agriculture and industry, or a larger region. The planning of recreation and natural beauty now going forward in connection with the development of the Potomac River is an example. Land-use proposals deal with land well back from the river's edge, and recreational uses of the river are related to recreational trends and developments in a four-state region.

The time has come when we must conceive rather large park and outdoor recreation systems made up of numerous land and water areas, scenic highways, trails, camping and picnicking facilities, educational and interpretive programs, conservation experiences, and so on, spread over quite extended regions. Examples would be the Maine coast, the Appalachian hinterland to the west and north of the Boston-to-Washington megalopolis, the northern Great Lakes area, the northern California redwoods-mountains-shoreline complex, and the Olympic Peninsula–Puget Sound–Cascades region.

The development of these large park and recreational systems has to be based on trends in population and family-income levels, changes in travel habits, and new kinds of recreation demands. On the supply side, the variety of sites for land and water recreation has to be considered, but so must we explore the alternative ways that these sites can be developed and managed as interrelated parts of a system. We already have state park systems and a national park system, but these are defined for administrative convenience rather than in broad functional terms. I have thought, for example, that much of the present unprofitable controversy regarding a Northern California redwoods park—should it be state or federal? how should private owners and even whole communities be compensated for loss?—could be dissolved by looking at the whole coastal California region north from San Francisco as a recreation and preservation system of many interrelated parts including seacoast, redwood trees, small drainage basin complexes, mountains, and even exhibition areas to instruct people in forest or fishing industries. Such a system could be planned to meet projected needs for forest products, outdoor recreation, scenic preservation, and viable communities. Per-

37

haps it could be brought forward under some new kind of organization that would embrace federal, state, local, and private elements.

Neither engineering efficiency, economic development, ecological balance, nor aesthetic satisfaction can provide, by itself, the answer as to the best way to develop water resources. A typical water project should be analyzed in its several relevant contexts. The Central Arizona project, for example, has engineering, economic, ecological, and aesthetic impacts on the Colorado River, its immediately adjacent land and scenery, the heavily populated parts of Arizona centering on Phoenix and Tucson, the Pacific Southwest region, including Southern California, the whole country, and to a degree the world. At the national level, the project has a financial effect because of the federal subsidy involved; it will also have effects on recreation visitors from other parts of the country and on national markets for the crops and manufacturing products that will result.

The same kind of story could be told of the Arkansas, the Ohio, the Potomac, or the Delaware where an innovative interstate, multipurpose program has been launched over the past several years. It is critical that those who draw up the plans for water development and those who will make the important decisions—whether they be in the government or in the private sector—have asked the right questions and have the best possible information available to them. The planning and decision process becomes the key to better water conservation and use; in this process, a look at water in its several contexts furnishes helpful guidelines.

REFERENCES

1. An earlier version of this essay was presented at the 1967 Annual Meeting of the American Forestry Association.

2. Irving K. Fox and Orris C. Herfindahl, "Attaining of Efficiency in Satisfying Demands for Water Resources," *American Economic Review* (May, 1964).

3. Charles W. Howe, "Competition for Water in an Expanding Economy, Economic Objectives and Issues," American Society of Civil Engineers Conference (Sacramento, California, November 1-3, 1967).

4. G. S. Tolley, "Reclamation's Influence on the Rest of Agriculture," *Land Economics*, Vol. 35, No. 2 (May, 1959).

5. Nathaniel Wollman, *The Value of Water in Alternative Uses* (Albuquerque: University of New Mexico Press, 1962).

AZRIEL TELLER

Air-Pollution Abatement: Economic Rationality and Reality

I

A STAFF Report to the Committee on Public Works of the United States Senate stated: "There is strong evidence that air pollution is associated with a number of respiratory ailments. These include: (1) nonspecific infectious upper respiratory disease, (2) chronic bronchitis, (3) chronic constrictive ventilatory disease, (4) pulmonary emphysema, (5) bronchial asthma, and (6) lung cancer."[1]

Air pollution affects vegetation and livestock and causes property damage. "Most common materials are adversely affected by pollution. Metals corrode, fabrics weaken and fade, leather weakens and becomes brittle, rubber cracks and loses its elasticity, paint discolors, concrete and building stone discolor and erode, glass is etched, and paper becomes brittle."[2]

Residents of such areas as Chicago, New York, Philadelphia, Los Angeles, Cleveland, Detroit, St. Louis, Pittsburgh, and Boston are demanding that something be done to reduce the level of air pollution. For most pollutants, the question is not how to control air pollution, but rather how much to control it. Pollutants like fly ash can be controlled to the 99.9 percentile, but is this necessary? One must ask this question because air-pollution abatement is not free. In fact, the cost of air-pollution abatement rises at an increasing rate as the level of abatement increases. Assume, for example, that there are three identical control devices, each with a rated efficiency of 90 per cent, in series with one another. This means that for every thousand particles in the gas stream, nine hundred will be removed by the first device, and one hundred will remain in the gas stream to enter the second device. Ninety particles will be removed by the second device, leaving ten to enter the third device, where nine will be removed. This leaves one particle remaining in the gas stream to be emitted into the atmosphere. Thus, one control device removes 90 per cent of the particles; two control devices, 99 per cent; and three control devices, 99.9. A 100 per cent increase in expenditure, therefore, results in a 10 per cent increase in abatement. A 200 per cent increase in expenditure results in an 11 per cent increase in abatement. Is this extra expenditure worthwhile? At the present time, no one can prove that it is. Nevertheless, a number of people firmly believe that the extra expenditure is necessary. Dr. E. Cuyler Hammond of the American Cancer Society, for example, has cautioned: "While we do not yet know the importance of various components of general air pollution, it would appear to be wise to reduce general air pollution of all types insofar as possible."[3] It is such specious reasoning that compels me to present an economic rationale for air-pollution abatement.

II

Economic Rationale

Clean air is a scarce resource. So are land, trees, human beings, animals, petroleum, and water. Like water, air is essential to life; however, unlike most resources, there is no market place in which air is bought and sold. This situation is not due to the inherent role air plays in our daily lives. (Food is also a necessity, but it is bought and sold daily.) It results, rather, from the nature of the product: The services of air are demanded by all but owned by none. Air is a collective good, and, therefore, it is society's responsibility to see that it is allocated efficiently.

Economics has two main applications to the study of air pollution. It enables one to estimate either the extent of the damage resulting from air pollution (that is, the external diseconomies of production) so that it can be rectified, or the market structure for clean air so as to determine the necessary amount of abatement. Since there is no formal market for the services of air (approach two), firms are allowed to impute their cost of production to some members of society (approach one). Thus, the two approaches are not separate and independent. There is a difference, however, between the two implications. The first approach implies that firms have not been "good citizens" of society and consequently must be prohibited from contaminating the atmosphere. It suggests that it is unjust for producers to transfer their costs of production to an innocent party, that such practices should be stopped, and that the damages be rectified. But this is an all-or-nothing proposition. If approach one is used and it is decided that these diseconomies should be eliminated, there is no halfway point in eliminating the costs to society.

But there is another side of the problem that is rarely discussed —the diseconomies of consumption on the part of human beings, plants, and animals. Because they demand the resource air to be of a certain quality, they are imposing a cost on industries that also use this resource. Firms that would normally not abate are forced to, but the consumer of clean air does not pay directly for any costs of abatement.

This inconsistency can be demonstrated by an analogy. Let us assume that two brothers jointly own a piece of property. One brother uses the air over the property for testing high-altitude jet airplanes. The other brother uses the property to make sound movies. Obviously, the airplanes can be tested while movies are being made, whereas the opposite is not possible. These two activities could operate simultaneously if the noise from the jets were muffled. Who should pay for these mufflers? The jet pilot argues that both his brother and he have the right to use the property as they please. The pilot contends that since the moviemaker has selected an endeavor requiring quiet, he should pay for the mufflers. The moviemaker argues that his brother should bear the full cost, since his planes are disturbing the natural state. Approach one implies that the moviemaker has a just argument.

Analogically, no individual has the endowed right to obtain clean air free, simply because it is a necessity. A person does have the right, however, to have the opportunity to purchase clean air. Similarly, a person does not obtain food free because it is a necessity. Just because it is a necessity, a person has the right to have an opportunity to purchase food. Nevertheless, there are differences in the opportunities to obtain food, which is a private good, and clean air, which is a collective good. With a private good, if an individual wants a resource of a certain quality, he can purchase it himself. But with a collective good, the individual may not be able to obtain the quality he desires in a particular resource. Society as a whole might not want it. Society must simulate the market structure for collective goods like clean air and attempt to allocate them efficiently. It can only do this if it can estimate the demand and supply schedules for clean air.

In attempting to simulate the market for air, it is important to realize that demand and supply schedules are different for those sectors of society that produce air pollution and those that are affected by it.[4] The sources of air pollution have a demand for "air," whereas receptors have a demand for "clean air." These are different commodities; as such, the "demands" cannot be aggregated. In reality, there is no schedule for either the supply of air or the demand for air. The supply is there and, from our point of view, is essentially infinite. It can also be assumed that a source's demand for the resource air is infinite, since it could not operate without air. This is equivalent to the normal assumption that an individual's demand for air is infinite, since without air a person dies. Thus, there is no market for the commodity air, and no possibility of simulating one. In contrast, the supply of clean air increases as the degree of pollution decreases. The supply schedule for clean air can, therefore, be determined by estimating how much it would cost sources to reduce pollution. The demand for clean air can be determined by estimating the cost of the physical and psychic damage that results from different levels of air pollution and assuming that receptors would be willing to pay up to this amount so as not to incur such damage. This is, of course, not to say that they actually pay this amount.[5] This procedure can be illustrated with an example.

Let us assume that Table 1 lists the costs of the annual total

TABLE I:	Cost to Society from Air-Pollution Damage Cost to Society for Air-Pollution Control		
Level of Abatement (per cent)	Total Damage TD	Total Cost of Control TC	Total Cost to Society TD + TC
10	$370	$ 15	$385
20	270	25	295
30	200	35	235
40	140	50	190
50	90	70	160
60	60	105	165
70	45	145	190
80	30	210	240
90	20	320	340
100	0	430	430

damage to society that results with no abatement and also the estimated damage that would occur after different degrees of abatement. With 100 per cent abatement, no damage occurs. Table 1 also lists a schedule of the total cost of abatement. These two schedules are graphed in Figure 1 in the damage curve and the

Figure 1: Cost to Society from Air-Pollution Damage
Cost to Society for Air-Pollution Control

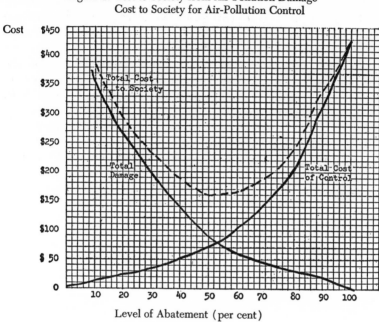

cost-of-control curve. Society desires to minimize the total cost from both types of expenditures, as both are costs to society. With no abatement, too many of society's resources are being used to offset the effects of air pollution. Conversely, with 100 per cent abatement, too many of society's resources are being used to control air pollution. The objective is to select a level of abatement that minimizes the total cost to society. In the example, the optimum point is 50 per cent abatement. At this level, the resources of society are being allocated efficiently.

One can also determine the optimum level of abatement by charting the benefits and costs of abatement. The benefits from abatement can be defined as the value of the damage that is averted by abatement. There are other benefits to society besides those from air-pollution abatement. These are the benefits from national defense, automobile safety, foreign aid, production, clean water, recreation, and so forth. In order to achieve each of these benefits, one must incur a cost. With respect to private goods, it is a private cost. With collective goods, it is a collective or social cost. The value of abatement to society is the difference between the benefits from abatement and the cost of abatement. If society simulates the market structure for collective goods and attempts to allocate them efficiently, it must choose that level of abatement with the greatest value to society.

A benefit-from-abatement schedule can be obtained from the cost-of-air-pollution schedule listed in Table 1. With no abatement, the damage resulting from air pollution is valued at $370. With 10 per cent abatement, the annual cost from pollution decreases to $270. Thus, the benefit to society from 10 per cent abatement is $100, the difference in damage between no abatement and 10 per cent abatement.[6] The resulting benefits-from-abatement schedule is listed in Table 2. The cost-of-abatement schedule is the same as in

TABLE 2: Benefit and Cost of Abatement

Level of Abatement (per cent)	Benefit TB ($)	Cost TC ($)	Value to Society TB–TC ($)
0	0	0	0
10	100	15	85
20	170	25	145
30	230	35	195
40	280	50	230
50	310	70	240
60	325	105	220
70	340	145	195
80	350	210	140
90	360	320	40
100	370	430	−60

Table 1. It shows the total cost of achieving each degree of air-pollution abatement. Figure 2 illustrates the two curves. The objective is to select the level of abatement that maximizes the value to society. From Table 2, the optimum level of abatement is at 50 per cent with the total value of $240. Any other level of abatement would not be efficient, as it would be of less value to society. Two other important points can be seen from this simple example. First, the level of abatement selected when the benefits and cost of abatement are compared is the same as the level selected when total costs to society are minimized. Second, simply

44

Figure 2: Benefit and Cost of Abatement

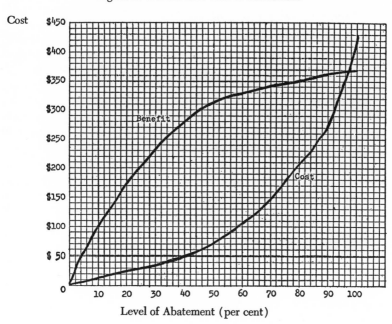

Level of Abatement (per cent)

knowing that the total benefits for any single level of abatement are greater than the total cost does not help society in deciding where to operate. It does not indicate to society whether to increase abatement, as is the case for 10-40 per cent abatement, or to decrease abatement, as is the case for 60-90 per cent abatement. People often justify erroneously a level of control on the basis of the benefits of abatement being greater than the costs. C. W. Griffin, Jr., for example, stated in the *Saturday Review:*

Even if air pollution presented no human health hazard whatsoever, we could justify a tremendous strengthening of control on purely economic grounds. . . . The nation's total bill is estimated at $11 billion a year, about twenty times the most optimistic estimate of the total national expenditures by industry and by all levels of government for control devices, research and enforcement programs.[7]

Even though Mr. Griffin states otherwise, his dubious estimates do not justify the conclusion that more abatement is necessary.[8] In order for society to determine the desired level of abatement, both the total-benefit schedule and the total-cost schedule are needed.

III

Economic Rationality and Reality

The greatest impediment to applying the theoretical determination of the level of abatement is the difficulty of estimating the benefits from abatement. In order to make such a calculation, the first and most important requirement is that there be a knowledge of the effects of air pollution. The short-run effects of an increase in the concentration, as well as the long-run cumulative effects, must be known. At the present time, there is some evidence, but there is no proof. This fact was clearly illustrated in a paper recently presented by E. Cuyler Hammond.[9] The paper, entitled "Epidemological Evidence on the Effects of Air Pollution," surveyed the present knowledge of the influences of occupational, personal (for example, tobacco smoke), and general air pollution on morbidity and mortality. With respect to general air pollution, his findings on some diseases are as follows:

Lung Cancer

I want to make it clear that I am not dismissing general air pollution as a possible contributing factor to the occurrence of lung cancer at some future date. I doubt that general air pollution will ever rise to such a level as to present a large risk of lung cancer to the non-smoker; if it should do so, then lung cancer would probably be the least of our worries. However, if general air pollution should continue to increase in the future as it has in the past, it may well result in a considerable increase in the risk of lung cancer among smokers and among persons exposed to certain types of occupational air pollution.[10]

Chronic Bronchitis

Goldsmith has reviewed the literature on chronic respiratory disease in relation to general air pollution. As he points out in this connection: "No excess mortality from chronic respiratory diseases has been documented." On the other hand, available evidence appears to me to indicate that at least in England an "urban factor" of some sort increases morbidity from such disease. Presumably, the "urban factor" is air pollution. . . . The evidence is overwhelming that personal air pollution, in the form of cigarette smoking, causes a very great increase in both mortality and morbidity from chronic bronchitis.[11]

Emphysema

Both among non-smokers with occupational exposure and among non-smokers without occupational exposure, the rural percentages were a little higher than the metropolitan percentages. . . . This was generally

46

the case among cigarette smokers (age and amount of smoking being taken into consideration).[12]

Coronary Heart Disease

Extreme general air pollution also appears to lead to an increase in deaths from coronary artery disease. . . . So far as I know, there is little or no evidence concerning the possibility of an association between coronary artery disease and general air pollution not exceeding the levels ordinarily present in many large cities.[13]

While there is some evidence that air pollution influences morbidity and mortality, there is no substantiation to the statement that "it would appear to be wise to reduce general air pollution of all types insofar as possible."[14]

The paucity of data does not imply that nothing should be done while further research is conducted on the effects of air pollution on material property and plant, animal, and human life. Air-quality standards should be established with the understanding that they may be changed as more evidence is accumulated. In the future, they may be made either more restrictive or more lenient. Two rationales are used in establishing air-quality standards. Each calls for a different approach to abatement.

Rationale One

The air-quality standard is set at that concentration which, if exceeded, would be "harmful" to society. If it is possible to predict when the standard will be exceeded, then it is necessary to abate only when trouble is expected.

Tragically, there is too much evidence on the effects of high short-run concentrations of pollutants. In recent times, serious air-pollution episodes have resulted in numerous deaths. The most acute was in London in 1952 when an excess of four thousand deaths occurred in a five-day period. These episodes can be predicted and abated. One approach is the air-pollution warning system proposed by the New York-New Jersey Co-Operative Commission on Interstate Air Pollution.[15] The proposal is worthwhile, first of all, because it recognizes that acute air-pollution episodes occur sporadically and can be predicted. Secondly, the degree of abatement reflects the situation at that moment. If the situation worsens, a greater amount of abatement can be used. According to the proposal, an air-pollution watch would be called if the meteorologists forecasted stable weather conditions for the next

47

thirty-six hours, or if the air-pollution concentrations for sulfur dioxide, carbon monoxide, and smoke exceeded the levels listed in Table 3 for one hour. If the air-pollution concentrations and meteorological conditions further deteriorated to the levels listed in Table 3, an air-pollution alert would be called. The standards and the control actions taken under each alert are discussed below.[16]

TABLE 3:   Standards for Air-Pollution Alerts

| Alert Status | Air Concentrations | | | Duration Sustained Levels of Air Concentrations (Hours) | N.Y.-N.J. Metro. Area Meteorology High Air-Pollution Potential Forecast for Next Hours | Action Plan |
	SO_2 ppm	CO ppm	Smoke Level COHS			
Air-Pollution Watch	.5	10+	5.0	1	and/or	36	
FIRST	.7+	10+	7.5	4*	and	36	1
SECOND	1.5+	20+	9.0	2	and	12	2
THIRD	2.0+	30+	10.0	1	and	8	3

First Alert: When air-pollution measurements exceed the standards for a first alert and the meteorological forecast indicates that profound stable air conditions will exist for the period of time tabulated on Table [3] . . . the Interstate Sanitation Commission recommends a first alert. If the states declare an alert, the following control measures will be taken by co-operating governmental agencies:

1. Large consumers of fuel are notified that an emergency is pending and are asked to reduce voluntarily their total fuel consumption to a minimum and substitute low-pollution-potential fuel where possible.

2. Industries and operators of municipal and commercial incinerators are asked to limit their activities which contribute to air pollution, except in those cases that are considered exempt, such as hospitals and other institutions essential to public health, safety, and welfare.

3. Motor vehicle operators are asked to reduce their activities to a minimum.

4. The public and refuse disposal operators are asked to cease open burning.

Second Alert: A second alert is recommended by the Interstate Sanitation Commission to the state agencies when the concentrations of air pollutants have reached the values established as the standard for this alert, when the weather forecast is for continued stable air conditions, or if the first alert has been in operation for twenty-four hours without a reduction in pollution. If a state declares a second alert, the co-operating government agencies require that all measures for the first alert be continued, with more stringent limitations on the consumption of fuel other than natural gas or Grade No. 2 fuel oil. Limitations are also set on the heating of homes and buildings, the use of domestic incinerators, and industrial operations. Motor vehicle operators are asked to cease operation on a voluntary basis.

Third Alert: It should be noted that a third alert indicates a serious danger to public health. The Interstate Sanitation Commission recommends a third alert to the state agencies when the concentrations of pollutants have reached the standards established for this alert, when the weather forecast is for continued profound stable air conditions, or when the second alert has been in operation for twenty-four hours (that is, a total of forty-eight hours after the initiation of the first alert) without reduction of pollution. If a state declares a third alert, the following actions are taken by the co-operating agencies and organizations:

1. All control activities of the first and second alert are continued.

2. Stringent limitations are imposed on traffic throughout the metropolitan area except for emergency vehicles.

3. Action is taken to reduce to a minimum industrial and commercial activity and public transportation.

Consideration is being given to limiting pollution by the following ways:

1. Stringent restrictions on the use and delivery of fuel oil, diesel oil, and motor fuels

2. Stringent restrictions on the burning of fuels other than gas

3. A curfew on lighting and heating similar to the brownout and heating limits during wartime.

Since operating and maintenance costs are functions of the number of hours a piece of equipment is utilized, the use of a regional warning system suggests an economical approach to the selection and use of air-pollution-control equipment. Depending on a city's industry, topography, and climate, the frequency of air-pollution episodes may range from zero to 100 per cent of the time. When a problem day is forecasted, it may be decreed that companies utilize their control equipment. This does not mean that companies cannot use their equipment more than is required or install more efficient equipment than is necessary. It does imply, however, that companies need not operate their abatement equipment 100 per cent of the time in order to satisfy the air-quality standards established by the control authorities. They may, therefore, invest more economically in control equipment.

The value of any warning system depends on how well weather conditions can be predicted. Like most other subjects within the area of air pollution, there is very little information on the ability of meteorologists to forecast air-pollution potential. Lawrence E. Niemeyer found that the highest particulate matter concentrations occurred in those periods when the following criteria were met:

1. Surface winds less than 8 knots

2. Winds at no level below 500 millibars (approximately 18,000 feet) greater than 25 knots

3. Subsidence, the slow sinking or settling of air from aloft, below 600 millibars (approximately 14,000 feet)

4. Simultaneous occurrence of the above with the forecast continuance of these conditions for thirty-six hours or more.[17]

From August, 1960, to July, 1961, the criteria established by Niemeyer were tested in the area of the United States east of the Rockies.[18] Within this period of time, twelve stagnation cases occurred, ten of which were forecasted. Another eight cases were forecasted, but not verified. Thus, with a total of eighteen forecasts issued, 83 per cent of the stagnating cases were predicted. As the meteorologists gain experience in forecasting air-pollution potential, their ability to predict will presumably improve.

Rationale Two

There are short-run, single-dose effects and long-range cumulative effects from air pollution. Also, there is a known relationship between a single high concentration and the long-run average concentration. Thus, the air-quality standard can be set so as to reduce the single high concentrations. If society always abates to satisfy this standard, then the long-run average concentration will also be reduced to a desired level.

This appears to be the approach followed by most air-pollution-control authorities even though, as illustrated by Hammond's survey, there is little evidence on the cumulative effects of air pollution. It is sometimes argued that Rationale Two is necessary to forestall any acute build-up of air-pollution concentrations. This is equivalent to saying that a region must abate 100 per cent of the time since a serious air-pollution episode is expected to arise, without warning, one or two times a year. This reasoning underestimates the ability of meteorologists to forewarn control authorities.

In general, then, the choice is between constant abatement and forecasting abatement. Within each choice, a number of approaches may be utilized in determining the necessary degree and cost of abatement. The naïve approach, which incurs the greatest cost to society, guarantees that there will not be an air-pollution problem. Each variation on the naïve can be considered a refinement and is based on the extent of our knowledge of the state of the environment. As more modifications are made, however, the probability of satisfying the air-quality standard declines, whereas the probability of finding the least costly solution increases. There is a trade-off between achieving the desired air quality and the determination of the least costly method. The latter involves an associated probability that the standard will not be satisfied. But there is also a cost in not utilizing the minimum-cost solution. Thus, the extent to which each model is used is determined by the knowledge of the environment, the desire to satisfy the standard, the desire to achieve accuracy in the estimates, and the desire to find the least costly solution to the air-pollution problem.

Two possible approaches are equiproportional abatement and selective abatement.

The Naïve Approach—Equiproportional Abatement: The naïve approach is the simplest method to apply in determining the degree and the cost of abatement. The approach assumes that all sources will reduce their emissions in the same proportion as the desired reduction in air-pollution concentration. Many people believe that this is the most equitable procedure since a source that accounts for x per cent of the total emissions is thus responsible for x per cent of the reduction. In reality, however, a source that emits x per cent of the emissions may be responsible for less than, or more than, x per cent of the concentration.

Selective Abatement: Selective abatement aims to find the minimum cost combination of abatement while still satisfying the air-quality standards. The theory behind selective abatement is that the cost of a unit reduction of emissions is not necessarily the same for all sources, and that the effect upon a particular receptor of a unit reduction of emissions is not necessarily the same for all sources. Thus, for each source it is necessary to know the cost of abatement, the amount of emissions, and the relationship between that source and any receptor. The latter is sometimes known as a meteorological diffusion model.[19]

City-wide or industry-wide emission standards are examples of equiproportional abatement. They generally state that all sources of pollution of a given magnitude must reduce their emissions to a certain level. Even if a source is located on the downwind side of an air-shed, it must control its emissions to the same degree as a similar source located upwind. The consequence of emission standards is that some sources do not control their emissions enough, while others must exercise too much control. Moreover, firms do not have an incentive to relocate in an effort to reduce their effect on the level of concentration. In some cases, relocation might be a more efficient method of control than abatement by equipment. Emission standards make relocation impotent. Nevertheless, emission standards are more efficient than selective abatement when the cost of implementing and supervising selective abatement is greater than the additional benefits that result from selective abatement. For most sources of air pollution, the cost of administrating equiproportional abatement is equivalent to that of selective abatement. In those cases where the sources are small but numerous, however, the cost of administrating selective abatement may be exorbitant. Examples of such sources are private residential units, small incinerators, back-yard burning of refuse, and automobiles. Moreover, because automobiles are mobile, the relationship between the emissions of any particular automobile and air quality cannot be accurately ascertained. In general, however, if society uses only equiproportional abatement, it has chosen an inefficient method of reducing air pollution.

In Table 4, the costs of different approaches to abatement are

TABLE 4:   Estimate of the Relative Cost of Sulfur-Dioxide Abatement
Through Fuel Substitution
1960 Estimate for Nashville Metropolitan Area[a]

	Air Quality Level[b]			
	1 %	2 %	3 %	4 %
1. Constant Abatement				
a. Equiproportional	48.5	66.4	86.8	100.0
b. Selective	13.0	25.8	39.4	71.5
2. Forecasting Abatement				
a. Equiproportional				18.0
b. Selective				12.9

[a] Low-sulfur coal was substituted for high-sulfur coal
[b] Sulfur-Dioxide Air-Quality Standards:

Level	2-hour average concentration (ppm)	24-hour average concentration (ppm)
1	0.50	0.30
2	0.40	0.25
3	0.30	0.20
4	0.20	0.10

compared.[20] The relative cost of constant abatement and forecasting abatement differ substantially. To satisfy air-quality level 4 by constant abatement costs per year five and a half times as much as forecasting abatement. Within constant abatement, equiproportional abatement is relatively more expensive than selective abatement. Generally speaking, the more severe the air-pollution problem or the more restrictive the air-quality standard, the smaller is the difference between equiproportional abatement and selective abatement. Thus, each city or air-shed must determine, in light of its own air-pollution problems, the relative worth of equiproportional abatement and selective abatement.

IV

The Mayor's Task Force on Air Pollution in the City of New York reported: "If New York had the sheltered topography of Los Angeles, everyone in this city would long since have perished from the poisons in the air."[21] This is true, but the point is that New York City is not Los Angeles. Each city is different and has its unique problems. The sources of pollution, types of pollution, receptors of pollution, and meteorology vary among cities. What is good for Los Angeles may not be good for New York. What is good for New York may not be good for Chicago. There can be neither a national blueprint for solving the air-pollution problem nor national emission standards. Each city or air-shed must approach air-pollution abatement with respect to its own particular situation, determining for itself whether it needs constant abatement, forecasting abatement, or a combination of the two; and, within the alternative selected, whether it needs equiproportional abatement, selective abatement, or a combination. Each city must decide the air-quality standards it needs. This does not imply that every air-shed is unique, that one city cannot learn from another city. Nevertheless, one city should not follow another city's air-pollution program without questioning the reasons for a particular action. Such reasoning does not abrogate the role of the Federal Government. The Federal Government should concern itself with studying the short-run and long-run effects of air pollution. It should help to develop and improve methods of abatement, conduct research on more extensive meteorological diffusion models and better meteorological forecasting models, serve as a center for air-pollution information, and assist in organizing interstate air-pollution commissions. On the other hand, the Federal Government should not establish national air-quality standards and, more important, must not establish national emission standards.

REFERENCES

1. U. S. Congress, Senate, "A Study of Pollution—Air," A Staff Report to the Committee on Public Works, 88th Congress, 1st Session, September, 1963, p. 14.

2. *Ibid.*, p. 20.

3. E. Cuyler Hammond, "Epidemological Evidence on the Effects of Air Pollution." A paper presented at the 60th Annual Meeting of the Air Pollution Control Association in Cleveland, Ohio, on June 14, 1967.

4. Sources of air pollution include such things as automobiles, industry, and incinerators. Receptors encompass humans, plants, animals, and property.

5. The demand for clean air can also be estimated by questioning everyone

on how much they would be willing to pay for clean air (that is, how much is clean air worth to them). Assuming that there is complete information on the damage resulting from air pollution, that the marginal disutility of damage can be measured in monetary terms, that everyone has the same marginal utility of money, and that everyone is honest, one should obtain the same answer as by the previous method.

6. In general,
   $$TB_a = TD_{a=0} - TD_a$$
   where a: per cent abatement $0 \le a \le 1$
   TB_a: total benefit from "a" per cent abatement
   $TD_{a=0}$: total damage with no abatement
   TD_a: total damage with "a" per cent abatement

7. C. W. Griffin, Jr., "America's Airborne Garbage," *Saturday Review* (May 22, 1965), p. 34.

8. In 1913, the Mellon Institute estimated the cost of smoke nuisance in Pittsburgh. The $11 billion a year estimate for the United States is a 1959 price and population extrapolation from the Pittsburgh data.

9. Hammond, "Epidemological Evidence on the Effects of Air Pollution."

10. *Ibid,* p. 8.

11. *Ibid,* pp. 13-14. See also, J. R. Goldsmith, "Epidemology of Bronchitis and Emphysema," *Medicina Thoracalis.* Vol. 22 (1965), pp. 1-23.

12. Hammond, "Epidemological Evidence on the Effects of Air Pollution," p. 19.

13. *Ibid,* p. 20.

14. *Ibid,* p. 23.

15. T. A. Glenn, Jr., "Regional Air Pollution Warning System," *Journal of the Air Pollution Control Association,* (January, 1966), pp. 22-24.

16. *Ibid,* pp. 23-24.

17. Lawrence E. Niemeyer, "Forecasting Air Pollution Potential," *Monthly Weather Review,* Vol. 88 (March, 1960), pp. 88-96.

18. Marvin Miller and Lawrence E. Niemeyer, "Air Pollution Potential Forecasts—A Year's Experience." *Journal of the Air Pollution Control Association,* Vol. 13 (May, 1963), pp. 205-10.

19. For example, see D. B. Turner, "A Diffusion Model for an Urban Area," *Journal of Applied Meteorology,* Vol. 3, No. 1 (February, 1964), pp. 83-91.

20. Azriel Teller, *Air-Pollution Abatement: An Economic Study Into the Cost of Control,* unpublished Ph.D. Dissertation, Johns Hopkins University, 1967.

21. *Freedom to Breathe,* Report of the Mayor's Task Force on the Air Pollution in the City of New York (June 20, 1966), p. 27.

55

DAVID ALLEE

American Agriculture—Its Resource Issues for the
Coming Years

FARMING IN the United States has been increasing its over-all
productivity at a rate perhaps unmatched in the history of man.
A large share of the natural resources and labor force normally
devoted to food production has, consequently, been released to
other uses. The sophisticated application of chemicals and power
to food and fiber production promises more than adequate supplies
for expanding domestic demands, at least for some years to come.
Larger contributions of American output to assist countries with
food deficits should be possible.

But all the problems created by this success are by no means
solved. Compared to the recent past, future demands will be for
greater quantity with more rigorous specifications of product
quality and with substantially more constraints on the industry
with respect to its indirect impact on other resource uses and community welfare. Problems of adjustment within the industry continue to seek solution, as is evidenced by low labor returns. The
shift to national and regional suppliers of inputs and marketing
services and shifts of production from one region to another have
left some rural areas with a community structure suited to a past
era. In many regions, productive land and water, once sought only
for farm use, are more and more under pressure for other uses.
Questions have been raised about the reasonableness of some shifts
to other uses. Increasing the use of chemicals and power to further
raise the productivity of land and water will multiply the potential
for objectionable impacts on the environment and the natural areas
that a more wealthy and sophisticated population is seeking to
enjoy.

We should find more effective ways to decrease the social costs
of rapid technological change in agriculture without undue sacrifice

in either direct output or alternative uses for the resources involved. This concerns, first, controlling and preventing "exotic" as well as "common" forms of pollution. Second, increases in the local intensity of lands used for farming must be consistent with other potential values such as wildlife habitat, other uses of water, and patterns of urban growth. Third, the social effects of displaced resources must be recognized and the use of resources redirected. Owners of resources must be assisted in their adjustment to resource displacement caused by a publicly stimulated technology, shifts in the economies of size in farming, or shifts in the relative ability of lands to remain in agriculture. And fourth, the size of the entire productive sector must remain consistent with long-term and short-term adjustments in the use of land for agricultural purposes, reflecting both domestic requirements and foreign commitments.

Pollution

The complexity of farm production is increasing and makes evaluation of its social effects more difficult but also more necessary. Individual dramatic items of farm technology, such as the tractor or hybrid corn, may be harder to distinguish in future changes. Still, even the tractor and new seeds represent but single features of a complex of past changes. Linked to the tractor was a wide variety of changes in the application of mechanical power. With hybrid corn came a complex of closely linked changes in fertility, tillage, pest- and disease-control practices; interactions between the parts of the package were as important as the independent effects of any one part. These systems of practices, more common and more complex today, have resulted in tremendous increases. Output per dollar of input has been rising between 3.5 and 4.5 per cent per year. Only by an exit of land and labor from farming have output levels been kept to an increase of around 2 per cent per year.

Some disturbing side effects accompanied the application of higher levels of inputs per unit of land used in farming. Chemicals of a tremendous variety, in large absolute quantities and in forms not normally found in the biosphere, are in use today, and this use will probably be expanded. But in most cases, there is only incomplete information about either the secondary distribution paths of these chemicals through the larger environment or their biotic effects. There is even less insight into the social losses that can result.

Questions have also been raised with respect to more "common" forms of pollution. Applications of fertilizers, a form of chemical input, can conceivably produce an increase in the plant nutrients normally leached from soils. To some poorly understood degree, this may well increase the level of nutrients in receiving waters. Such nutrient changes can step up algal activity and result in other changes which in many situations would be a deterioration of the quality of the receiving waters.

Animal wastes are also a possible source of such enrichment of our waters. Greater concentration of animals has been responsible for some recent problems. New technology has made possible economies of larger size within farm operations, and this larger size is irresistible to many producers because of competition. Nowhere is this more spectacular than in poultry production and beef-cattle finishing. Thousands of animals can be handled at one time and in one place where hundreds could only a few years ago. Hog and dairy operations are, in general, less affected today, but these will have "caught up" before very long. The decline in the relative value of manure as a soil additive compared to artificial fertilizers and the frequent incongruence in time and space of the location of such concentration away from enough cropland that might receive and break down these wastes suggest a growing potential for animal-waste pollution.

In each of these cases—pesticides, inorganic nutrients, and animal wastes—varying efforts are being made to find technical solutions that will avoid conflict situations. Pesticides are being more carefully screened, tested, and labeled; biological-control mechanisms are being explored; and distribution paths, biotic effects, and social costs are being studied in a limited way. Like so many resource problems, the results of pollution are likely to be diffused, indirect, future, and relatively small in their absolute effect on most people. Little basis may exist for effective political organization and action by individuals who do lose by such pollution. On the other hand, those who seem to have the power not to use the chemicals, to cut back on fertilization, or to disperse their animals see the results of such actions as sharply and immediately direct personal losses of significant size, especially if a similar burden is not placed on their competitors.

The situation calls for greater understanding of the processes involved and the development of evaluation and control mechanisms that will balance public and private interests.

Alternative Uses of the Resources

The day of "new" land development in the United States is not at an end. These new lands may not have the character of the homestead or the frontier, but potentially productive wetlands are being drained, and the bloom is moving across the desert as water is being provided. New applications of mechanical power to soil problems will remove other limitations and enable a more intensive use of some areas. At the other end of the spectrum, the amount of land being idled at the edges of urban areas may exceed future urban needs. Further, it is increasingly recognized that selective preservation of some types of farming in urbanizing areas has amenity value as open space and offers a land-use tool in efforts to shape the city, restrict scatteration, cut urban service costs, and reduce commuting distances.

Where land drainage reduces the quality of wildlife habitat, we have another excellent case in which the market may reflect imperfectly the full range of social values involved. Increasingly, however, drainage projects are only feasible through group action supplemented by governmental sponsorship. This provides an opportunity for greater attention to the broader public interest and for evaluation of compensatory features. Important exceptions exist. For example, the potholes of the North Central states, important in migration and reproduction of waterfowl, are amenable to individual action.

Existing irrigation with its highly consumptive use of water offers in some cases less net value per unit of water used than potential alternative uses of the water. But once an area is committed to irrigation with heavy investments in other farm development and operation, and service facilities and community organization, the water developed for irrigation can be a much more expensive source of supply for alternative uses than new-source development. In other words, taking the water away from a region that has developed on the basis of irrigation to make it available for growing urban, industrial, and recreational uses entails such a wide impact that developing new sources has been the favored alternative. Such economic irreversibility is a common feature of resource problems and suggests the need for careful planning. It also suggests that we should find reasonable ways to facilitate reversing what is now irreversible. For example, promising technological changes may allow agricultural production to use much less water per unit of output through improved application and inhibition of evaporation losses at many points. Changes in the basis of pricing water to irrigators would be one way to provide incentive for such conservation practices. While the range and flexibility of possible water use per unit of output may never approach that of many industrial processes, it should be possible to make substantial strides in the next few years.

Within many miles of our rapidly growing urban centers, farmland owners are affected by existing and potential increases in land value. The possibility of selling the land for capital gains, as large as or even many times the total equity of the farm family, hangs like a silver-lined cloud over the rural landscape near our growing cities. "Rain" from this cloud may fall in one spot and not next door for some years. In the interim, capital investments may be allowed to deteriorate prematurely, and current income may fall. Rising taxes, problems with new neighbors, with labor, with vandals, and the offer of a speculator who is not able to keep the land in production may be all that is required to shift the land to idleness. An unresolved question is how much output is really lost in this process. The more productive the land, the more likely it is to be rented to some remaining operation, or at least so it would seem. Although some estimates have been made of the amount of idle land, none have been noted that evaluate the production foregone.

Several contradictions, probably more apparent than real, exist in our use of land at the urban fringe. While land is being idled, on the one hand, there is concern for open space, on the other hand. But the location of land that is idled is usually not favorable to open-space needs. Frequently only those who border on it have access to it. And too often it is more of an eyesore than a contribution to the environment. Also, the term *open space* implies that the area in question is left open because it serves *non*-open land in some identifiable way. Idled land implies that whatever service may be provided to the used land, it is only fortuitous and has an uncertain future. The challenge is to find ways to encourage those mixes of land use that stress the complementarity and not the conflict between activities, that provide the common amenities that few private persons can provide for themselves alone.

It is sometimes suggested that an appropriate intermixture of farms with houses enhances the living environment of extended suburban communities, and that enhancing the prospect for farming around our cities may be a means of reducing urban sprawl and of producing more compact and efficient development instead of the present scatteration. Yet modern agriculture can produce smells, chemicals, and water problems for nonfarm neighbors. Problems also exist in the reverse—adjacent urban communities can attract nuisance litigations, cause farmers worries over vandals, smog damage, and taxes for public services little used. If farming is to be used to maintain the landscape or to control the form of urban development, these difficulties, as well as the capital-gains pressures, will have to be recognized.

A more orderly process of urban growth, with controls and incentives applied to achieve a wide variety of objectives, will be more common in the future than it is today. The role of commercial agriculture in this process should be clarified.

Displacement of Farmers

The new technology in agriculture characteristically increases the cost advantages of larger operations (larger size is best expressed in dollar volume per unit). Large farms are, in turn, leading many people who are prepared to farm to shift to other occupations. Acreage per farm has risen dramatically even though the amount of land in crops has fallen, but acreage is a poor measure of the change in size of farms. A two-man wheat farm uses far more land than a two-man dairy farm, but it may have increased output less over the years. Labor used per farm also does not reflect this change. The bulk of the labor in agriculture is still provided by the family that owns and operates the farm, a fact identified with a willingness to accept lower levels of money return per hour of work. The farm family provides three quarters of the total labor used on farms and has consistently done so over the last fifty years. With the seasonal change in tasks and a family labor supply, high levels of specialization in labor have been difficult. There is, however, a trend for the farms that use more nonfamily labor to increase their share of total output. Farm families that leave agriculture have tended to be those that have not increased in size either by this means or some other.

More significant than changes in labor or land use have been the increase in the volume of output per farm and the even greater increase in capitalization per farm. Some people have suggested that in the next decade there will be greater opportunities to develop skilled-occupation groups within farming. These would put further pressure on the generalist family farmer.

There is now and there will continue to be a problem of facilitating transitions to new employment. This is true for any industry that is undergoing rapid technological change, emphasizing size, capitalization, and more specialized labor. Agriculture has several inherent disadvantages in this process. Farming is one of the few means of livelihood where, by their very home environment, a man's sons learn many of the skills and habits involved in their profession. Although it is less and less true, farm families have tended to be large and to have a strong ethos of sons following in the father's footsteps. This is reinforced by the advantages of inheritance as a means of acquiring the resources required to begin farming, if on a small scale. As a result, we have far more ready replacements for the declining number of jobs in farming than we need. Also, men are too often prepared for yesterday's agriculture.

By 1976, we should have more effective programs for retraining farm workers to be better farm workers, for redirecting farm youth to other professions, and for equipping better those that do farm. In the past, such needs were present as a result of many innovations; there is little expectation that new technology, including potential breakthroughs for food analogues, will produce very different effects in the next decade and beyond.

Displacement of Land

The new agricultural technology is not equally applicable to all land resources. Sandy soils that were considered infertile are still naturally infertile, but cheap fertilizers have made them much more productive than many fertile soils. Mechanized equipment is of more advantage to flatter, larger fields than to smaller, steeper fields. Most new technology produces better results on soils with good water-handling capacities: They drain well, but not too well; hold water, but not too much. Such soils lend themselves to better timing of more precisely performed operations with more intensive applications of seed, fertilizers, and other inputs. Consequently, lands that were once adapted to commercial agriculture are becoming obsolete. Probably more acres have been displaced by this process than by erosion or poor conservation practices. Millions of acres in the Northeast and the Southeast, with significant amounts elsewhere, have passed out of farming, and more can be expected to shift in spite of efforts to retain them in farming.

This has caused unique displacement problems for the regions in question. When farmers are displaced but the land continues to be cropped by those that remain, the level of output increases, and servicing facilities and community organization are less affected. (Many rural trading centers have declined in the face of expanded local farm output, but this reflects, among other things, shifts in transportation and communication that are, in turn, reflected in local trading patterns.) In the Northeast, land that is displaced will be taken up by people who will use it for houses, vacation cabins, and recreation. The availability of nearby urban employment facilitates the transition of the community to a recreation orientation. In the Southeast, commercial timber production is much more significant. Wherever this phenomenon occurs, there is scope for improving the adjustments of the people and land involved.

Adjusting Agriculture to National Goals

The "farm problem" has long occupied part of our national debates. Through price manipulation, plus a few resource diversions, income policy has been attempted, but with only partial success. At the same time, the incomes of some farmers have been enhanced through cost sharing of some soil fertility and conservation practices, plus land and water development. Nevertheless, specific public policy has produced much of the technology that has made the tendency for agricultural overproduction and price and income instability more acute. Indeed, the problems we now face with pollutants, displacement of land and people, and unsatisfactorily low levels of family income are in large measure the bitter fruits of our success in freeing the great bulk of our population from the need to be farmers. With the affluence gained comes the freedom to treat new generations of problems.

Much of what has been discussed thus far has strong implications for insuring that adjustment in farm production meet our hopes and expectations. Actions taken to enhance the movement of redundant labor and obsolete land out of farming can be accelerated or slowed down depending upon the need for more or less farm output and for higher or lower incomes for workers. Rising and falling farm prices can be expected to achieve much, as they have already, in keeping resources in farming or urging them out. Manipulation of prices can still be an important means of adjusting agriculture to national goals. Retraining and relocation programs, as they exist or as they may be improved, or proposed transition payments, should they be used, can either direct people out of farming or bring a few people with special skills back into it in more productive ways. Resource-development projects can be accelerated as needs become apparent. Large potentials still exist for enhancing output through investment in land and water conservation. Although expensive, renting resources out of production will still offer a feasible way to reduce production when this is required. Government purchases can still take products off the market.

But recurring throughout the long "farm problem" debate have been suggestions for more systematic and long-range procedures to introduce both greater price and income stability and to achieve production goals. In part, this has been a recognition of the social losses associated with overcommitment of resources in the farm production plant. "Too many" people and "too much" land in farming are often the result of investments that, once made, make staying in production more attractive to the individuals involved than the alternatives open to them. We should devise better long- and medium-range targets for output and, through somewhat closer co-ordination of production with targets, insure sounder resource use. While it is doubtful that these hopes can be achieved with very great precision, it should at least be possible to recognize and to utilize better the degree of flexibility that has been achieved by price-support and food-aid programs.

As part of our price-support operations, we have acquired large quantities of storable products, notably wheat and feed grains. The Korean War decreased our stocks at a time when they might have become embarrassing. By the time they had been built up again, we found that we were able to use large quantities—worth $1.5 to $2.0 billion in United States farm values—in our foreign-aid programs. Today a combination of increasing foreign commercial sales and aid, increasing domestic use, and output limitations has dwindled these stocks. At the same time, world populations are expanding, and although there is some promise of eventual stability in world population, this may clearly be contingent upon improvement in world diets as well as acceptance of family limitation and other changes in life styles. This diet requirement is made in the face of a world food output that has barely kept pace with population. If the United States is to assist in a more meaningful way, our commitment will have to be increased significantly. As much as five times the current level of food aid ($2.0 billion per year) may be required, although a doubling in the next decade is more realistic, and even this may be difficult to get adopted. Strict commercial sales would have to increase from a $4.0 billion-plus level to several times that. Foreign shipments represent some $6 billion out of a total output of around $36 billion; both the proportion dependent upon shipments and, even more to the point, that dependent upon government policy would have to increase drastically.

Once built up, such a high level of government purchase could provide stability in the market through purchases that attempted to move, cyclically, counter to prices. It could also be a source of uncertainty, since annual federal funding would be so important. A sudden withdrawal of this much purchasing power from a market so sensitive to small quantity changes would be extremely damaging to farm incomes at home, but perhaps such a withdrawal would be politically unthinkable. As the residual supplier for the world, even a year or two of good crops in the world would drop the demand for United States shipments drastically. Stockpiles to be drawn upon in years of heavy world demand and built-up in other years would seem to be necessary both to insure stability for domestic producers and to meet the unpredictability of being the residual supplier. Thus, such a commitment can only be made with the recognition that it will be for a long period of time—the longer the period, the larger the noncommerical commitment; the larger the commitment, the larger the stockpile carrying costs.

An expansion in farm output beyond domestic needs would, if carried far enough, affect the rural landscape. The first areas to be affected would be the forty or fifty million acres of cropland now retired by government programs. Doubling the average level of food aid would bring back some twenty million acres—possibly including some land that would be better left untilled. The short-term gains in output might be offset by the losses due to wind and water erosion. Initially, it would also mean some slowing down of the exit of marginal land; eventually, it could contribute to an increase in the use of land and labor in farming. It is, however, by no means certain that a commitment of this size is likely in the next decade. Also, unless past patterns of food aid are dramatically shifted away from the prominence of wheat, the domestic impacts of food aid will be concentrated in the major grain producing areas.

As in recent expansions of farm output, those lands most responsive to new technology will bear the major burden. And as in past increases in output, the adoption of new methods, new inputs, new systems or complexes of practices will provide the largest gains. We will have to be even more prepared to deal with the problems of side effects. We may hope that this will be a minor price to pay for the good that will be done.

This paper was prepared for the "Natural Resources, Recreation, and Conservation" panel in the study by the American Academy of Arts and Sciences entitled, "1976: Planning the American Future." Comments and ideas shared by many of my colleagues at Cornell are reflected throughout this paper. A special debt is owed to Marlin Cline, Howard Conklin, Robert Kalter, David Pimentel, Kenneth Robinson, Lee Taylor, and Robert Young.

HAROLD GILLIAM

The Fallacy of Single-Purpose Planning

This nation leads the world in wealth and power, but [it] also leads in the degradation of the human habitat. We have the most automobiles and the worst junkyards. We are the most mobile people on earth and we endure the worst congestion. We produce the most energy and have the foulest air. Our factories pour out more products and our rivers carry the heaviest loads of pollution. We have the most goods to sell and the most unsightly signs to advertise their worth. —*Stewart L. Udall*

THE PARADOX of which Secretary Udall writes—the befouling of the American environment by a fantastically productive economy— results from a persistent fallacy that afflicts the American mind and misguides our energies. It is the fallacy of single-purpose planning, both public and private.

Most engineers, developers, industrialists, and government officials are single-purpose planners. They assume, for example, that a power plant exists simply to produce power, a factory to turn out goods, a dam to store water, and a highway to move traffic. In each case they are wrong. These structures have a far more complicated purpose. If, as Lewis Mumford maintains, the purpose of a city is the care and nurture of human beings, each of the city's aggregate parts—every street, school, factory, and highway—must contribute to that care and nurture.

A human being needs fresh air and clean water, space and beauty, the opportunity not only for exercise and rest in quiet surroundings but for stable social relationships. He needs to consider his work worthwhile and to participate in decisions that affect his community. If any single structure is subversive of these purposes, it is a bad structure, no matter how efficient or well-designed it may be from a single-purpose standpoint.

The term *single-purpose planning*, as used here, does not imply

67

that the planners close their eyes completely to all other considerations, but that they subordinate other considerations to the predominant or intended purpose of the immediate project. These single-purpose planners may landscape their highways and their factory sites; they may conscientiously avoid the biggest trees in building a road through a park. But these amenity values are incidental.

Single-purpose projects are normally analyzed for their feasibility in terms of calculations that measure potential benefits against potential costs. The benefits and costs considered pertain only to the predominant purpose of a project. No attempt is made to analyze the benefit-cost impact of the project on other environmental values—social, aesthetic, recreational, or ecological. Single-purpose planning calculates only the immediately intended effect of proposed projects; it fails to account for the total environmental impact.

If a proposed highway would disrupt a neighborhood, displace homes, increase air pollution, destroy jobs, or invade a park or scenic area, these detriments should be calculated and subtracted from the potential benefits in determining whether the highway should be built. They seldom are. Normally, the highway engineer's overriding concern is to speed automobiles on their way. To accomplish this, he believes that he is justified in uprooting thousands of people, bulldozing trees, invading parks, and destroying scenic values. Similar prerogatives are claimed by legions of engineers, administrators, builders, and developers.

Such myopic planning is clearly capable of causing intolerable damage. Ways must be found to move toward a concept of multipurpose planning that recognizes the full spectrum of human needs. This kind of planning would require broad research to determine precisely what those needs are and how priorities among them are to be allocated. Multipurpose planning agencies would have to be created to make the environmental decisions consonant with those needs.

Some of the damaging effects of single-purpose planning and the problems involved in inaugurating multipurpose planning will be evident from an examination of some recent environmental controversies in the San Francisco Bay area—at Bodega Head, Napa Valley, Golden Gate Park, and San Francisco Bay itself.

In the late 1950's, officials of the Pacific Gas & Electric Company decided to build a nuclear power plant on several hundred acres at Bodega Head, a coastal promontory some fifty miles north of the Golden Gate. The decision drew the fire of conservationists who maintained that the headland was of outstanding scenic value and should be reserved for public recreation. Both the National Park Service and the State Park Commission had previously recommended that the area be preserved in public ownership for its scenic and historic values. The legislature had authorized the purchase of the head as part of the state park system, but the state was delayed in acquiring the land because the cost of the property was greater than anticipated and because Bodega Head had never been designated as a park in the Sonoma County master plan—a prerequisite for any state park. Moreover, a majority of the county supervisors clearly preferred a power plant to a park, since the taxes paid by the plant would loom very large in the county's attempt to broaden its narrow tax base.

Consequently, P.G. & E. acquired the property over a period of years, most of it by condemnation from reluctant ranch owners. When the application to build the plant came before the State Public Utilities Commission early in 1962, the P.G. & E. arguments followed a familiar pattern: The region would need vastly increased power to accommodate a booming population. From the engineering standpoint, Bodega was an almost perfect site for a power plant. Cooling water could be drawn from Bodega Harbor on the east and discharged into the ocean on the west. To conservationist arguments that the new populations would need not only electric power but open space for recreation, particularly along the scenic coastline, P.G. & E. representatives replied logically that they were in the business of providing power, not parks; that deciding whether an area should be a park was beyond their responsibility and jurisdiction.

The Public Utilities Commission granted the application, explaining that its business was to regulate utilities, not to decide how land could best be used. (State park officials had testified that they currently had neither funds nor plans to purchase the head.) P.G. & E. had demonstrated that Bodega was a good place to produce power, and the Commission, by its own reasoning, had no choice but to approve the application (although a vigorous dissent by Commissioner William Bennett held otherwise).

P.G. & E. next applied to the U. S. Atomic Energy Commission, and discussion centered thereafter on the safety of building next to the San Andreas Fault. The plan was ultimately abandoned for this reason. P.G. & E. had spent some $3 million for "improvement" of the site, including the excavation of an abyssal hole, which was to have held the reactor and which remains a scar on the landscape.

The Northern California Association to Preserve Bodega Head and Harbor, headed by David Pesonen, led the fight against the P.G. & E. plant at the grass-roots level. For the conservationists, the abandonment of the project seemed a remarkable triumph over the corporate Goliath. But the defeat of P.G. & E.'s Bodega plant cannot be viewed as conservation's victory. Had the offshoots of the San Andreas Fault not been discovered on the reactor site, the plant would have been built over the conservationists' protests. A non-nuclear plant could probably still be built there. Although P.G. & E. has leased the property to the county for park purposes, it can revoke the lease whenever it wishes to do so.

It became quite clear in the course of the battle that there exists in the State of California no agency to protect the people's interest in maintaining scenic open space. Single-purpose planners have a free hand. Open land is condemned by P.G. & E. for power plants and by the Division of Highways for freeways. Developers convert it into subdivisions, shopping centers, and factory sites. Historical, scenic, and agricultural factors remain mostly ignored. No one in authority in California is qualified to analyze and evaluate other possible uses of land in terms of public interest.

Although the State Park Commission can condemn land for park purposes, it is perennially short of funds and is merely an impoverished country cousin of such affluent agencies as P.G. & E. or the Highway Commission. The latter has even condemned portions of state and local parks for its freeways. In any case, the amount of land that can be purchased for parks is only a fraction of the total undeveloped land in the state. Hundreds of acres that may be needed in the future for recreation, breathing space, or agriculture are being pre-empted daily—paved over, subdivided, industrialized, commercialized. There is, in short, no multipurpose planning.

There is an unfinished sequel to the Bodega story. In 1966, P.G. & E. purchased property for another nuclear plant in the Nipomo Dunes, about two hundred miles south of San Francisco. In a 1959 coastal survey, the National Park Service described the area as being "unexcelled . . . in scenic quality" and recommended it for public recreation. P.G. & E. listened to conservationists more attentively on the Nipomo Dunes question than it had during the Bodega debate. Company officials conferred with representatives of the Sierra Club, the chief guardian of the California landscape, and with a special conservation task force set up by the State Resources Agency. P.G. & E. subsequently agreed to shift its site from the Nipomo Dunes to a little-known location at the mouth of Diablo Canyon, some twenty miles to the north. To save the dunes, the conservationists consented.

Few of them were well acquainted with the Diablo Canyon area, however, and some may have been unaware that the National Park Service's 1959 report had described a fifteen-mile stretch of coast, including this area, as possessing "excellent seashore values" and had recommended it for public acquisition. It is the only long stretch of California coastline—other than one area near Oregon—that remains in its natural state, unmarred by highways, railroads, or any other development.

This time the state could correctly claim to have set up an organization to safeguard conservation values, and P.G. & E. could maintain that it went out of its way to co-operate with the conservationists so that another Bodega could be avoided. Yet it is evident that the procedures employed bore little resemblance to multipurpose planning.

At Diablo Canyon, as at Bodega, there was no agency to answer—or even to ask—the essential question in multipurpose planning: What is the best use of this land in the long run? Conceivably the best use for Diablo Canyon could be precisely that intended by P.G. & E., but in the absence of any systematic analysis of alternatives, it is impossible to make such a determination. Despite efforts to take conservation matters into account, there was no attempt at rational land planning that would consider all the needs of all the people, particularly those of future generations.

The Diablo Canyon plant could be relatively harmless to the values considered by the state task force—water quality, existing beaches and parks, fish and game—and still be seriously damaging to other environmental values. The Department of Beaches and Parks testified only that it had not set a priority on the acquisition of Diablo Canyon and had neither available funds nor plans for its purchase; the Department did not testify that Diablo Canyon was undesirable for future park purposes.

The scanty funds available for parks have to be spent on areas closer to metropolitan centers. There is no master plan for state parks to indicate which areas would be desirable over the long range. Even if an area were deemed unsuitable or unavailable as a state park, there might be other uses of the land far more compatible with preservation of environmental values than a power plant—agricultural use, for example, or a combination of a local or regional park with the kind of high-quality residential development that does minimal damage to the landscape. Examples of such residential areas in California are Sea Ranch in Mendocino County and the Del Monte Properties' developments on the Monterey Peninsula, including the famed Seventeen-Mile Drive.

Within many cities and counties, rational land planning is accomplished by a planning department that zones or recommends zoning of lands for certain broad purposes—residential, industrial, commercial, agricultural, or public, usually with sub-categories in each classification. It would seem time to consider extending such zoning practices to the regional or state level when regional or state interests are involved.

Local zoning cannot cope with the issues raised by the Bodega and Diablo Canyon projects. Local governments are at a considerable disadvantage when confronted by large outside organizations that possess the power of eminent domain. Moreover, the single-purpose planners wield, inadvertently or otherwise, great financial power. San Luis Obispo County officials were as anxious as their Sonoma counterparts to have a large plant that would add substantially to the county's tax base; they scrupulously refrained from any action that might cause P.G. & E. to take its investment elsewhere. Thus, the utility clearly exerts an overwhelming influence by virtue both of its size and the largesse it can distribute in the form of taxes and payroll.

Regardless of its own intentions, such a superorganization inevitably has a potent "steamroller effect" on local affairs. To the county supervisors, the present benefits of an increased tax base and payroll vastly outweigh the intangible, long-term benefits of preserving scenic coastal areas for future generations. We can formulate a theorem here: Local multipurpose planning cannot be effective when local government agencies must deal with outside single-purpose organizations of immense size and wealth. The steamroller effect takes place whether the single-purpose organization is a public utility, a government agency, or a private developer.

Obviously, in such cases, multipurpose planning must take place at a higher level. It must be accomplished by a public agency large enough to match the size and power of the single-purpose organizations involved. Its absence in California indicates that the state has not yet learned the lesson of Bodega.

In the Napa Valley, local officials dealing with a large single-purpose organization were rescued from the steamroller, at least temporarily, by help coming from two directions. For generations the vineyards of the Napa Valley have produced some of the nation's finest wines in a beautiful pastoral setting. The Napa River, the heart of the valley, flows from Mount Saint Helena south for fifty miles, past rolling hills, redwood canyons, bottomland vineyards, ancient stone wineries, and through the small city of Napa. Like most rivers, it sometimes spills over its banks during winter storms and floods hundreds of acres of residential, agricultural, and commercial property. A few years ago, Napa County officials appealed to the Army Corps of Engineers, the agency responsible for flood control on navigable waters, for help.

The Corps' preliminary report, delivered in 1964, advised a straight, concrete-lined ditch, 160 feet wide and 30 feet deep, surmounted by a five-foot concrete wall topped by a high cyclone fence, an immense barrier through the center of the city. Within the city and downstream, trees and vegetation were to be stripped away and the river channel converted into a sterile storm drain.

The blame for the aesthetic brutality of that scheme cannot properly be laid to the Corps of Engineers; they were merely doing what they had been authorized to do. Their job was not beautification but flood control—at minimum expense to the Federal Government. They were, in short, a single-purpose agency. A more elaborate design would cost more, and the Napans would have to secure these additional funds themselves. To a community of a few thousand people, the prospects for raising a million dollars or more did not look bright. On the basis of the engineers' preliminary report, Congress approved $18 million for a flood-control project, the final design to be worked out by the Corps.

If Napa had been merely the somnolent pastoral community it appears to be, there probably would have been no effective opposition to the big ditch. Unlike most similar agricultural communities, however, Napa has special advantages. Because it is only fifty miles from San Francisco, its populace includes a good many former or part-time urbanites. With a few exceptions, the leadership in the campaign against the big ditch came from the members of this group. Napa clubs raised money to send a delegation to Washington to confer with officials in several federal departments; Napa's Congressman offered help.

In 1966, Napa acquired an energetic new planning director, Richard A. Oliver. He proposed, as an alternative to the Corps of Engineers' cement ditch, twenty-foot walls topped by a walkway and sloping banks leading to an upper promenade suitable for sidewalk cafés, river-front houses, and shops. The lower walkway and landscaped slopes would contain the occasional flood waters. Instead of interposing a mammoth barricade across the city, the Oliver plan would reorient the downtown area toward the river as the heart of the community.

All the work of Napa's citizens might have been insufficient, however, had it not been for substantial help from Washington, D. C. A Special Message to Congress from the President launched the natural beauty program in 1965. The White House Conference on Natural Beauty followed in May of that year, and the President's Council on Recreation and Natural Beauty was created.

Two consequences of the program were particularly important to Napa. A recreation and landscape-design specialist joined the Corps of Engineers' staff in San Francisco to enable the engineers to give environmental matters due weight in their planning, and the San Francisco office received a directive from Washington permitting as much as 3 per cent of flood-control funds to be devoted to beautification measures. The Corps of Engineers is presently considering Oliver's proposals for the Napa River and planning its own report. Even if the Corps were to adopt the Oliver plan, the $540,000 available for beautification would fall short, possibly by a million dollars, of enabling Napa to purchase and landscape the additional riverbank property necessary. Federal urban-renewal and open-space funds may be available for this purpose, but they will be difficult to obtain. Even the $540,000 for beautification will not necessarily be available: The "3 per cent" provision is permissive, not mandatory. A similar provision existed in the Federal Interstate Highway Act for several years and was totally unused until it was made mandatory, principally because local officials were either unaware of its existence or felt themselves unable to take the initiative against a large agency.

The Napa experience indicates that even small steps in the direction of multipurpose planning require pressure from both above and below. Pressure from below demands a degree of specialized knowledge about government programs and political techniques that is not likely to exist in communities that do not share the geographical advantages of Napa. Even there, after a long uphill fight, the outcome is in doubt. It would seem desirable, therefore, to establish procedures and agencies to support this kind of community action.

Not only small communities but large cities as well need such help, as San Francisco's freeway controversy indicates. Even before the passage of the Federal Interstate Highway Act of 1956, residents of the city had registered vehement protests against routes proposed by the State Division of Highways to connect freeways and bridges leading in and out of the city. Some of the routes would have invaded Golden Gate Park, developed over nearly a century from one thousand acres of sand dunes. Concern for the park was augmented by residents' fears that their homes would be affected.

In January, 1959, the Supervisors voted a blanket resolution against seven freeways that the State Division of Highways was planning to build in the city. *Architectural Forum* described the measure as "the first concerted revolt of a city against the highwayman's single-minded urge to drive freeways through by the most convenient engineering routes without regard to the city's tissue and fabric of life." The magazine failed to note, however, that the highway engineers were doing precisely what they had been charged by law to do. The Division of Highways is a single-purpose agency whose responsibility is not safeguarding social and environmental values but moving traffic.

Recent San Francisco freeway disputes have revolved around attempts to revive in a piecemeal fashion some of the routes killed in the 1959 revolt. On each occasion, the State Division of Highways, backed by the U. S. Bureau of Public Roads, bore down upon the city with potent promises and threats: the chief promise, the expenditure of some $290 million in federal funds available for freeway construction in San Francisco; the chief threat, the withdrawal of the money if no agreement was reached by a certain deadline. Each time the city failed to agree on a routing by a specified date, the highway engineers extended the deadline and made a new proposal that turned out to be a slight variation of the old. Cynics concluded that there had never been a real deadline and that the threat was being used to club the city into submission.

There was also pressure from below. Construction trade unions and contractors urged city officials to accept the route through the park. Even the Recreation and Park Commission was induced to give its approval; it evidently did not want to be responsible for the city's loss of $290 million. So vociferous was public protest, however, that each proposal was defeated by the Board of Supervisors—most recently, in 1966, by a one-vote margin. San Francisco has presumably succeeded in rejecting the $290 million; a shift in the balance of power on the Board of Supervisors could, however, renew the struggle.

San Francisco's sad experience offers convincing evidence that the single-purpose planning of highway engineers does not adequately take into account a highway's effect on the environment. The civil turmoil, the engendered bitterness, and the neglect of other urgent municipal business could have been avoided had the engineers initially calculated the cost of the freeways in terms of the total environment, rather than deriving their judgments on freeway routings almost entirely from engineering considerations.

The engineers' failure to assess properly nonengineering values was not a result of perversity or malfeasance. Neither by training nor by experience were they qualified to evaluate the effect of the freeways on recreational, aesthetic, ecological, social-welfare, or urban-planning patterns. Highway authorities hold public hearings and listen to protests, but in practice this procedure merely means that engineers or engineering administrators listen to objections on matters lying outside their field of competence. Single-purpose agencies are constitutionally not capable of doing multipurpose planning.

Theoretically the San Francisco city-planning department should have performed this function. But the few professionals of the underbudgeted, understaffed planning department were no match for the multi-million-dollar Division of Highways or the multibillion-dollar Bureau of Public Roads. An alternative to this kind of municipal chaos would be well-budgeted planning agencies at regional, state, and national levels with enough political muscle to override the large single-purpose agencies. Steps toward an effective multipurpose regional planning agency have been taken in regard to San Francisco Bay itself, and what has happened there is worth examining.

The filling of San Francisco Bay began more than one hundred years ago when the first Forty-Niner dumped dirt and rock into the water along the beach, and it has continued, reducing the surface area of the bay by one third. During the 1950's and early 1960's, it was greatly accelerated under pressure of population increases. There were fills for subdivisions, municipal facilities, industrial purposes, and "sanitary" garbage dumps—each fill diminishing the areas available for recreation, wildlife, fish breeding, and oxygenation of shoreline wastes. Further filling threatened to turn the bay into a biological desert, to curtail navigation, to diminish the natural beauty of the region, and to affect adversely the weather conditions of the shoreline cities.

Some residents of Berkeley, disturbed at this exploitation of the region's greatest single natural resource, formed the Save San Francisco Bay Association to promote multipurpose planning for the body of water and its shores. A battery of single-purpose planners opposed them, myopically concentrating on the single "need" for a subdivision, an industrial site, or a garbage dump. Single-purpose planning promised profits not only to the bay fillers but to building contractors who had large quantities of excavated dirt to dispose of, to the truckers who hauled the dirt to the shores of the bay for fill material, and to the finance concerns lending money to the developers. Their economic interest in single-purpose planning quickly became a political interest as well, and in more than one case the developers had financial connections with local officials.

For these reasons local control over the exploitation of the bay could not succeed. Moreover, nine counties, a score of cities, and federal and state agencies shared jurisdiction over the bay. It became clear that any plans to control the haphazard filling of the bay would have to be made by an agency with jurisdiction over the entire area.

As a result of the energetic Save the Bay movement and the political skill of San Francisco's State Senator, the late Eugene McAteer, the legislature created the San Francisco Bay Conservation and Development Commission. The Commission is charged with developing a master plan for the bay within four years, and it possesses the power to grant or deny permission for any fill project during the interim period. Since September, 1965, when the Commission began its work, it has been successful in holding the line on major fills, despite steadily increasing political pressures. The Commission's future will bear watching.

There is now considerable sentiment for an effective regional government in the San Francisco Bay area, and the Bay Commission's scheduled report to the 1969 legislature may recommend that its functions be merged with those of existing agencies in charge of regional air- and water-pollution abatement, regional parks, transportation, and other regional functions—creating thereby a truly regional multipurpose agency. In some cases, such an agency would still be dealing with public and private power structures much larger than itself and would thus need help at even higher levels. Practical proposals for higher multipurpose agencies have come from California's Planning and Conservation League, a new organization formed to give planners and conservationists a legislative voice in Sacramento. The League has recommended a "Coastline Conservation Commission" with powers similar to those of the Bay Commission. An enforceable master plan for the entire coastline would, in part, solve the dilemmas involved in the Bodega and Diablo Canyon controversies.

The League also recommended a statewide Land-Use Review Commission that would "hold hearings and make advisory recommendations on all land-use decisions which it considered to be of statewide interest. The Commission would represent the general public interest and would include members competent in social, economic, legal, conservation, planning, recreation, and design fields." Hopefully, such an advisory agency could ultimately be superseded by a state planning agency capable of making a master plan for all the state's undeveloped lands. The State of Hawaii is presently experimenting with statewide land-use zoning.

Consideration should also be given to corresponding agencies at the federal level that could deal with cases involving either federal programs or the national interest. The residents of Napa, for example, should have access to a federal environmental agency that would listen to their problems, consult with the Corps of Engineers, and advise them on the possible use of other federal programs, such as those for open space or urban renewal. San Francisco might have turned to such an agency when federal funds were proposed for use in a freeway that would have damaged environmental values in Golden Gate Park. As it was, the city could only protest to the Bureau of Public Roads, which remanded complaints to the State Division of Highways.

The kind of damage that can be done to the national interest by single-purpose planning is illustrated in the proposal of California's Division of Highways to build a freeway through groves of redwoods that have been preserved with the help of contributions from all over the United States. Owing to the lack of any regular federal agency to assert the national interest in the preservation of these redwoods, the freeway plans have been held up only by the emergency intervention of the President's Recreation Advisory Council (now the Council on Recreation and Natural Beauty). The Council was not set up as a court of appeal, however, and does not have the facilities to act in all cases that may involve the national interest. Logically, such matters should be worked out at lower echelons of government and reach the Council only as a last resort. At present, the local officers of the Bureau of Outdoor Recreation endeavor to keep track of the impact of federal programs on recreation. This function might be extended to other environmental values as well, but such a move would require the Bureau to be staffed by professional members competent in various environmental fields.

Whether such an agency should have planning as well as advisory functions is questionable. Here, as with multipurpose planning agencies at lower echelons, there would be serious risks involved in the concentration of power. Determining the interests of all the people is a formidable responsibility that cannot be entrusted to any single body, no matter how wise or conscientious. Various measures can, however, be taken to diminish the danger of such a concentration of power. The first is to create viable institutional frameworks through which an agency's decisions can be appealed—possibly providing recourse to the courts at various stages in the procedure. The second is to require that all single-purpose agencies whose work has an environmental impact include staff members professionally trained in environmental matters—ecology, landscape design, recreation, social relations, or economics. Environmental values would thus be brought into each agency's planning from the beginning, giving it a multipurpose aspect and diminishing the need for intervention by superior multipurpose agencies.

The power of the planning agencies can also be restricted by defining as explicitly as possible the standards to be used in determining the best use of the land. Such definition would minimize reliance on arbitrary judgments. Land-use standards might be developed by extending the feasibility analysis beyond the project's immediate single-purpose costs and benefits to include its social costs and benefits as well. In determining the feasibility of a proposed freeway, it might, for example, be necessary to calculate the effect on nearby property values. When a freeway would increase the value of the adjacent commercial property, the benefit could be calculated; when it would have a negative impact on a residential neighborhood, the depreciation of property values could be added to total costs. The impact of a freeway on public property would be somewhat more difficult to determine, but it may be possible through research to develop applicable standards. How much would the value of Golden Gate Park, for example, be diminished (or enhanced) by the construction of a freeway through it? The answer might involve anticipated diminished usefulness of the park in terms of visitor-hours, and the cost of providing equivalent park values elsewhere. The calculation should include the cost of replacement of destroyed trees, with allowances for the time required to grow specimens of equal size. (In the case of virgin redwoods in public parks, the cost of replacement would probably make any freeway through prime groves prohibitive.)

In the case of the Napa River, a multipurpose feasibility study of the benefits of an attractively landscaped channel—as an alternative to the engineers' proposal—should include the anticipated increase in the value of nearby property. The focusing of the downtown area of Napa on an enhanced river channel might well increase the value of all downtown property. A multipurpose analysis might, therefore, show the landscaped channel to be far more economic than the plain concrete channel, despite higher acquisition and construction costs.

The problem becomes more complicated when it is necessary to consider the impact of a project on undeveloped land. Here, multipurpose cost-benefit analysis would involve a comparison of possible future uses, both public and private. In determining the multipurpose costs and benefits of a power plant at Bodega Head or Diablo Canyon, for example, it would be necessary to consider alternative costs and benefits of using the same land for other purposes—agricultural, recreational, or residential. To do so would involve estimates of future needs of projected populations—needs for electricity, for farm products, for recreation, for housing. It would also necessitate comparison of cost-benefit analyses for alternative locations. Such calculations might indicate a multipurpose cost-benefit advantage in building a power plant at an inland site of less value for alternative uses. The greater cost of operating a plant at an inland site—in single-purpose terms—might be offset by the greater social benefit of using the relatively rare coastal land for residential or recreational purposes. The calculations, of course, might prove the reverse. But this kind of multipurpose analysis, whatever the result, is essential for rational land-use planning.

Many of the tools necessary for the full development of this kind of planning have yet to be formulated. How are we to determine, for example, who is to pay the extra project costs that may be involved in meeting the social needs that are revealed by multipurpose analysis? If it is necessary to build a freeway around a park rather than through it, at greater acquisition and construction costs, should the difference be charged to the highway budget or to the park budget? Should the federal flood-control budget be charged for the extra cost of landscaping the Napa River channel or should the difference be made up by other federal or local sources? If multipurpose cost-benefit analysis indicates that P.G. & E.'s nuclear power plant should be built inland, at higher costs of construction and operation, rather than on the coast, should P.G. & E. be required to supply the extra funds or should some public budget make up the difference? And if Diablo Canyon or Bodega Head is to be used as a public recreation area, how are the owners of the land to be compensated?

Although these are not unanswerable questions, they reveal the need for special arrangements—fiscal and otherwise—to implement multipurpose planning. The San Francisco Bay Conservation and Development Commission is confronted with such questions and will presumably answer them in its 1969 report to the legislature. The Commission's existence indicates that the public has recognized the need for multipurpose planning pertaining to the bay. The manner in which the Commission handles the inevitable conflicts between multipurpose and single-purpose planning will bear watching.

Apart from the problems involved in the implementation of multipurpose planning, we do not have all the tools necessary for measuring social needs. We lack adequate measures of the individual's needs for recreation and scenic beauty. We must develop standards as to how much open space is necessary or desirable for given population sizes and densities. And because this kind of research deals with the human psyche, it is probable that multipurpose planning can never be accomplished by the use of cost-benefit formulas alone. Some leeway must be allowed for the exercise of informed intuitive judgment. Nevertheless, land-use planning should be subject to a far greater degree of rationalization than its current methods employ.

We may hope that by 1976 we shall have set up environmental planning agencies and be moving toward a new science of human ecology that can measure our environmental needs, drawing on the biological sciences as well as the social disciplines of psychology, psychiatry, sociology, and anthropology. We should also look to the humanities. In the end, the poet may be able to teach us as much about human needs as the biologist.

ANN LOUISE STRONG

Crisis Mentality and the Deteriorating Environment

CAN AMERICANS face, consider, and resolve problems before their crisis proportions are palpably and tangibly manifest to us as individuals?

Can a crisis afflicting a large segment of society be comprehended as a crisis by those whom it does not yet afflict?

Even were we aware of emerging crises in the environment, is our concept of a desirable environment clear enough for us to demand its creation or preservation?

Assuming that we agree on environmental goals, will we accept short-term costs and limitations on freedom of action for long-term benefits?

Or, until our garbage rots uncollected in the streets before us, until our septic tanks overflow and foul our gardens, until fetid weeds choke our favorite swimming beach, will we cling to our belief in a God-given right to use the land as we please?

What does "this land is my land . . ." mean to the landowner: my land to nurture and cherish or my land to exploit and destroy? Today's urban land ethic is shaped by a search for the top dollar and by a relic of the frontier mentality—devastate one site and then move on over the horizon. Land is to be used, reused, and discarded when worn out or destroyed, like an old car. Also like a car, land has symbolic value. Ownership of land creates an aura of solidity, status, and security. Under today's land ethic, land is a personal possession, man's fief, as his home is his castle; for many, it is also the most desirable form of investment. This is more because it is a tangible symbol of wealth than because land ownership assures a higher return than ownership of intangibles such as stocks, bonds, and bank accounts.

Because of these symbolic and proprietary attitudes toward land, government regulation of its use is bitterly resented. There is a ready resentment of government as an intruder, whether the intrusion is direct, as to build a road, or indirect, as to forbid building in a flood plain. Government regulation through zoning, for decades reviled as communistic, is more readily tolerated today, because the landowner has learned to manipulate, change, or evade it.

The Rural Land Ethic

Where is the American's vaunted love of the land as his heritage and his roots? Out beyond the greedy, grasping reach of megalopolis, it's still there. Not everywhere—the exploiters are there too—but for many rural landowners away from the rising land market of the urban scene there is a different land ethic. For them, the right to use the land carries with it an obligation to care for the land. Man sees himself as the transitory custodian of the land, successor to ancestral custodians and, he may hope, precursor to descendant custodians. The land is husbanded and its fertility maintained; it is a partner with man. When a man is in a continuing partnership with nature, their interdependence is simple for him to comprehend. It is visible in the quality of the harvest and the amplitude of the ground water. The effects of degradation and neglect are soon and clearly manifest.

Certainly this is an oversimplification. There is no one rural land ethic. Nevertheless, these attitudes of love and respect for the land, of responsibility for its management, and of independence from government intervention remain the most prevalent ones among rural residents. Still, the rural land ethic is of continually diminishing significance in determining our actions as a society toward the environment. The rural-urban population distribution has dramatically altered with shifts in the scale and nature of rural land tenure. Mechanization, chemical fertilizers, the economies of scale in production and marketing, the harvest from government investment in agricultural research—all these have led to greater yields, larger holdings, and less need for manpower. For those who remain, there is quite possibly a wiser use of the land than ever before. Erosion is controlled, fertile soils are kept fertile by crop rotation and fertilization, and steep or poor soils are planted in trees to prevent further deterioration. Large-scale single-crop planting may tempt pestilence, and widespread use of pesticides to avoid this poses one serious threat to the environment.

On balance, however, it is megalopolis that is poisoning our land, our sky, our lakes and streams. Most of us are citizens of megalopolis, and we have chosen, by avoiding or postponing a confrontation with the facts, to allow the quality of the natural environment to deteriorate.

The Developer's Land Ethic

On the urban fringe, where the farmer may sell out from five to ten years before development is profitable, the real estate investors and developers may control the future character of the countryside. Their motivation is simple: Make the most profit possible by investing wisely and turning the money over rapidly. Land, though unique, is seen as an economic asset given value by location, access, and nearby development and, although to a lesser extent, by such natural characteristics as topography, climate, and water supply.

With profit the sole motive, planning and land development controls should be welcome. Rational public action would clarify and simplify private investment decisions. Given knowledge of where and when public investments in transportation and infrastructure would occur and make development profitable, the land investors could maximize their possibilities for gain.

If the large-scale developers don't support public planning and land use controls today, it is largely because they have no confidence that any plan will be carried out or any controls enforced according to plan. Without such public adherence to plans, the land investor is in a far more speculative position; he must personally assess the likelihood of multiple public and private actions by scores of agencies, companies, and individuals. While he must resist individual actions imperiling his investment—such as installation of a trailer camp adjacent to his proposed high-priced residential development—it also is prudent for him to resist the usually uncoordinated and unpredictable plethora of government controls so as to leave freedom for maneuvering.

The developer's land use ethic is concerned with treatment of environmental resources only insofar as it affects his profit. If trees help sell houses, keep the trees. If industries demand an assured clean water supply, take steps to provide it. The client of the developer states his demands from the environment; if these demands are nonexistent, there is no motivation for the developer to preserve any of the natural resources that he finds on the land. To him, without demand they are not assets.

The Land Ethic of the Megalopolitan Landowner

We, then, who live and own property in megalopolis are the ones who determine what happens to the natural environment as it is urbanized. We are the client of the developer, and we are the government of megalopolis with all its fragmented municipal subdivisions.

In becoming urban dwellers, whether of center city or the urban fringe, what changes has our rural land ethic undergone that can explain our disregard even of prudent self-protection? We still believe that the natural environment is healthier than the city, that our children will grow up stronger and our lives will be happier if our home has a garden and trees and if there are clean streams and green pastures nearby. We cherish a dream of life in rural America, a dream often remote from reality or personal experience. Perhaps because it is now but a dream, the acceptance of responsibility toward the land has been lost while the insistence on freedom in use of the land has been retained.

Man in megalopolis still attaches to his land and his residence the psychological attributes of home, sense of place, and personal territory. But because he and his family are mobile socially and economically and because the land contributes to his livelihood only through its development value, he also views it as his major marketable capital asset. This leads to a conflict in values toward the land.

Were he solely a developer and not also a homeowner, megalopolitan man would shed his emotional links to the rural past and respond with economic rationality toward his land.

Alternatively, if the resident landowner in megalopolis held his land because of his affection for it as a site to raise his family and to enjoy his leisure time and were he not concerned with it as a source of possible gain, then the sense of responsibility for land management could reemerge. Given a greater psychic investment in his own land, such a landowner might also accept a share in the responsibility for managing use of the nearby environment.

Today, the land ethic of the resident landowner in megalopolis is an unsuccessful amalgam of the land ethics of the rural landowner and of the urban developer. Yet, despite this unresolved conflict toward use of the environment, it is we who live and own land in America's urban areas who will decide whether or not to arrest and reverse the past record of destruction and devastation of the natural environment by the expanding metropolis. Although most of our land is rural, urban America must bear a responsibility quite disproportionate to the space it occupies for damage to the natural environment. Furthermore, with almost all growth occurring in metropolitan areas and with the population increasingly concentrated there, this responsibility is increasing. The influence of the rural residents will decrease. The real estate investors are powerful and can be expected to endorse actions to protect the natural environment only if convinced that it is good business to do so. Whether or not it is good business turns upon what values we—the residents of megalopolis, both landowners and potential landowners —place on use of the natural environment. Unless the current conflict of values between respect for the environment and regard for the "fast buck" is resolved, and unless we are willing to look ahead to see where our selfish and uncoordinated land use practices are leading, the real estate investor can hardly be criticized for fighting to keep his land use options open. If we don't know what we value and are ready to pay for, why should he be a resource altruist?

The Brandywine Experience

This rather gloomy view of our current land ethic has crystallized during a two-year effort to develop and gain public endorsement of a watershed protection plan for part of the Philadelphia urban fringe.[1] It was the planners' aim to determine what type of residential environment present residents, and potential future residents, of the urban fringe want and then to propose a long-range plan for the projected growth of the watershed compatible both with the people's wishes and with preservation of the present quality and quantity of water resources.

To determine people's view of the role that the natural environment plays in their lives, how it influences their choice of residential location, and how they value the importance of its preservation, an attitude survey was conducted before planning began.[2] The unanimity of response—95 percent—stating that the natural environment is "important" or "very important" as part of people's way of life far exceeded the planners' expectations.

Asked next, "What part does the natural environment play in your life," 33 percent stressed the appearance of the countryside, 31 percent valued its contributions to a good life, such as climate, healthy conditions, leisure activities, and general enrichment of life, 20 percent cared most for the restful and private feel of natural surroundings, 14 percent mentioned specific activities, such as gardening or children's play, and fewer than 2 percent listed negative characteristics.

When asked the following question, however, the response revealed the conflict between economic investment and concern for the environment.

As you know, the suburbs are getting bigger and bigger. Because of this expansion, forests and farmlands are developed for homes, stores, industries, and offices. Some people say that parts of the countryside, especially the most beautiful parts, should be kept the way they are for future generations to appreciate. Others feel that this land should be used in any way the landowners want. What do you think about it?

To this question, 53 percent of the people living in the Brandywine watershed answered that natural areas must be preserved, 15 percent favored preservation combined with properly planned development, and the remaining 32 percent thought that development should occur at the landowner's option. The answers to this open-ended question often were mixed, with one view or the other dominant, showing the conflicting attitudes referred to earlier in the discussion of the megalopolitan land ethic. Many of those concluding that preservation was necessary also voiced a concern about loss of money or freedom to act, while many preferring to maintain the landowner's freedom to use the land as he sees fit also were desirous of preserving the beauty of the countryside. With almost half of the Brandywine residents giving answers reflecting both attitudes in varying degrees, 72 percent spoke of the need for preservation, 23 percent recognized a need for a mix of development and preservation, and 47 percent expressed concern for self-determination of land use.

Consistent with the view that recognition of the need for action usually occurs only after deterioration has taken place, the study showed that substantially more people in settled suburbia, where nature has been trampled, believe that preservation is more important than maintenance of personal determinism of land use.

Given the answers discussed here and many more, it was possible to characterize the types of residential areas and the environmental setting desired by people living on the urban fringe, in suburbia, and in the towns of Chester County. On the basis of the attitude study, it seemed reasonable to hope that, given an opportunity to assure achievement of this character of land use throughout a small watershed, the residents would endorse a moderate degree of local government control and would forgo the possibility for speculative gain on part of the land. They did not.

The plan proposed that 25 percent of the watershed—the flood plains and buffers three hundred feet on each side of streams and swales—be kept in open space uses, that another 25 percent—large woods and slopes of 15 percent or more—have a density no greater than one dwelling unit per four acres, and that development on the remaining 50 percent of the land be subject to regulations to control erosion, solid waste and sewage disposal, water supply, and tree cutting. The plan further proposed that the landowners voluntarily sell easements to the Chester County Water Resources Authority limiting use of the flood plains, buffers, woods, and slopes as specified in the plan. The price to be paid by the county for the easements was the difference between the current market value of the land and the market value after sale of the easements.

No referendum of citizens of the watershed was held. Based on response at township public meetings, telephone calls, and letters, however, the supervisors of six of the eight townships with land in the watershed voted to reject the plan. Responding to the wishes of the township supervisors, the Water Resources Authority decided to drop the plan.

The response to the plan was illustrative of the urban landowner's attitude toward the environment. Almost everyone, except a small and aggressive group organized to fight the plan, endorsed the principles. There was some minor difference of opinion concerning definition of the areas in which development was to be limited, but support for clean and ample water, for preserving the beauty of the countryside, and for fertile farms and fine fishing was about unanimous. No one wanted new roads, power lines, or schools on their land, but everyone wanted their services. No one wanted subdivisions, trailers, shopping centers, or factories next door or down the road. But many, and maybe most, would want them on their own land if the price were right. After all, the argument went, if a developer should offer you a tempting price, why shouldn't one be free to take it? Who is the county to put a crimp in this deal between you and the developer by buying an easement which would prevent or restrict development? It would be unconstitutional; people just felt this, though no one ever would say why. The prospect that enactment of the plan would make the location of future development more predictable and thus create better opportunities for investment was not convincing. Partly this is because of the bond people feel to the parcel of land they own. Buying and selling land held for investment just isn't the same as buying and selling securities.

Then there is the absence of a felt crisis. Change may be coming, but, even though the nearest shopping centers and industrial areas are but a few miles away and neighboring streams are open sewers, no one really believes that it will happen where he lives. If it should, that frontier relic is still there: we can sell out and get out.

What about government? Isn't it answerable to somebody who wants a decent environment to go to as well as to somebody who wants the right to ruin the environment and flee? Not today. Control of land use is the prerogative of local government, and the residents of the urban fringe are fighting tenaciously not to lose any of that local power, not even to the county with its somewhat broader constituency. The state and federal governments cajole, review, and offer financial incentives, but the power to determine what happens to the land is a local government power. It may not be exercised, because local residents don't want any constraints, or it may be exercised to advance the wishes of the local constituency, completely regardless of the wishes of the residents of megalopolis or of the nation. This is how the urban fringe residents want it, and it is they who soon will hold the balance of power in our state and federal legislatures. It is possible that the "one man one vote" case, *Baker* v. *Carr*, will result in a backward step for environmental protection, if we compare the rural land ethic with the land ethic of the urban fringe. One can hope that this is too pessimistic a view, but the grounds for a more sanguine outlook are not clear at this time.

REFERENCES

1. "The Brandywine Plan," Chester County Water Resources Authority, West Chester, Pa., 1968; "Plan and Program for the Brandywine," Institute for Environmental Studies, University of Pennsylvania, Philadelphia, Pa., 1968.

2. For detailed information about the attitude study see Mark Menchik, "Brandywine Residents and Their Attitudes Toward the Natural Environment," in "Plan and Program for the Brandywine," Institute for Environmental Studies, University of Pennsylvania, Philadelphia, Pa., 1968.

R. BURTON LITTON, JR.

Landscape and Aesthetic Quality

RAYMOND DASMANN has observed that it has not been considered good form to speak of aesthetics or natural beauty in circles of western resource management.[1] The image of forestry projected by Gifford Pinchot, and hence an official stance within the early twentieth century for professionals and Forest Service alike, denied any responsibility for scenic resources or related amenity.[2] Chief Forester Pinchot took his stand not on personal grounds, but in order to fight the pressing conservation battles of his era. Indeed, those battles are still with us in new guise or with other objectives, and this earlier posture has not been readily put aside. But it seems quite safe to suggest that no forester or other resource manager would have entered his profession without a general and abiding interest in the outdoors.[3] Now it is permissible and even mandatory to consider the visual landscape as a concrete resource in its own right. But how do you think, speak, and act with goals of aesthetic purpose when it has not been a cogent part of your training and fundamental responsibility? For those who are still reluctant, it might be reassuring to repeat Aldo Leopold's guidelines: "Quit thinking about decent land-use as solely an economic problem. Examine each question in terms of what is ethically and esthetically right, as well as economically expedient. A thing is right when it tends to preserve the integrity, stability, and beauty of the biotic community. It is wrong when it tends otherwise."[4]

We can all call to mind environments, man-made or natural, with physical and visual characteristics that we have found pleasing or displeasing. But we are not apt to assess such experiences by explicit aesthetic standards.

Psychologists, sociologists, and members of related disciplines are just now beginning to explore the impact—both aesthetic and

91

psychological—exerted by our surroundings: architectural and urban spaces, the landscape. Kenneth Craik suggests that the entry of psychologists into the realm of the "real" world has been tardy, but notes that it could not have been made without the earlier basic investigations in scientific psychology and the development of reliable laboratory techniques.[5] Albert Parr has made some keen observations about city-dwellers and their surroundings that hold broad implications for an analysis of landscape and aesthetic content.[6]

The reasons for encouraging a liaison between psychologists and landscape architects or other designers appear to be many and complex. The general affluence of the times, the new questions being asked and new criticisms given, the need for more objective standards to replace subjective, traditional standards—all seem to require a more scientific investigation of the relationship between the physical environment and the criteria of design. Not all designers will agree that they want their work or their professional procedure scrutinized in this way. Yet such a scrutiny presents an opportunity for the sometimes blunt instrument of design to become a sharper, more precise tool. Through such a honing process, aesthetic criteria will be clarified, and communication between designers and nondesigners should improve.

Designers seem to communicate better within their circle than they do outside it. They are prone to define their work in terms of economics or practicality rather than on aesthetic merit. Placing the discussion in such a context helps a designer when he is working with engineers, foresters, or members of various boards who, directly or indirectly, are also concerned with design in the broad sense of the word. But how well can the designer talk with an engineer when he thinks of design from an aesthetic base, whereas the engineer may not? For clarity in communication, aesthetic principles ought to be defended directly rather than shielded with arguments of economic efficiency or political expedience.

Design in the landscape aims to establish appropriate relationships in the context of a particular place. The psychologist or sociologist can provide the designer with valuable insight into the methodical analyses of human responses to the initial characteristics of the landscape and the subsequent man-made changes. Additionally, the psychologist or sociologist can also arbitrate or interpret when communications between designer and nondesigner break down.

Staying within the context of landscape and its aesthetic dimensions, the designer is first forced to draw a series of aesthetically based hypotheses with which the psychologist can work. It should then be possible for the psychologist or sociologist to plumb the nature of the human response to visual stimuli. These responses may reveal symbolic or hidden meanings that various compositional elements within the landscape hold for an observer. Testing for perceptual response to visual design elements is not suggested as a substitute standard for that of design specialists, but it should direct effort into more promising channels.

I assume that the landscape—or at least obvious segments of it—can be classified on aesthetic and perceptual bases. Several implications for resource management should follow from such a procedure. First, once graphic and understandable inventories of landscape, based on visual criteria, become part of planning documentation, the visual landscape is less likely to be the mute victim of the nonaesthetic factors influencing any given decision about the environment. Second, if evaluations of quality are made, as would be most feasible in comparing similar kinds of landscape, then areas in danger can be determined and protected. Third, such inventories should enable environmental decisions to be made on the bases of the best alternatives available. With explicit visual or aesthetic criteria built into the design process from the very beginning, the landscape would not continue to be the misbegotten offspring of single-purpose planning. Fourth, the costs of maintaining environmental quality would come to be considered as long-term needs or potentials; values should not be wholly pecuniary, but social and aesthetic as well. Diversity as a source of landscape quality is undoubtedly more economical to keep than it is to create artificially, if that is even possible.[7] With the possible exceptions of some forms of agriculture, we have not yet produced any man-made continuum that is even a close equivalent to native landscape. We do not know what future needs the landscape will be called to fulfill, but flexibility and diversity should hold the promise of their attainment. Some people will be shocked at these notions of cataloguing and classifying landscape as being inimical to landscape's essence of elusiveness and heterogeneity. But probing, weighing, and institutionalizing may be the only way to defend the landscape so that it can continue to contribute to a better human environment.

Some of the elements that tie aesthetic quality to landscape are offered here in terms of propositions, with photographs providing

93

visual evidence of a visual resource. They are stated as a means of isolating certain aesthetic characteristics that reside in the landscape. After this stage—and with evaluation—these characteristics can be recorded in an inventory to assist planning. Yet any attempt to be pragmatic about the landscape and its design quality is apt to be naïve or overly simplistic. Perhaps the most fascinating aspect of the landscape is that another variation lies just behind the next hill, and response is compounded by chance circumstances as well as individual perception.

REFERENCES

1. Raymond F. Dasmann, "Aesthetics of the Natural Environment," remarks at the Ohio State University, Natural Resources Institute Symposium (May 24, 1966).

2. Henry Clepper, "The Forest Service Backlashed," *Forest History*, Vol. 2, No. 4 (January, 1968), pp. 6-15.

3. C. Frank Brockman, "The Recreational Use of Forest Lands in the United States," in H. Clepper and A. B. Meyer (eds.), *American Forestry: Six Decades of Growth* (Washington, D.C., 1960), p. 158.

4. Aldo Leopold, *A Sand County Almanac* (New York, 1949), pp. 224-25.

5. Kenneth H. Craik, "The Comprehension of the Everyday Environment," *Journal of American Institute of Planners*, Vol. 34, No. 1 (January, 1968), pp. 24-37.

6. Albert E. Parr, "Psychological Aspects of Urbanology," *Journal of Social Issues*, Vol. 22, No. 4 (1966), pp. 39-45.

7. John V. Krutilla, "Conservation Reconsidered," *American Economic Review* (September, 1967).

Figure 1: Tomales Bay State Park, California

Proposition 1: Unity can come from spatial limitation. Although only a segment of the outdoor continuum, an enclosed landscape is a visual whole defined by terrain walls or trees bounding a floor. The positive nature of the enclosure, variety in surfaces, and proportional contrasts developed within the parts contribute to the level of quality.

Figure 1a: Whiskeytown Lake, California. Enclosure limits attention, emphasizing quality deterioration due to the impact of construction.

Figure 2: Drakes Beach, Pt. Reyes National Seashore, California

Proposition 2: Boundless space, quite as much as enclosed landscape, establishes unity. Seascape is an abstract expression of panoramic landscape—not different in principle from that of the Great Plains or mountain ridges receding to the horizon. The seascape is potentially monotonous, but relief and change occur in sky and clouds, in wind motion above and on surface. Foreground and middleground elements become significant indicators of scale and distance, establishing contact with base plane or recurrent horizontal lines.

Figure 2a: Minarets Range, John Muir Wilderness, California (Credit: U.S. Forest Service)

Figure 3: Cathedral Peak, Yosemite National Park, California

Proposition 3: Unity is obvious as derived from the dominant-subordinate relationships of a feature-dominated landscape. The central solid form creates a zone of visual influence—producing a landscape essentially the opposite of a bounded, enclosed landscape with central void. The ascendant form is repeated in minor or more distant peaks, in talus slides, in forest patterns, and individual trees.

Figure 3a: Church Rock, Moab, Utah. Isolated mesa-lithic form also dominates, but how much does it take to erode quality?

Figure 4: Sierra Nevada foothills, vicinity of Clovis, California

Proposition 4: Vividness, a conspicuous mark of design quality, can come out of form development and contrast. Hills become clear through difference between crisp, dark edges and plain, light surfaces. Skyline silhouette is the strongest contour and coordinates the landscape. The image is further strengthened through form repetition and variations of proportion.

Figure 4a: Subdivision, Oakland, California. A shaky and incomplete concept of new forms laid down in conflict with original form.

Figure 5a: Aspen Grove, Sierra National Forest, California

Proposition 5: Line domination and spatial limitation are the fundamental characteristics of the forest landscape. Vertical stems to horizontal base, canopy, and side closure make the generalized whole. Infinite variations of contrast may then occur: dark-light, massive-delicate, dense-sparse, opaque-translucent.

Figure 5: Coast Redwoods, Humboldt County, California

Figure 6: Childs Meadow, Tehama County, California

Proposition 6: Ephemeral changes over time—diurnal, seasonal—wash the landscape with variation. Light, weather, or animal life can give brief distinction to the most ordinary landscape. Whether this is a saving grace or confusion in the search for quality is debatable. The design configuration and nature of some landscapes will appear to have a constant basic quality to which temporary change is an incidental bonus.

Figure 6a: "Signs," Russian River, California. Knowing one's relationship to the landscape may influence signs left behind.

Figure 7: Canyon de Chelly National Monument, Arizona

Proposition 7: To be clear, proportions and the scale of the landscape must finally relate to the human observer and the yardstick of his body. Trees here provide a crude sense of size between parts. But the ancient dwellings give an acute understanding of the monumental face with its rich line patterns and moon shapes. These clues help indicate that this is a landscape of unique and vivid quality.

Figure 7a: Bridges near Oso, Washington. Handsome new bridge—but solution to complex speedscale problems that cars present to landscape awaits.

Figure 8: Whitebark Pine, Stanislaus National Forest, California

Figure 8a: Sandstone, Mendocino Coast, California

Proposition 8: Details and parts, as building blocks, should demonstrate a richness and a diversity comparable to that of the larger landscape in which they occur. Individuality of the place and environmental circumstances should be detected from small parts as readily as from the whole. Fullness and variation that suggest a state of good biotic health in landscape are also marks of aesthetic quality.

Figure 9: Conway Summit, Mondo County, California

Proposition 9: Aligned elements and linear guidance can focus attention, ordering a gradation ending in climax. Diminutions of apparent size and outline, of colors and their value due to distance, are visual facts of perception. A selected viewpoint can sharpen these expectations. A focal landscape reflects the combination of observer's position, aerial perspective, and linear order.

Figure 9a: Tioga Road, Yosemite National Park, California. Positive virtue from a segment of straight road responding to surroundings.

ECONOMICS AND POLITICS

HANS H. LANDSBERG

The U. S. Resource Outlook: Quantity and Quality

IT WILL soon be sixty years since Gifford Pinchot published *The Fight for Conservation*, as informative and succinct a guide to the Conservation Movement's views and judgments as one can hope to find. With regard to resource adequacy, it presents a generally somber picture, supported by careful projections based on the idea that the volume of economic resources in the United States is defined by their identified physical occurrence. The lesson that only careful husbanding can stretch the supply is the logical sequel. Governor Pinchot summarizes the findings of approaching resource exhaustion as follows:

The five indispensably essential materials in our civilization are wood, water, coal, iron, and agricultural products. . . . We have timber for less than thirty years at the present rate of cutting. We have anthracite coal for but fifty years, and bituminous coal for less than 200. Our supplies of iron ore, mineral oil, and natural gas are being rapidly depleted, and many of the great fields are already exhausted.

Later in the book, Pinchot points to our "limited supply" of coal, a substance that he holds to be "in a sense the vital essence of our civilization."

If it can be preserved, if the life of the mines can be extended, if by preventing waste there can be more coal left in this country after we of this generation have made every needed use of this source of power, then we shall have deserved well of our descendants.

On that last point there is unfortunately no direct way of judging how well we have, in fact, done. Not only is the evaluation of resources and reserves a very imprecise art at any point in time, but criteria and methods themselves undergo change. Thus, the nation's first estimate of coal resources, published by the U. S.

Geological Survey in 1909, one year before Pinchot's book, reckoned that 3,200 billion tons had been in existence "when mining first began." This estimate held for four decades but was trimmed to 2,500 billion tons in 1950, and to 1,900 billion tons in 1953, not because of intervening consumption (not more than 40 billion tons or so, a minute fraction of the amount estimated to exist, has been mined in the entire history of the country), but because of more sophisticated and extensive methods of measurement.

Governor Pinchot would probably judge us kindly on the score of coal consumption, for the American of 1966 used about two and a half tons of coal per year where his forebear of 1910 consumed almost twice as much. The decline was not, however, motivated by thrift or avoidance of waste, as the Conservation Movement understood these terms. Rather, the prime reasons were vastly greater efficiency in burning, especially in steam-electric plants, and the emergence of other energy sources that have almost totally replaced coal in ships, railroads, and homes, and partially replaced it in factories and power plants.

Indeed, in the case of coal, we have come full circle. Today the U. S. Department of the Interior is investing millions of dollars a year in research that is aimed not at conserving coal but at developing new uses. Two of them, liquefaction and gasification, could, if successful, increase future coal consumption spectacularly. But few considerations, we may be sure, prey less on the Department's mind than the fact, incontestable as it is, that the country's coal supplies constitute a finite resource and thus are subject to eventual exhaustion.

How We Have Made Do—The Big Picture

What has wrought this radical change in our view of things is, of course, the cumulative and joint impact of increased knowledge and improved technology—in short, the forces generally lumped under the broad heading "The Scientific Age."[1] Change induces change. Diminishing returns from exhaustion of resources with better characteristics are staved off not by lucky discoveries, as was once the case, but by advances that are both systematic and cumulative. Moreover, we have learned the advantages of "disaggregation"—that is, the separate utilization of the different inherent features of natural resources, as opposed to their joint use in the form in which they occur in nature. To illustrate the technique and realize its advantages from a conservation point of view, one need only think of the way in which the chemical industry, prominently including oil and gas processing, typically breaks down its raw-material stream.

We have thus enhanced our ability to upgrade old resources (for example, cropland through the addition of fertilizer), to discover new ones (oil, gas, nuclear fission, and so forth), to utilize them more efficiently (coal in power generation, low-grade copper ore, wood waste for pulp mills and building board, and the like), and to adjust to relative resource availabilities (aluminum replacing copper, or air-cooling replacing water-cooling). Consequently, the relative importance of the country's resources as inputs into the economic hopper has steadily diminished. A few gross examples will suffice to support this statement.

At the end of the Civil War, 6.5 million people were employed by the resource industries, which represent the sum total of the agriculture, forestry, and extractive industries (lack of suitable data prevents inclusion of water-associated activities). By 1910, this figure had climbed to 12 million, but it has now dropped to 5.5 million—one million less than it was ninety years ago. Resources now claim less than one tenth of all the labor in the country, instead of the half of a century ago, but this tenth produces five times as much as the half did.

Almost the same relationship is revealed when the output of resource industries is compared with the output of all goods and services. A quintupling in the resource field has been accompanied by a twenty-five-fold growth in the economy's total output. Not surprisingly, prices of resource commodities have, in general, not risen above prices for all goods and services.

A Quick Rundown in Some Detail

One might, therefore, say so far so good. Things have not worked out badly, at least not for the United States. Fossil fuel reserves have held up well, even though we have drawn on them at rates that were unimaginable not so long ago. Because rising yields allow us to grow what is needed on fewer acres, land in crops has been on the decline. And were it not for booming food exports, partly financed by ourselves, the problem of surplus farm land would loom much larger.

The most recent survey reveals that our forests are adding new growth at a substantially faster rate than that at which the annual cut is removing them. In 1962, when detailed estimates were last made, growth exceeded cut by 60 per cent. To be sure, behind this favorable aggregate comparison lurk problems of quality, species, location, marketing, and so on. For example, we still cut more sawtimber softwood—a highly desirable product—than we grow. Moreover, some of this apparent good fortune derives from improved measurement. This would mean that we were better off in the past than we had thought and that part of the apparent improvement is a mirage, but it would not negate the finding that current growth exceeds cut. The products of new technology—metals, plastics, and other synthetic substances—have reduced the demand for forest products; and in some lines, such as pulp and paper, we have been able to rely extensively on imports to supplement domestic production.

Perhaps nothing reflects so dramatically the changing tide of events as the conditions of timber resources. As Harold J. Barnett and Chandler Morse have pointed out, the Conservation Movement's "sense of impending scarcity derived directly from a concern for the future of America's forests, dating back at least to the 1870's."[2] As early as 1877, Carl Schurz, then Secretary of the Interior under President Hayes, forecast a coming "timber famine," with supplies to last only another twenty years. Today the concern for forests focuses on their role as part of the environment rather than as a source of materials.

In the field of nonfuel minerals, we are intermittently plagued by specific shortages—copper, sulfur, tin, and the like—but a stretch of high prices and concern has never as yet failed to engender successful efforts to locate new deposits, to exploit old ones more efficiently, and to promote substitution of more abundant, natural or man-made, materials, sometimes temporarily, sometimes permanently.

The Role of Technology

The current condition of ease regarding sufficiency of quantity is rooted largely in advancing technology, with its twin offspring: efficiency and substitutability. This trend has accelerated in the recent past. Only fifteen years ago, the authors of "Resources for Freedom" (the name under which President Truman's Materials Policy, or Paley, Commission released its findings in 1952) commented that "in the U. S. the supplies of the evident, the cheap, the accessible are running out."

The Commission would probably not phrase it that way today, for there are abundant examples of the nonevident becoming evident, the expensive cheap, and the inaccessible accessible. Broadening scope, increasing variety, and rising volume of man-made products exemplify the nonevident that is becoming evident. So do nuclear power generation and telecommunication by microwave and laser.

Hardness, low-metal content, fine-grained structure, and the nonmagnetic nature of part of the deposits made the extensive iron-bearing ores of Minnesota, Michigan, and Wisconsin that are commonly lumped under the generic heading of taconites too costly to mine until after World War II. New processing technology has since made it not merely possible to extract usable material at acceptable costs, but has turned the initial handicap of having to agglomerate the fine particles into pellets into a major advantage, because the pellet feed greatly enhanced the productivity of the industry's furnaces. Similar evidence testifies to the changing circumstances of accessibility. Thus, the deposits of oil in offshore fields, buried under hundreds of feet of water and thousands of feet of ocean bottom, have become accessible. So have many and varied underground ore deposits that have yielded to the search by airborne magnetometer, sensing devices, chemical anomalies, and other new exploration tools.

But while that Commission, from the vantage point of 1967, appears to have underestimated the speed of population growth, of economic growth, and of industrially useful new knowledge and technology, its place in history is secure, for its decisive emphasis was not on the "running out of resources," which had been a popular concept in earlier years, but on resource availability at a cost, on the role of costs as a barometer of scarcity, and on future technology as a factor in determining costs and availability. Thus "running out" becomes a relative matter. Copper may "run out" for fabricator A, but not for fabricator B who, for one reason or another, is able to pay the higher price that reduced availability engenders. At the same time, the higher price is likely to bring closer the threshold at which deposits with poorer characteristics can be commercially exploited. The "running out" process is a dynamic one, subject to changes in direction, and thus is quite different from the straight-line, down-trending concept current early in the century.

Barnett and Morse have suggested that a major cause of this development is the flowering of the scientific advances.[3] In such an environment, there are no diminishing returns from improvements, for the improvement is in turn improved upon before its advantages have been dissipated or squeezed to a zero return. We have reached constant cost plateaus, at which increased amounts of resources are available without cost increases.

Others suggest that the curve of technological improvement will soon begin to flatten out and that we may already be moving along the upper leg of the sigmoid development curve. The bigger part of many technical revolutions, says John R. Platt, appears to lie behind us.[4] We have reached "science and technology plateaus." From horse-and-buggy to the current version of the jet plane is a bigger quantum jump than the impending advance to the SST. The invention of the telephone marked a bigger break with past communications methods than will the transition to satellites.

Perhaps this is so, although the odds in speculating on unknown technology are notoriously long. Nevertheless, no amount of speculation on the kind of plateau we may be approaching can relieve us of the need or impair the usefulness of taking a long look ahead for a test of how well, under carefully spelled-out, realistic assumptions, our resource situation is likely to hold up. Such a look involves a wide array of guesses, the worth of which will depend as much on the effort that goes into making them as on the investigator's success in recognizing and overcoming his biases.

A Look Ahead

Resources for the Future has engaged in making and publishing such informed guesses or projections.[5] I can, therefore, be brief and summarize the picture that emerges for the balance of this century. It is not one to provoke undue concern, at least not on the score of quantity and for this country.

Farm Land

Rising crop yields—based both on further advances in agronomy and on a large-scale catching-up of the bulk of the growers with the best—can confidently be expected to keep land from becoming a limiting factor to food production. A few years ago, contemplation of past history led Resources for the Future to project 1970

112

corn yields at 70 bushels per acre. Because yields ranged between 53 and 55 bushels per acre in the three years preceding 1961, the year in which we had to make our projections, we thought our prediction a little daring; some scholars who were asked to review what was then a manuscript thought we were very daring. But by 1965 the yield had climbed to 74 bushels and had outrun the projection. The average yield in Iowa had jumped above 80 and in Indiana and Illinois above 90 bushels per acre. Our projected yield of 100 bushels in the year 2000, a faraway guess when made, had begun to move into clearer view. This projection and those for other feed grains stand a good chance of being overtaken before the end of the century. Little can as yet be said about other major crops.[6]

Forests

It is difficult to speak with assurance regarding the long-run adequacy of U. S. forests to supply the domestic market. A few years ago, Resources for the Future had grave doubts that even allowing for a generous drawing on imports, prospective demand could long be satisfied by domestic supply without impairing the size and quality of our forests. These doubts have diminished. Demand continues to lag. Wood prices seem high in comparison with nonwood alternatives, especially when the latter offer advantages in handling and maintenance. Also, there has been a less than buoyant housing market. Moreover, the existing volume of trees now appears larger than was believed a few years ago. The most recent figures (1962) compiled by the U. S. Forest Service show a significantly higher timber inventory than does their previous estimate (1953). For the time being, emphasis has shifted from forest products in the aggregate to adequacy and quality of given species.

Outdoor Recreation

Considerable uncertainty attaches to those uses of land that do not lead to production of commodities. This is true especially for outdoor recreation. Even cautious projections of the use trend of parks and other recreation land translate into very large acreage figures.

On what some might consider quite conservative assumptions

regarding both the rate of increase in visits and tolerable density of recreation acreage, Resources for the Future estimated that by 1980 there might be need for 76 million acres for outdoor recreation; and by the year 2000 this need should call for an additional 58 million acres. For comparison, in 1960 there were only 44 million acres of land in national parks, monuments, recreation areas, state parks, and in national forests used primarily for recreation.

In terms of new policies and of magnitude of outlays required, such figures put a wholly new face on a hitherto secondary aspect of land use. On the other hand, until we know more about such factors as the carrying capacity of outdoor acreage for recreation and the potential of private land for such purposes, we must handle these statistics with some sense of detachment. Unfortunately, it will take some time for research to catch up with the speed at which use of this new resource has been growing.

Other Uses of Land

A common complaint of the sixties is the "asphalting over" of America's land. Houses, offices, factories, highways, airports, parking lots, and the like have such high visibility to so many people that their presence and growth tends to distort perspective. It is the view during the occasional airplane ride that restores it.

In cold figures, the 25 million acres or so occupied by the urban population at this time is less than 1.5 per cent of the country's surface. Highways, railroads, and airports take up perhaps 27 million acres, for a grand total of built-up terrain of, say, 50 million acres, not quite 3 per cent of the face of America. By the end of the century, this might grow by 50 per cent, to 75 million acres, due overwhelmingly to expansion of urban land use.

I do not mean to suggest that problems of land use—especially in urban areas—are meaningfully measured in terms of acres. If they were, the task of finding the additional 25 million acres of land that we may need for urban living between now and the end of the century could be entrusted to a child equipped with nothing more than a map and a ruler. Nor does dealing in aggregates, unqualified by reference to land characteristics, do justice to the issue. Pointing to European population densities that typically run five to ten and, in some cases, fifteen times the U. S. density merely shows that other countries have problems too.

On the other hand, nearly 500 million acres are devoted to

commercial raising of trees, and about 700 million acres are primarily grazing land (there is room for arguing over proper land classification here, but these rough figures will do for the purpose). Thus, 75 million acres for urban centers and transportation facilities pose less a problem of "space shortage" due to "asphalting over" than of inventiveness in efficient use of the country's surface.

The Demand for Energy

The demand for energy is likely to be three times as high in the year 2000 as it is now, but the entry of new or newly derived energy resources (from nuclear reactors to oil and gas from coal, shale oil, oil sands, and so forth), combined with more efficient utilization and conversion of conventional energy sources, is likely to ward off rising costs. Indeed, we may well be entering an era of slowly declining energy costs. There is unprecedented activity in developing new coal technology to widen the scope of our largest fossil fuel resource; research and development leading to a breeder reactor, which may begin to bear fruit by the mid-seventies, will multiply many times over the country's uranium resources as a basis for power generation.

Metals

Enough deposits of the major metals, supplemented by imports and rising amounts of scrap, have been identified that emergence of sustained supply problems due to inadequate resources seems unlikely given our demonstrated ability to handle ever lower-grade material. This does not, however, insure against shortfalls in times of national emergency—to be provided for through special measures, such as stockpiles. Nor does it offset temporary and, perhaps, even prolonged difficulties like those that have in recent years plagued copper, which is mined in major quantities in countries that are subject to political upheavals or uncertainties. Supply cannot always keep up with quickly rising demand, but it has a habit of catching up, sometimes to a greater extent than is required.

Ability to process low-grade material carries one great advantage: Such material usually exists in very large volume. For example, the previously mentioned taconite ores, most of which are likely to become subject to commercial exploitation during the balance of the century, equal four times the cumulative demand

115

for iron projected through the end of the century. Perhaps a turn to unconventional sources, such as the ocean floor, will help the situation for others, as will substitutions by nonmetallic materials. Thus, despite projected levels of consumption that between now and the year 2000 could cumulate to the equivalent of 60 to 70 times the 1960 consumption for iron, copper, lead, and zinc, 90 to 100 times that for nickel, chromium, and tungsten, and 125 times that for aluminum, it is difficult to envision serious supply problems because of resource limitations.

Water

Judgments about water are often confusing because of fuzzy concepts and poor terminology and complicated because of the attention that must be given to problems of quality. It helps to realize initially that in many of its uses water is either a free or nearly free good and that incentives for economizing are the exception rather than the rule. Thus, projections of future consumption are based more on what people have been led to take for granted as "needed" than on what they would be willing to buy at prices that more nearly reflect cost.

Another aid to understanding is a clear distinction between *withdrawal* of water with subsequent discharge back into the original source and withdrawal followed by consumption, or *depletion*. All uses have elements of both, but the proportions vary greatly. In municipal use, for example, most water—about 90 per cent—is discharged after it has served its function, while irrigation depletes from 60 to 90 per cent, depending upon the circumstances. Since water can be used over and over again, the item to keep one's eye on is, for most purposes, depletion—not withdrawal. Unfortunately, most popular discussion is conducted in terms of water "use," without further definition of the term.

The need for sharpness of definition applies equally to the supply side. The total supply of surface water—precipitation—is a multiple of what becomes accessible in the form of runoff. The latter is, in turn, normally a multiple of withdrawal, and withdrawal typically exceeds depletion. (Instances where the entire flow is diverted without any return to the source are the exceptions.) Moreover, ground water, as distinguished from annual replenishment, constitutes a separate supply. Finally, there is a variety of techniques for adding to available supply. Some, such as storage, predate the era of recorded history; others, such as desalinization, weather modification, and evaporation control, are undergoing active development. They are paralleled on the demand side by techniques for reducing consumption. Substituting air-cooling for water-cooling, less wasteful irrigation techniques, and a more efficient use generally (for example, having a smaller flow or depletion per unit of service required) belong in this category. As our political and administrative approaches to water management, as well as our costing and pricing mechanisms, receive attention and review, channeling water into the highest-yielding alternatives will assume increasing importance.

Differences in natural endowment and climate have combined with a different mix of use categories to produce a sharp cleavage in situation and outlook between the eastern and western United States, using these geographic terms in the loosest of meanings. Because of the large role played by irrigation, the West (excluding the Pacific Northwest) depletes nearly five times the volume of water depleted in the East. Since it only disposes of about 20 per cent of the runoff available to the East (which is, of course, the reason why the West needs irrigation if it wants to have agriculture), the West depletes about 40 per cent of the water it can count on.

Before long, the West may find water supply a serious obstacle to economic growth if flows are not diverted to uses other than irrigation, prices are not brought into line with costs, and techniques for adding new supplies do not soon become commercially feasible for meeting the needs of cities and industries at prices they can afford.

In sharp contrast, and for the opposite reasons, the East depletes less than 2 per cent of its runoff and faces no long-range physical shortage, provided rainfall deficiencies during the past few years do not represent the beginning of a basic long-term change in climatic conditions. Meteorologists are divided on this issue, and conclusive evidence one way or the other will not be forthcoming for some time. Meanwhile, whatever the ultimate trend, the East faces decisions associated with pricing and allocating water and with encouraging economizing by means other than admonitions and exhortations (though in the face of uncertainty the "muddling-through" approach has the merit of preserving options).

Above all, however, the eastern United States is confronted with growing deterioration of water quality. This increasingly narrows the usefulness of many streams and lakes for purposes that

117

demand clean water. It imposes costs on users that draw their supplies from stretches polluted by others. Moreover, it raises in full not only a host of new technical problems but economic, political, and administrative questions about equitable and efficient remedies to the situation. For those who try to appraise the degree of adequacy of the nation's resources, it opens up a new dimension —the quality of resources.

The size and characteristics of domestic resources, in combination with imports, are such as to exclude any significant limitation to U. S. growth because of resources. This picture would no doubt look different if one were to widen the geographic scope and consider the world, or a major portion of it. The number of critical resource areas would increase, and the time horizon for which one would have a reasonable assurance of adequacy would shrink. Specifically, it is unlikely that these conditions will affect the terms on which the United States obtains its imports sufficiently to alter significantly the general perspective outlined above. Except in the case of food, however, only the most general quantitive appraisals have been made of the resources that the developing countries are likely to need for the decades ahead.[7] Analogies of trends and patterns of material use that have prevailed in Western industrialized nations and extrapolations of short trends in the developing countries can both be misleading. Exploration of future development patterns in terms of claims on specific resources is badly needed, however, if we are to gain a realistic picture of what faces this country in its role as a member of the world community.

Quality of Resources: How Good?

It would be convenient to deal with the quality problem in much the same fashion as with quantitative adequacy. We would, in other words, assess the degree of past acceptability for each of the resources, project the demand into the future, and judge whether the supply will be forthcoming, or whether, where, and when "quality shortages" will develop.

Unfortunately, we can barely begin to measure the state of adequacy at the present. How good or bad the past has been we can deduce, at best, from the presence or absence of comments and protests. Moreover, we are as yet woefully short of methods that can help us pick our way between those who see the population tobogganing toward physical and emotional decay and those who regard the current concern over quality decline as but another phase of modern life with which common sense and technology will in time come to grips.

Technology—Two Sides of the Coin

Technology, it seems, has played a cruel hoax on us: It has assured enough, but in the process it has led to degraded quality. Excessive use of the waste-assimilative characteristics of water and air by cities, factories, coal mines, oil wells, chemical-bearing agricultural land, and many other concomitants of life in the industrial age has created a complex technological and economic problem: to devise ways and means other than natural stream and air flow for disposing of waste material, and to determine and apportion the costs and benefits that arise in the process. Undesirable by-products have made their mark on both the rural and the urban landscape. The settings are different but the adverse consequences and the problems of measurement, evaluation, and policy are similar.

Deploring technology's side effects—which range from unpleasant to highly dangerous—is not tantamount to decrying technology as such. In one of his recorded songs, Tom Lehrer, Cambridge's gift to social satire, finds it a sobering thought that at his age Mozart had been dead for two years. Similarly I find it a sobering thought that I would have been less likely to accept the invitation to contribute to this symposium at the turn of the century, for a man in his fifties would at that time have outrun his mean chance of survival. Life expectancy at birth in the United States has since moved from less than fifty to seventy years.

One is apt to view the more disagreeable aspects of modern life, including most prominently those due to the impact of technology, with partiality—often unconsciously. We take for granted that we may drink tap water, eat uncooked fruit or vegetables, and consume milk with no thought of falling victim to a lurking bug. We are reminded of our good fortune only when we travel in parts of the world that require preventive or remedial countermeasures, or when the exceptional case in this country hits the front page. But, customarily, we fail to do much balancing of pluses and minuses. We tend to overlook the fact that the chemical industry produces not only controversial pesticides, but also antibiotics and vaccines; that the automobile whose incomplete fuel combustion fouls the city air does, at the same time, enable us to escape its boundaries and to know the world in a way available a generation or two ago only to the daring or the rich. We are quick to lament the fallen sparrow, but slow to celebrate the fall of "Typhoid Mary."

This is not the same as inviting, or welcoming, or even being indifferent to the negative aspects and abuses that can be or are associated with technological advance. To reconstruct what is in terms of what could have been is generally a misleading venture, for people commonly engage in such reconstruction for the purpose of excising the obnoxious features while leaving untouched those they sanction. They forget or ignore that both are usually part of one and the same fabric. To show that we could have had one without the other requires more than saying so.

Nor can it be taken for granted that accurate and timely anticipation of the adverse consequences of a particular action necessarily produces decisions to prevent them. For example, the failure of cigarette-smoking to decline or of repeated disasters to discourage occupancy of flood plains raises doubts about the level of individual response. Failure to have acted long ago on such matters as provision of adequate, common-carrier urban transport or nonpolluting incinerators suggests that we act no more wisely in matters of collective response.

Beyond the need of adequate motivation and appropriate institutions, there is the great difficulty of balancing the gains and the losses. Let us look more closely at the cigarette-smoker, and let us assume that he is well informed about the effects. Presumably the smoker has achieved a balance of gains and losses: The gain from inhalation more than offsets the pain from possible illness and shorter lifetime. Arriving at the balance is likely to involve several elements—among them, the weighing of pleasure *now* against pain *later*, with the distant event, as is customary in such situations, heavily discounted; the reluctance and remoteness of applying to oneself a cause-and-effect relationship that is only statistically demonstrated, a reason for additional discounting; the calculating of odds; allowance for personal habits and characteristics; appeasement through change to presumably less harmful brands. Clearly some such calculus underlies the decision to smoke and how much to smoke.

One might go on to speculate that those smokers who have digested the new knowledge have adjusted to it by setting their daily intake at a level at which they judge reduction would gain them less in future health than they would forego in current pleasure; a level, conversely, at which the improvement in current well-being derived from the extra cigarette, the marginal revenue, is not worth the incremental health hazard, the marginal cost. At that point, the smoker is in equilibrium. This point comes at different levels of smoking for different people, and the motivation—the type of gain extracted—differs widely among smokers. Thus, rationality of decision is not the issue. Rather, what is open to discussion and represents a proper area for education are the value scales on which pleasure from smoking and pain from ill health are traded off.

A serious economic problem arises not when an individual's actions affect adversely only himself (though costs of medical attention will in varying degrees not be defrayed by the individual, and there is, therefore, a public interest), but when those actions affect, primarily and often exclusively, other people. This is the heart of the quality aspect of resources.

Quality Versus Grade Differential

One could argue that to distinguish quality from quantity is merely a semantic nicety; that supply must always be understood as supply corresponding to appropriate specifications; and that if there is not "enough" by whatever the qualitative yardstick, then we have a quantitative shortage, whether it be water, air, iron ore, copper, or softwood sawtimber.

To some extent this is true. For example, within a large excess of aggregate forest growth over aggregate cut, there is too much poor hardwood from small trees and too little good softwood from large ones. Why do we not customarily speak of this as a separate dimension in judging resource adequacy? In part, we do not because there is a market on which poor hardwoods are traded and have, in different uses, found acceptance as satisfactory substitutes for good softwoods. Taconite ores are undoubtedly poorer bearers of iron than the traditional ores, but poor quality did not prevent their acceptance as soon as they could be processed at a cost low enough to make their use lucrative in blast furnaces. Copper mines today go after ores that hold only five pounds of metal per thousand. In the end, there is nothing that distinguishes the copper ingot derived from poor ore from that derived from rich ore; all that matters is that their costs be in a range that finds them a

121

market. These grade differentials are handled satisfactorily by the market that reduces the offerings to quantities of some commonly agreed upon standard or equivalent. Provided we have an appropriate processing technique, six tons of .5 per cent copper ore are neither better nor worse than one ton of 3 per cent copper ore.

But one hundred cubic feet of slightly polluted water or air cannot presently substitute for fifty or ten of clean water or air— at least not for most purposes. Given a choice, one could not be indifferent, as in the case of copper. But above all, the choice is not one the consumer can effectively make, except in the most roundabout way.

Examples of these kinds of quality problems are abundant. There is the discharge of municipal, industrial, and agricultural waste into watercourses, of pollutants into the air; there is disfiguration of the landscape through mining activities, transmission lines, or other symbols of the industrial revolution; there is ugliness along highways, be it beer bottles or billboards, interference with plant life and wildlife through the use of pesticides, disturbance of the atmosphere through vibration caused by fast-flying planes and of the sound waves through indiscriminate use of portable radios.

A new wrinkle in the quantity-quality relationship, best exemplified in the energy field, should be mentioned here. The traditional conservation doctrine maintains that use of natural gas as boiler fuel signifies an "inferior" use of an exhaustible resource. In the past, both the Federal Power Commission and the courts have upheld this viewpoint. As late as 1961, the Supreme Court confirmed the Commission's authority to make end use a factor in deciding upon certification for service (in a case involving shipment of gas from Texas to New York for use as boiler fuel). "One apparent method of preventing waste of gas," said the six-man majority, "is to limit the uses to which it may be put, uses for which another, more abundant fuel may serve equally well."

This was before air pollution became a pressing problem and made natural gas the preferred boiler fuel, given its low pollution quotient. The Federal Power Commission has not yet made this feature a basis for granting electric-utility applications for increased gas deliveries. It does not deny that gas is a less polluting fuel; the "inferior use" argument would sit badly with urban communities today. It does, however, contend that steam-electric plants are not the major villains in the situation and that additional gas would be, at best, a temporary palliative—at worst, a block to more radical remedial action. In any event, appraisal of adequacy can obviously be heavily affected by such changes in judgment.

Economic Characteristics of Side Effects

The "side effect" syndrome has a number of characteristics, all of which distinguish it from simple grade differentiations and make it a highly controversial object of economic analysis and public policy.

Certain effects arise apart from and beyond the primary purpose. Not confined to the user, these affect others. Gains are reaped and costs are incurred, but there is no market that relates the two. Most importantly, the costs that arise are borne not by those that cause them but by others that happen to be around but are outside the process—bystanders, so to speak. Not all the costs of the process end up as costs to the producer; a slice is lodged outside. With inventiveness, but at the peril of losing their nontechnical audience, economists refer to these as "external diseconomies" or "externalities"; less elegantly, one might think of them as "someone else's headache."

Unless these headaches are brought home to the originator in such a way that they are included as costs in his profit-and-loss calculations—or "internalized"—private costs will understate total, or social, costs. Consequently, production decisions will lead to misallocation of resources, for the producer will be faced with production costs that are lower than they would be if he had also to foot the bill for the external diseconomies—the unpleasantness, nuisance, or other aggravation caused to his neighbor or environment.

The cause-effect nexus of such phenomena is often difficult to establish. Sometimes this may be due to the low intensity of the degrading substances or activities or to the low degree of quality deterioration that takes place. At other times, damage may be long delayed in appearing, or it may turn up in areas remote from the locus of emission. Finally, effects seldom occur with laboratory-like purity and in isolation, but are intermingled with a variety of other factors. Thus, presumption is more common than proof. And when the causal relationship can be satisfactorily established, it is often difficult to identify the offender, or when he can be identified, to assess his share in the total effect.

Typically, there is a widely dispersed multiplicity of the

offended. In marked contrast to traditional "nuisance" cases that are actionable in the courts, this raises questions of both efficiency and equity in remedial action, if not of the feasibility of starting any action at all.

Changes in the environment are not easily, and often not at all, susceptible to meaningful evaluation in dollars and cents. This impedes comparison with costs incurred or avoided by the producer of the side effect in question, which as a rule lends itself to expression in monetary terms.

There is no answer to "what price beauty?" that would furnish a zoning authority a ready method of weighing the claims of, say, a stone quarry, a wildlife refuge, and a resort hotel where they are competing for the same tract of land. Psychic values are not traded in the market, at least not directly and not obviously. One is, therefore, limited to seeking surrogates and proxies that reflect such values. (For example, movements into and out of specific areas may be prompted by changes in environmental conditions and may be reflected in real-estate quotations.) This search has only just begun. Moreover, there are, as yet, few institutional and administrative arrangements that offer a mechanism for bringing together the offended and the offender, even when both can, in principle, be identified.

For the sake of efficient management, it is frequently desirable that measures dealing with questions of environmental quality be considered for large areas at a time. This is almost a necessity where air and water are concerned. Action then tends to become collective and regional, rather than individual and local. The rationale is that the smaller the community considered, the more the costs will be of the "external" kind. As the area widens, they become internal and, therefore, part of the proper economic calculus. If the decision-making unit is my home, then the costs of my dumping trash in my neighbor's backyard are "external" as far as I am concerned. If the unit is my street, then the costs are "internal."

Thus, one way of catching up with side effects is to extend the area within which they cannot be "external." Decisions made on the basis of rather large areas—the community, the river basin—are likely to produce a result closer to the optimum than the sum total of many individual decisions. One consequence of this spatial relationship, incidentally, is that for reasons of both efficiency and equity the role of the Federal Government as well as that of interstate and regional compacts, commissions, and similar multi-state bodies will inescapably grow larger.

While it may sound as though stressing the size of the decision-making unit as an important element in quality management is a highly academic point, it is actually a very practical one. A good topical illustration is the use of pesticides in crop production. One's balancing of the gains and losses incurred from use of pesticides would differ according to whether one focuses on the individual farmer and his immediate surroundings, the county, the state, a region, the country, or an even larger supranational area. It is one thing to weigh damage to the environment against gains in crop production in a given locality, but quite another to do so in a national or supranational framework. It could be argued that the United States might not now be able to ship one fourth of its wheat crop to India had it not been for the prolonged application of various chemicals to soil and vegetation. Such chemicals not only raise productivity in their own right but permit many other changes in farm practices and organization that jointly form a tight, almost ecological system. Evaluation of gains and losses from use of pesticides, thus, can be seen to depend greatly on the size of the decision-making unit—on where one draws the line.

The Case for Quantification

The above categorizing makes no claim to either comprehensiveness or uniqueness. But it does serve to bring out the principal difficulties that beset improvement of resource quality: identification of gainers and losers, ascertainment and valuation of gains and losses in the absence of a market, and lack of channels and institutions for arbitration of rival claims. If economists have not yet found many answers, they have begun to bring to this relatively new field of concern the integrating element of a common denominator—cost. Its applicability can be exaggerated, but its neglect surely leaves the field open to pressure and emotion. At the very least, even a rough casting of gains and losses into dollars and cents will convey a sense of magnitude that would otherwise be lacking. There is nothing dehumanizing in the process of monetary quantification.[8] Where efforts must be expanded to achieve a given objective, they are not available for alternative uses, and it is only fair that we establish at least the magnitude of what we must forego, so we can gain some idea of whether the environmental change contemplated is worth the price tag. This approach suggests a number of areas that call for better understanding. To a degree, they are corollaries of the characteristics discussed above.

We must learn more about the physical characteristics of the desirable objectives, of the undesirable side effects, and of the relationship of the one to the other. In such studies, attention should be directed not to the spectacular, which is usually accidental and ephemeral, but to the pedestrian, which is usually basic and lasting. From the study of physical aspects, we must move to the dollar values associated with them. Above all, we must ascertain and analyze cost relationships. We know, for example, that it is extraordinarily expensive to remove the final traces of pollution. In water treatment, costs double and triple as we approach a state of pristine purity. In removing successive amounts of coal dust from power-plant smokestacks, the capacity of precipitators must increase proportionately with the added removal efficiency, measured in terms of the remaining dust. Thus, if removal efficiency is to be raised from 96 to, say, 98 per cent, the increase is not 2, but 50 per cent, and consequently represents a steep rise in equipment size and cost. We must, therefore, ask how we determine the point of equilibrium, beyond which additional purity costs more than is gained in terms of health or aesthetics? Where does one reasonably stop? The more we can learn about cost behavior under different conditions, the easier it will become to establish criteria around which compromises can be built, even in the face of the difficulties that beset ascertainment of corresponding benefits.

Indignation over the manifestations of pollution comes easily; remedies do not. It has been estimated, for example, that it would cost some $20 billion annually to return all watercourses to an unspoiled state. This is about what the country spends each year on primary and secondary education. Will such knowledge affect specific decisions? It might, for decisions will tend to be more in accord with explicit value scales, openly arrived at. And these will frequently differ from what is merely presumed.

We must find ways of measuring society's demands for improving the quality of resources, the environment. The bafflingly unmeasurable must be made measurable. There are small beginnings today and much groping for answers, for it is clear that in the absence of acceptable measurements the debate will continue to produce more heat than light. Moreover, since funds will be appropriated and spent without greater guidance from any demand gauge, responsibility will remain above all with the resource manager, who must construe a demand schedule out of his own scale of preferences, what he believes are other people's preferences, and what he thinks ought to be other people's preferences. He will get some help from the political process, but that process is clumsy, especially when it comes to detail. Customarily, it permits choices only between approval and rejection, between yes and no; rarely between more and less, or among a whole spectrum of alternatives. As a consequence, decisions tend to be reached with little factual knowledge of the values that society as a whole puts on the results of the contemplated action.

Nor does the matter end here. Even though the individual consumer's choice is limited to the range of goods and services that are offered in the market, there *is* choice, both in quantity and in kind. This is not so in most decisions that are arrived at politically. As little as I can have a Federal Government that is part Democratic and part Republican, can I have a river that is both wild and provides storage for water supply and power. Thus, there is a problem of meeting the wants and needs of minorities whose desires are swamped in political decisions.

Finally, we must recognize that the decision-maker can err. Let us assume, for the sake of argument, that cigarette-smoking were considered a form of pollution and its practice made subject to public regulation. In the light of the last few years' experience, there can be little doubt that any restrictions put on smoking would not be in accord with the aggregate of private valuations rationally arrived at—not only, as J. W. Milliman has suggested,[9] because the political process is no freer from imperfection than the market mechanism, but because there is a real conflict between a theoretical cost-benefit calculus, made in all good faith, and one derived from the summation of an individual's preferences. Only by cranking in society's interest in a healthier population as a plus could one hope to redress the balance toward a net gain from restrictive regulation.

All of this demonstrates the need for greatly increased research efforts directed toward methods of ascertaining where in the hierarchy of rival claims people rank quality improvement and similar intangibles. Even without accurate measurements, however, we are not quite lost. Establishing a range of arbitrary quality standards and estimating the costs their imposition would imply is one way out. To initially recommend itself, the cost of an action would have to be at least commensurate with the value of the improvement that is sought or the deterioration that is to be prevented.

With the aid of such calculations of alternatives, we can begin to make intelligent choices among policy decisions—intelligent, but not necessarily easy. The cost tag is an indispensable aid: "No intangible has infinite value. All intangibles have cost."[10] Nevertheless, it is not the only nor perhaps always the determining criterion for decision. Still, the magnitude of what one has to forego, which is what cost is all about, is always relevant and usually lurks somewhere in the decision-maker's mind. Instead, it should be explicitly and prominently on the decision-maker's agenda.

Calculation of both gains and losses greatly facilitates dealing with quality changes. Whether it is more efficient to allow degradation to stand, or to reduce or suppress it, the course followed should leave nobody worse off and somebody better off than before. Without cost tags, this is hard to judge.

If the effluent from a paper mill muddies the water for the downstream resident, and the cost of removing the cause exceeds the cost of reducing such disturbance by treatment at the intake, it would clearly be efficient to let the offending effluent continue and to treat the water prior to its further use. In that event, the "winner," the paper mill, could compensate the "loser," the municipality, out of the savings that would accrue from not having to treat the effluent. Thus, both efficiency and equity would be served. The added cost (added, that is, in comparison to the previous condition of pollution without compensation) would most likely be reflected in higher costs of paper, at least initially, which only proves that you do not get something for nothing.

As has been pointed out, most situations of this kind are very complex, involving a multitude of participants, actions, and reactions. But it is easy to see the need for finding ways in which the external cost—in the simplified case above, the nuisance to the city residents—can be gauged and added to the private, or internal, cost, with the result that the polluter's cost will fully reflect the social cost of his activity.

Existing institutions and mechanisms need to be modified or new ones invented to facilitate making the cost of side effects a cost to the originator—that is, "internalizing" them. Imposition of taxes, charges, or other financial burdens on the producer is one way. These might be rigid or flexible so that the punishment could fit the crime. Their rationale lies in the consideration that the use of a congested facility, be this a watercourse, the air, a highway, or a park, should be reduced by putting a price on it.

At times, particularly when it is impractical or too costly to bar free access to the resource, a charge can be levied not on the activity itself but on the agent that causes the adverse effect (a pesticide, a detergent, a fuel), in the expectation that this will promote more sparing use of the offending substance and thus lead to a reduction of the noxious side effects. Also, raising the cost may stimulate the development of new technology, and the charges collected can be tapped for remedying the effects of the activity in question. In other situations, collective, administrative action may be more efficient. Unlike taxes, standard-setting regulations will not, however, produce revenue; also, flexibility will be less easily achieved, and policing and enforcement will present major administrative burdens, if not problems.

Technical considerations may, however, suggest collective action of a different sort—not through regulation—but through doing on a large centralized scale what is harder and more expensive to accomplish through the aggregation of a multitude of individual actions. To illustrate, a dollar's worth of aeration of dirty water performed by a public body according to a carefully laid plan is likely to beat a dollar's worth of waste-discharge treatment undertaken separately by a score of users.

When we can compare meaningfully the costs to society—which are, as we have tried to show, the producer's private costs plus costs to others that are not part of his calculus—with the many-sided benefits that are the counterpart of those costs, we shall have taken a long stride toward evolving a workable policy of preserving the quality of the environment without sacrificing the beneficial effects of advancing technology. Only then will we be able to appraise the present and future adequacy of quality of the resources as we have appraised that of quantity. If this means having the best of two worlds, then the time may be at hand to cease calling economics the dismal science. Until then, the economist will have to insist that the frontiers of cost and benefit measurement be vigorously extended—not necessarily to dictate action but to allow it to be shaped in the presence of the newly gained knowledge.[11]

REFERENCES

1. See Harold J. Barnett and Chandler Morse, *Scarcity and Growth: The Economics of Natural Resource Availability* (Baltimore, 1963).

2. *Ibid.*, p. 86.

3. *Ibid.*, p. 235 ff.

4. John R. Platt, *The Step to Man* (New York, 1966), pp. 185-203.

5. Hans H. Landsberg, Leonard L. Fischman, and Joseph L. Fisher, *Resources in America's Future* (Baltimore, 1963); and Hans H. Landsberg, *Natural Resources for U. S. Growth* (Baltimore, 1964).

6. A cautionary view of prospects for rising yields in developed countries was advanced by Lester R. Brown at the December, 1966, meeting of the American Association for the Advancement of Science. (See *Journal of Commerce*, January 3, 1967; no published version as yet available.)

7. For a recent attempt, see, for instance, Joseph L. Fisher and Neal Potter, *World Prospects for Natural Resources* (Baltimore, 1964).

8. Mason Gaffney, "Applying Economic Controls," *Bulletin of the Atomic Scientists* (May, 1965), pp. 20-25.

9. J. W. Milliman, "Can People Be Trusted with Natural Resources?", *Land Economics* (August, 1962), pp. 199-218.

10. *Ibid.*

11. Appreciation is expressed to the Cooper Foundation Committee, Swarthmore College, for permission to utilize material first developed in connection with a talk on conservation presented to a symposium in February, 1966.

NATHANIEL WOLLMAN

The New Economics of Resources

I

THE PREMISE that there is a "new economics of resources" is itself subject to debate, but if there is, it differs from the "old" in that it pays greater attention to constraints within which economizing behavior is observed and gives greater weight to so-called "intangibles." It is an economics for which the "proper" supply of nonmarketed goods and services is a question of considerable moment, as is the design of the machinery by which the proper supply can be ascertained.

The natural environment—its various dimensions and qualities —is an especially apt subject for the new economics. I shall assume that we all agree on the fact of environmental deterioration, and argue that the low value we put on the environment reflects deeply imbedded philosophic principles and historic sequences. The disregard of aesthetic factors and the dominating influence of the "economic man" were joint results of common causes. We still have no scientific way of determining how much "should" be spent on environmental quality, nor do we know what relationships, if any, exist between environmental quality and productivity. The knowledge we have of consumer preferences is inadequate, and we do not know how much weight should be attached to those consumer preferences that we can identify. Since environmental changes frequently trigger a sequence of irreversible effects, we cannot expect decisions to be both "correct" and based upon democratic authority unless the electorate is well informed and aesthetically sensitive. Lacking these qualities but aware of the deficiency, the electorate can proceed with confidence if there is a qualified body to whom it can delegate responsibility. Since all levels of government have environmental problems to solve, there is need for a corresponding hierarchy of environmental boards

131

of experts. These boards should possess the power and authority that is now accorded the military establishment, not only because the penalty of inexpert decisions may be just as disastrous for the human race as the effect of military weapons, but because the ability of most of us to make expert decisions is no greater in the field of ecology, broadly conceived, than in warfare.

In advising or manning a board of experts, the economist functions as a member of a team. The economic task of "optimizing" resource use consists of bringing into an appropriate relationship the ordering of preferences for various experiences and the costs of acquiring those experiences. Preferences reflect physiological-psychological responses to experience or anticipated experience, individually or collectively revealed, and are accepted as data by the economist. A broad range of noneconomic investigations is called for to supply the necessary information.

II

Economists, as Tibor Scitovsky has pointed out, tend to think in terms of money. "Exactness, precision, and rational calculation hinge on the use of money. In the words of Georg Simmel, 'money economy and the dominance of the intellect are intrinsically connected. They share a matter-of-fact attitude in dealing with men and with things.'" Thinking in terms of market prices, continues Scitovsky, yields a "consciousness of society's valuations; and when a person's actions are influenced by market prices, they conform that much more closely to society's needs and limitations."[1]

Scitovsky then goes on to discuss the deficiencies in the price system that grow out of its failure to account for all aspects of money transactions. The price system fails to account adequately for benefits or costs that are enjoyed or suffered by people who were not parties to the transaction. These "extra-party" costs and benefits are the "externalities" of economic analysis. (Familiar examples are the disfigurement of the landscape by billboards, the sulfuric odors that surround a paper mill, or the pleasure of a neighborhood in a well-landscaped front yard.) Economists have long recognized their existence, but have usually treated them as side effects of uncertain magnitude rather than as central points of interest. In general, these externalities have no monetary valuations because the machinery by which valuations are created—that is, a market—does not exist for them. The markets do not exist because the benefits that are gained or lost are not exclusive or appropriable, and, until recently, the costs have not imposed such a burden that society saw fit to make an issue of them.[2]

The market malfunctions not only when it fails to register third-party effects, but also when participants in the market fail to act in accordance with their own interests. We infer that market action is *per se* welfare maximizing, but this inference rests upon the prior assumption of adequate knowledge and foresight. To the extent that people act on the basis of restricted information and inadequate understanding of the consequences of their acts, market transactions fail to achieve maximum human welfare.[3] Reliance upon consumer sovereignty has its limitations.

III

The past's low regard for careful preservation of the environment stemmed from several circumstances. Those controlling the use of resources could usually avoid permanent contact with dirt and ugliness. Moreover, environmental control required collaborative action. One man could blight a region, but collective action was needed to prevent this. Furthermore, levels of income were not high enough to suggest a substitution of beauty for physical goods, and those in the business of developing and disseminating good taste and sensitivity to beauty usually had as clients not the public, but the wealthy. The classic examples of blight—polluted air, polluted water, and scarred hillsides—were more often than not concomitants to the process of accumulating private fortunes. Today's interest in public beautification stems in part, perhaps in large part, from the fact that those professionally concerned now have the public as a client. Interest has also grown because we find it increasingly difficult to escape, and because sectors of the society—the upper-middle class particularly—have become saturated with goods and services.[4]

The foregoing catalogue does not exhaust the explanations of why we inured ourselves to environmental decay. Several additional, perhaps more fundamental, reasons can be advanced. Blight was an inescapable part of the industrial revolution, which began, in Lewis Mumford's phrase, with the paleotechnic age—an age dependent upon coal and iron and, consequently, the disfigurement of the landscape.

After technological developments made the home inadequate as a production center, laborers began to concentrate in factories. These were probably related, aesthetically, to problems of pauperism and public charity. As a manufacturing center, the factory appeared late in the history of cities and was, therefore, relegated to the periphery. "The operators of workhouses [factories] first found their labor supply not from within the city, but among runaway serfs and country yokels. . . . [Industrial plants] are still striving for a rational place in the body of the urbanized region."[5] The aesthetic decline of the city to the level of the workhouse had greater force than the elevation of the aesthetic quality of the factory to the level that had been attained by the medieval city.

The Anglo-American understanding of man's nature, based upon epistemological questions raised by Galilean and Newtonian physics, focused attention on man as a thinking rather than a feeling being. F. S. C. Northrop points out that "when Locke made explicit the complete consequences of his friend Newton, this experimentally verified physics was found to provide a theory not merely of physical nature but also of conscious man."[6]

Northrop's explanation, dealing as it does with man's conception of man and with the elemental units which together comprise the comprehension of reality, is the closest we can come to fundamentals. The Lockean person was a "mental substance . . . a completely local, independent thing having nothing in common with all other persons and things." In his view of man, Locke erred in failing to recognize that, in addition to the "theoretic continuum, . . . there is an all-embracing indeterminate continuum of feeling common to all creatures in their aesthetic immediacy. . . . All these aesthetic materials, including the all-embracing aesthetic continuum, are the kind of thing which can be known only by being immediately experienced. No syntactically formulated, mathematically or logically abstract, indirectly and experimentally verified theory can ever designate them."

Northrop points out that Hume and his positivistic followers used the aesthetic materials mainly to develop a "mathematical, deductively formulated theory in the science of economics" and ignored the "purely empirical aesthetic factor in things for its own sake." Hume, Bentham, Mill, and Jevons erected the body of doctrine that has dominated our culture on the Lockean view of man. Northrop's quotation from Gautier's preface to his *Mlle. de Maupin* is worth repeating both because it reveals the deep sense of frustration felt by those whose aesthetic sensibilities were deeply scarred by what they saw, and because the attack on Hume and the economists who followed him was somewhat unfair.

Poor fellows! Their noses are too short to admit of their wearing spectacles, and yet they cannot see the length of their noses.

If an author threw a volume of romance or poetry on their desk, these gentlemen would turn round carelessly in their easy chair, poise it on its hinder legs, and balancing themselves with a capable air, say loftily— "What purpose does this book serve? How can a man, instead of making the great synthesis of humanity, and pursuing the regenerating and providential idea through the events of history, how can he write novels and poems which lead to nothing, and do not advance our generation on the path of the future? How can he busy himself with form, and style, and rhyme in the presence of such grave interests? What are style, and rhyme, and form to us? They are of no consequence (poor foxes! they are too sour). . . ."

No, fools, no, . . . a book does not make gelatine soup; a novel is not a pair of seamless boots. . . . There are two sorts of utility, and the meaning of the vocable is always a relative one. What is useful for one is not useful for another. You are a cobbler, I am a poet. . . . You will object that a cobbler is far above a poet, and that people can do with the one better than without the other. Without affecting to disparage the illustrious profession of cobbler, which I honour equally with that of constitutional monarch, I humbly confess that I would rather have my shoe unstitched than my verse badly rhymed, and that I should be more willing to go without boots than without poems. . . . I know that there are some who prefer mills to churches, and bread for the body to that for the soul. To such I have nothing to say. They deserve to be economists in this world and also in the next.

For my own part, may it please these gentlemen, I am one of those to whom superfluity is a necessity—and I like things and persons in an inverse ratio to the services that they render me. I prefer a Chinese vase, strewn with dragons and mandarins, and of no use to me whatever. . . . Of my talents the one I esteem the most is my incapacity for guessing logogriphs and charades.

Northrop comments that there is nothing in utilitarian economics "which requires that its basic concept of 'utility' be restricted to eliminate the aesthetic object in the manner which [Gautier] has suggested. The Chinese vase is as much an 'economic good' as is a jar of mustard or a ton of coal." He goes on to add:

Nevertheless, in their actual handling and use of the emotional and aesthetic materials given in the purely empirical component of human knowledge, the modern British empirical philosophers and economists did actually neglect the aesthetic and emotional values, which these empirical materials, pursued in and for themselves for their own sake, provide, and did tend to turn them into mere counters, entering them into theoretical scientific relations, for understanding and computing the course of prices in the market place. Thus the equally important aesthetic

135

values which their purely empirical knowledge could have given modern Western mankind were lost, and the modern Western world fell into the very serious fallacy, to which the Marxians as well as the Anglo-Americans are heirs, of tending to identify the whole human value with nothing but restrictedly utilitarian economic value.[7]

IV

If Northrop is right, we still lack the bridge in economics that links the aesthetic and theoretic continuums. We have no way of incorporating into the body of the state's "rational" economic behavior (or even into theoretical economic models of the state) the clues to collective action that are yielded by what is directly sensed. Economists have clearly avoided any calculation that depends upon a cardinal measure of sense perceptions and any scientific judgment regarding human welfare where, in the economist's phrase, an interpersonal comparison of states of satisfaction has to be made.

A completely puristic view on this question would have severely restricted the usefulness of economics in coping with real problems.[8] By limiting himself to situations in which no interpersonal utilities are compared, the economist is reduced to the conclusion that an act is good if no one loses and at least one party gains. This criterion does not let us go very far. For example, progressive income taxes (in fact, any kind of tax protested by one individual), agricultural price supports, Medicare, public education, interstate-highway programs, and most of our past military expenditures could never be supported on economic grounds in the context of a full-employment economy.

Economic decisions are being and will continue to be made by both economists and noneconomists, unrestrained by knowledge that interpersonal comparisons of utility cannot be scientifically made.[9] We should, therefore, be aware of what we can do in addition to balancing intuitively gains and losses that cannot be measured objectively. Occasionally we can bolster our conclusion with relatively well-supported arguments. For example, a reduction in bacterial contamination of water will reduce morbidity, raise life expectancy, and result in an increase in Gross National Product in excess of the resources absorbed by improving the water supply. Unfortunately, such arguments cannot be used for most of the problems we face. We cannot support a program of atmospheric-pollution abatement on productivity grounds.[10] If, in fact, there is a correlation between Gross National Product and atmospheric pollution, or between GNP and any other deficiency, such as lack of urban recreational facilities, congested living conditions, or failure to preserve adequate wilderness areas, we do not yet have the supporting data.

Does our ignorance mean that we should do nothing? There are two answers that support action. The first is that when in doubt, the burden of proof ought to be put on the backs of those who are responsible for deterioration. Let them demonstrate that no one's productivity is impaired. The other answer is that the value of the environment is measured less by changes in man's productivity than by man's direct sensual response—delight, repugnance, or unconcern. Measuring direct sensual response is more difficult than measuring productivity, but the validity of the thing measured, human satisfaction, is more compelling. After one has demonstrated that the improvement has raised GNP, one would still be faced with explaining why an increase in Gross National Product serves as grounds for saying that welfare is increased; measurement of satisfaction can end the matter.

Putting the burden of proof on the polluter, and thereby compelling him to bear all costs of abatement, does not serve as a guide for such questions as the adequacy of recreational facilities. The only rules we have are those that treat man as either a producer or a consumer. If man is considered to be solely a producer, we should have that quantity of recreational facilities for which the marginal dollar spent adds as much to national product as any other expenditure would add. Since this point of view conceives of man as something less than a dog, which is well treated on humanitarian grounds, we may seek to substitute a criterion based on human satisfaction, on the sense of well-being and fulfillment. (Any objective other than productive capacity can be specified.) We face the same problem in this area as in environmental quality: We possess no criterion other than our preference. Someone in authority has to make the decision on the basis of whatever information he can gather regarding the relative strength of our respective preferences.

V

The overriding importance Anglo-American culture attaches to the theoretic component at the expense of the aesthetic is partially matched by its view of "work" as a source of "negative satisfaction." Work is a duty rather than a privilege, a punishment imposed by God on man rather than an activity that is sought for its own sake. If work is negative utility, idleness is utility. But this is false. We know that man must be engaged in meaningful activity if his mental health is to be sustained. Throughout man's history, this need has been met by the production of goods and services. Now that we are faced with the prospect that man's involvement in the production process will be substantially reduced by the cybernetic revolution, his deep-seated psychological requirement for productive activity will have to be met by activities that now come under the heading of "recreation." (Income will no longer be a necessary inducement for work; nor will income differentials necessarily reflect differences in the ratios of the demand for and supply of various occupations or activities.[11])

An alternative proposition, or at least one that modifies the impact of increased productivity, argues that part of the labor force released from the production of food, shelter, clothing, and equipment will be available for other purposes. We can, therefore, polish up the environment without "sacrificing" any of the goods and services we now consider essential. Increases in labor productivity in the past were met by a general rise in the level of consumption of "necessities," a proliferation in the variety of goods and services, and an increase in leisure—all at the expense of a decay in environmental quality. Given a positive desire for work and the probable reduction in per-capita effort needed to supply goods and services, the necessary outlay on environmental improvement for daily living could be costless. In other words, the effort required to improve the environment may itself yield satisfaction that would not be enjoyed otherwise. On top of the positive pleasure of the work, we would have the pleasure of the improved environment.

If human needs for work could be filled in part through opportunities to improve the environment, the burden on recreation to supply the satisfactions of meaningful activity would be lightened. To the extent that we reduce the need for recreation, we reduce those environmental pressures that are hardest to meet, namely, broadly based access to outdoor facilities of high quality. (Compare the ease with which we can meet a recreational demand for bowling alleys with the difficulty of meeting a demand for lonely contact with nature.) Furthermore, as we devote more work to environmental improvement, we expand man's contact with nature and thereby satisfy those recreational needs that are uniquely dependent upon nature.

VI

I shall assume that in a democratic society we do as well as we can in selecting responsible public officials. In coming to a decision with regard to environmental quality, these officials face a double-barrelled question: What do the people want—how much of other things (measured as a sum of money) are they willing to give up to enjoy these benefits of nature? And do we accept the idea that the people's judgments truly reflect their welfare?

We can find out what people want in various ways: directly, by asking them; indirectly, by inferring preferences from observed action; and, combining the direct and the indirect methods, by exposing people experimentally to alternative situations and asking their reaction as well as observing their behavior. Gilbert F. White has concluded that attitudes toward the environment vary widely, and that we do not fully know how to elicit and interpret information regarding what people think they want.[12] I assume that we shall learn more about what people want, and that knowledge of consumer preferences will help us reduce guesswork.

Better knowledge of what people want leaves unsettled the question of how much reliance should be placed upon expressed preference. The question does not arise in market transactions merely because we choose that it be suppressed: By hypothesis, each consumer is free to act as he chooses in the market, and therefore he acts in his best interest. So long as transactions are no more consequential than picking tonight's soup, the consumer is able to survive poor decisions and learn to make better ones. In the private sector, most decisions are perhaps marginal and reversible. The opposite is likely to obtain in the public sector; for this reason, there is less rationale for reliance upon consumer preference. Only if we are also assured that preferences are based upon adequate information, adequate exposure to and experience of alternatives, and adequate appreciation of the future consequences of present actions, will expressed preferences be consistent with maximum welfare. A broad "base of citizens who have the maturity to deal with complex and probabilistic conditions" will, as White points out, allow us to reduce our reliance upon a technical elite for making the correct decision. But, as David Lowenthal remarks in commenting on White's paper, many attitudes are formed and can only

139

be stated *"after* an environmental decision has been acted on."[13] Richard Neutra has observed:

Plans for public garbage collection, incineration, and elaborate sewage disposal first appeared as doctrinary, idealistic dreams conceived in a vacuum of any possible "financial facts" and altogether devoid of practical sense. . . . The most ordinary sewer systems of today would have seemed like black fantastic nightmares to the taxpayers of only one hundred years ago.[14]

In short, transcendental guidance on the question—How much should we spend on environmental improvement?—does not exist. The economic guide that indicates a *minimum environmental quality control level* can be specified as those standards that yield the maximum Gross National Product net of environmental control costs.[15] Apart from the fact that we have little information that relates environmental quality to productivity, this guide is limited because it excludes the aesthetic factor—that is, consumer preference for high-quality environment at the expense of other goods and services.

VII

Where does this leave us? I think that we are where we always have been, namely, facing the questions of what we want and of what machinery we can rely upon to reconcile conflicting individual and social goals. Environmental quality, no less than food, shelter, clothing, and comic books, comes at a cost. In some instances, the cost is ours; in others, it is transferred to the future; in still others, it can be transferred to foreigners. Often there is no well-defined net social cost or social benefit, but rather a transfer of income (real or psychic or both) from one group to another at a given time. The way in which these conflicts are resolved is the stuff of economics, but their resolution is not the economist's responsibility. In fact, if we are to live in a world that is aesthetically and ecologically more satisfying than the one present trends promise, the responsibility is clearly on those whose aesthetic insights are clear and whose knowledge of ecological, physiological, and biological change can be communicated persuasively to society. Deciding what to do is only weakly an "economic" decision; the decisions once made, however, may have various economic impacts.

The most likely effect of a decision to upgrade the physical environment is a change in the pattern of goods and services produced, with no change in Gross National Product—at least in the short run. Long-run effects on Gross National Product will depend upon several different forces, about which we can only speculate. If we are faced with economic rootlessness and lack of purpose as a result of the technological destruction of the psychic importance of work, expenditures on environmental improvement that are economically justified on a long-term basis may be much greater than appear appropriate on the surface. Furthermore, *recreational* experiences may have to provide a psychic substitute for work; such need may justify much larger expenditures on the natural environment that anyone today believes reasonable.

The most significant aspect of the full-employment economy when viewed in a static perspective is that we can have more of A only by sacrificing some of B. Hence "costs" are impressive. For example, Allen Kneese has pointed out that if we were to adopt a standard of pristine purity for all effluents returned to a water-course, it "might cost $20 billion a year—about as much as we spend for primary and secondary education. I am sure that most people would find such an undertaking ridiculous."[16]

If we shift to a dynamic perspective, the absurdity of absolutely pure water in all our streams diminishes. Twenty billion dollars a year is roughly one third to one half the amount by which one year's GNP exceeds the previous year's GNP at current rates of output. Should we decide, therefore, to restore our streams to purity, the cost is a delay by four to six months of the expected *increase* in all other goods and services that we would otherwise enjoy. (One could argue with equal validity that a doubling of the outlay on primary and secondary education would have a similar effect and would be of even greater merit.)

Another dynamic problem about which we know little but which we should approach optimistically is the impact of alternative environmental standards on technology. The direction of research and development and the flow of new goods and services would be modified in proportion to the rigor of the standards. We can imagine the effect on Du Pont: Instead of devoting technical know-how to developing new yarns from petroleum and adding thereby to the industrial waste problem, it would be developing low-cost tertiary treatment of sewage. Changes in other policies would also affect environmental quality. If highway programs were reduced sufficiently, automotive traffic would become so snarled that cities would be compelled to turn to mass-transportation systems, thereby reducing air pollution and releasing land for other uses.

Outlays to improve the environment cannot be described wholly as "consumption" or "capital" expenditures, since both are involved. As a consumption outlay, the effect on GNP of increased expenditure on environment would probably be imperceptible, provided it was offset by reduced expenditure on other forms of consumption. If the offset were a reduction of investment, the net effect would probably be a reduction in the rate of economic growth. Increased outlays by government on natural resources would most likely have a negligible effect on savings and investment if they were financed by consumer charges rather than by taxes. The fee to enter a national park, for example, is likely to compete against other travel items in the family budget. At the same time, changes in outlays on environment made without regard to revenue collected from users serve as an extremely desirable anticyclical device. Furthermore, should we ever be serious about the abolition of poverty, large outlays on environmental improvement would serve as an appropriate vehicle for employment of unskilled and other disadvantaged labor classes.

Some forms of blight can be corrected at practically no cost, if we exclude heightened emotions, short-run dislocations, and some income redistribution. In fact, the improvement would be accompanied by a net release of resources to other uses, hopefully less injurious to aesthetic standards. I refer here, of course, to the eyesore created by outdoor advertising—highway and urban. We have generated some momentum toward improving conditions along federal highways. Measured by man-hours of impact, highway beautification will achieve negligible results, since most of us spend most of our time in the city. Efforts to improve conditions are even weaker in town than in the country.

All effects that fall under the heading of "external costs"—that is, all cases where marginal social costs exceed marginal private benefits—imply that there has been a transfer of income from one group to another. The incidence of this income transfer has probably been regressive; the poor have suffered for the benefit of the rich. As we examine alternative ways of financing environmental uplift, our eyes naturally fall upon the polluter. Costs imposed on the polluter will, in the course of events, probably appear in the market price of the goods that are responsible for the pollution. Since products that are a serious threat to environmental quality are likely to be produced and consumed on a large scale, the ultimate incidence of the costs of pollution control is also likely to be "regressive," but no more so than the costs of any widely consumed product. Only if we start with the premise that we have a "natural right" to use the environment for "free" waste disposal would a different incidence of pollution-abatement costs be appropriate.

The "appropriate level" of expenditure on environmental quality is not a figure that can be ascertained any more accurately than the appropriate level of expenditure on education, national defense, or television entertainment. The cost of doing nothing in the face of environmental decline is itself quite high. Only by continuous negotiation, via political and market mechanisms, between those who have demands and those who have resources or control over resources can we determine what we should spend. The "new economics" can help in these negotiations by bridging the aesthetic gap—by developing new methods of analysis that will show us how to incorporate into a measured system the direct sensual responses that up to now have figured solely as intuitively valued side conditions. For what is now measurable, the "old economics" is good enough.

One task of the new economics is to decide when things should *not* be done. For example, new roads into places now accessible only by trail constitute the main threat to continued existence of the relatively small amount of undisturbed country still left. To protect against this, strong industrial and bureaucratic interests must be opposed. There is no bureaucracy or industry organized to prevent unspoiled areas from encroachment, only organizations of amateurs. Perhaps the best immediate solution is a merger of existing like-minded private groups into a national federation that would adequately reflect the growing interest in a primitive natural base.

Most environmental needs can be satisfied only collectively. In order to generate public awareness, expert findings must be broadly disseminated. Occasionally environmental problems are dramatic enough to stimulate a spontaneous response, but more often they reflect, in Secretary Udall's phrase, a "quiet crisis," recognized by relatively few people. For this reason, a network of citizen groups is needed to serve as a link between the experts and the electorate. A wide variety of groups would be desirable: urban, rural, county, state, regional, federal, landscape, air, water, wildlife, architectural, beach, mountain, and so forth. Citizen involvement can be facilitated by a modest federal matching-grant pro-

143

gram to finance costs. In addition, a staff position of aesthetician should be created in all agencies concerned with use of resources, public construction, and zoning. The plan of study of the North Atlantic Regional Water Resources Study Coordinating Committee prepared by the North Atlantic Division of the Corps of Engineers includes an appraisal of "aesthetic and cultural values," a step that should be taken as a matter of course in all projects.

If we accept the solutions offered by existing market forces, we shall probably waste and misuse part of our resources. This conclusion rests upon the probability that there is a bias in the "old economics" in favor of underestimation rather than overestimation of needs met by nonmarketed goods and services.

A partial cure for underestimation of the importance of nonmarketed goods and services is an extension of the price system to activities now excluded. This can be achieved by encouraging the growth of co-operatives and profit-making enterprises into new areas (tax benefits and other subsidies can be conferred), and by extension of user charges by governmental agencies. Such charges can be employed to measure demand as well as to provide a source of funds for the acquisition of new facilities. User charges are an especially attractive way of financing new and better facilities, since the consumer can usually find the funds by reducing outlays on complementary resources or other forms of consumption. So long as access to water is "free," the fisherman can afford to buy a more expensive trout rod. As a consequence, we tend to have better trout rods and poorer fishing waters than a different pricing arrangement would warrant—a condition analogous to the disparity between expenditures on automobiles and highways noted by John Kenneth Galbraith.

To the economist, a user charge also makes possible a more efficient allocation of existing scarce resources. In the absence of a charge, each user employs the resource up to the point where the last unit of use yields a zero benefit. This is socially justifiable only if there is such a large quantity of the resource in question that everyone has as much as he wants, which is patently not the case for most natural resources—such as wilderness, fishing streams, camping facilities, and national parks.

The "new economics" of natural resources and environmental quality will, one hopes, be concerned with deciding which choices should be made by the market and which by other devices, and with increasing the "efficiency" of the market not so much by removing frictions introduced by monopoly and oligopoly, as by improving the connection between aesthetic response and market response. But the economist will need help. Consumer preferences can be formulated sharply only if consumers have an understanding of alternatives. In order to help develop such understanding, the consumer must be exposed to a wider variety of experiences than he now enjoys. Expenditures for environmental improvement on the order of those now going into education are not unreasonable, especially since the needs to be met are not dissimilar.

Rather than question our ability to achieve a high-quality environment, we should ask whether we want it badly enough to pay for it. The costs are not likely to be so great as to absorb resources needed for adequate diet, shelter, clothing, education, medical care, national defense, and whatever else we are likely to include under the heading of "necessities." The debate will be over the kinds of luxuries we want. Yesterday's economics, overwhelmed as it was by the widespread incidence of poverty, malnutrition, slums, unemployment, and severely restricted health facilities, was preoccupied with the need for widespread distribution of necessities. Alfred Marshall has pointed out that not until low-cost coal was available could the poor heat their houses and enjoy decent ventilation at the same time. How many victims of the paleotechnic age would sacrifice a well-ventilated hearth for a more sightly countryside? Today such choices need not be made in the more prosperous countries of Western Europe and certainly not in the United States. If anything, the choices to be made in the United States may have an aesthetic multiplier effect: Outlays on environmental improvement not only yield direct satisfaction, but absorb resources that if used otherwise would contribute to environmental decay.

REFERENCES

1. Tibor Scitovsky, "External Diseconomies in the Modern Economy," *The Western Economic Journal* (Summer, 1966), pp. 197-202.

2. See papers by Ralph Turvey and Roland N. McKean, *Environmental Quality*, ed. Henry Jarrett (Baltimore, 1966); also J. M. Clark, *Economic Institutions and Human Welfare* (New York, 1957).

3. "Maximization of welfare" by market transactions is assumed to be constrained by the distribution of wealth, the availability of natural resources,

and science and technology. There also are other reasons why a market may not function "efficiently": presence of monopoly, immobility of resources, and discontinuities that result from large fixed capital investments.

4. See Mason Gaffney, *Environmental Quality*, p. 101.

5. Richard Neutra, *Survival Through Design* (New York, 1954), p. 374. See also Lewis Mumford, *Technics and Civilization* (New York, 1934).

6. F. S. C. Northrop, *The Meeting of East and West* (New York, 1946), p. 81.

7. *Ibid.*, pp. 307-310.

8. Note the asperity with which Turvey refers to the turn that theoretical welfare economics occasionally takes. *Environmental Quality*, p. 49n.

9. Richard B. Brandt, "The Concept of Welfare," and C. W. Churchman, "On the Intercomparison of Utilities," *The Structure of Economic Science*, ed. Sherman Roy Krupp (Englewood Cliffs, N. J., 1966). Both Brandt and Churchman argue that the "purist" position taken by economists is extreme and cannot be sustained without being exposed to weakness. Brandt asks whether we cannot make some assertions about the consciousness of others: that, for example, a proctoscopic examination will hurt more than a mosquito bite; and that the economist will want his child to be anesthetized for an operation. For an excellent essay on "Values and Value Theory in Economics," see Jerome Rothenberg's paper in the same volume.

10. Allen Kneese, *Environmental Quality;* also Roger Revelle, "Pollution and Cities," in *The Metropolitan Enigma* (Washington, D. C., 1967), pp. 78-128.

11. See Michael Harrington, *The Accidental Century* (Baltimore, 1966); especially Chapter 8, "The Statues of Daedalus."

12. See the paper by Gilbert F. White, "Formation and Role of Public Attitudes," *Environmental Quality*.

13. David Lowenthal, "Assumptions Behind the Public Attitudes," *Environmental Quality*.

14. Neutra, *Survival Through Design*, p. 372.

15. This is tantamount to saying that we raise environmental standards to the point where the marginal cost of any environmental improvement is equal to the induced increase in Gross National Product.

16. Kneese, *Environmental Quality*, p. 71. See also Hans H. Landsberg, "The U. S. Resource Outlook: Quality and Quantity," a paper presented at Swarthmore College, February, 1966, for a valuable discussion of economic issues concerned with environmental quality.

AARON WILDAVSKY

Aesthetic Power or the Triumph of the Sensitive Minority Over the Vulgar Mass: A Political Analysis of the New Economics

How DOES the "old economics" of natural resources differ from the "new economics"? The old economics was mostly economics. The new economics is mostly politics. The agonizing question confronting the new economics has troubled political theorists from the time of the Hebrew prophets to this very day: How shall society be organized so that the preferences of the morally or aesthetically sensitive minority will triumph? Where majorities are rarely mobilized, the question may be rephrased to ask how our *good* minority may prevail over their *bad* minority. If only a superior few truly love the remote and virgin wilderness, for instance, how may this opportunity for solitary communion with nature be preserved against hostile masses or rival elites? The new economics of natural resources appears to be designed to answer this question indirectly without quite raising it to a conscious level.

The terms new economists use to describe the deterioration of the natural environment are sufficiently expressive to convey the feeling behind them. The landscape has been assaulted and degraded, if not raped; genocide has been practiced against certain animal species; the air threatens to become a poisonous gas; the odor of dead fish testifies to the pollution of our water; human marauders invade and despoil isolated areas. The tone is strident; the mood, a mixture of rage and disgust. The metaphors belong more to the battlefield than the market place. It is not surprising, then, that Athelstan Spilhaus urges us to take risks in enhancing the environment comparable to those we would take in war; nor that Nathaniel Wollman suggests a political structure with administrative environmental boards possessing "the power and authority that is now accorded the military establishment . . . because the penalty of inexpert decisions may be just as disastrous for the

147

human race as the effect of military weapons." Unfortunately, the old economics does not provide the necessary weapons for what many evidently see as the war for environmental quality.

In the beginning, the rationale for the Conservation Movement was one of preserving basic resources that were becoming increasingly scarce. Wood, coal, and iron were essentially fixed in given lumps; use was a kind of desecration. As demand increased and supply decreased in an industrial society, these resources would become more and more valuable. The larger the part played by natural resources in the economy and the higher their price in comparison with other goods, the easier it was to make an economic case for protecting them. To the extent that the votes of a misguided or ignorant people would not protect these precious resources through the political arena, the symbolic casting of ballots in the more rational economic market place would restrict use by raising prices. If politics were involved at all, it would be not for economic reasons, but merely to undo the evil restrictions upon the free market that special interests had worked out with conniving politicians.

Even when economic theorists arrived at a justification for governmental intervention to overcome certain imperfections in the market place, the political arena proved vexing. When a large dam would impose costs on those who did not benefit from it, for example, it was deemed appropriate for the government to intervene to rectify the situation. But, as it turned out, the politicians marched to music of their own and were only remotely interested in following the lead of economic science. The interest rate, that old puritan arbiter between present consumption and future desires, was kept artificially low so that many projects were justified on economic grounds without valid reason. Cost-benefit analysis, designed to increase national income by assuring that the benefits to whoever received them would exceed the costs to whoever paid them, was twisted out of shape in notorious fashion. Things were arranged so that general taxpayers received less and the direct beneficiaries far more than their economically justifiable shares. A project with a low benefit-cost ratio might be joined with another having a much higher ratio so that the "new" combined project could qualify. So-called intangibles like recreation values were credited with increasingly large shares of the benefits, thus representing a "finagle" factor that could be enlarged almost at will to provide justification. A decentralized party system and a highly fragmented national political system with strong regional interests proved resistant to making decisions on economic grounds. Comments about narrow local interests, selfish minorities, and violations of the public interest filled the economic literature. While politics was proving so disappointing, the former economic rationale for protecting resources suffered severe blows.

The market mechanism, together with man's remarkable technical ingenuity, drastically changed the supply-and-demand relationships for many natural resources. New sources of supply were continuously discovered, and new products substituted for old. Industrial and farm production grew exceedingly large and immensely more efficient. Consequently, the prices of resources commodities continually decreased in comparison with those of other goods and services. The contribution of natural resources to Gross National Product showed a corresponding, proportionate drop. The decline in the price of resource commodities made it more difficult to justify special treatment on the grounds of economic efficiency. The contribution that these resources made to production was too small, and it is getting smaller. This change in the economic importance of resources lies behind the plaintive cry that it is not possible to justify on economic grounds most large programs designed to improve the quality of the natural environment.

Re-evaluations of the abundance of natural resources illustrate another aspect of their new position. We now know that we have more forest resources than we had thought and that new growth may exceed demand. Although water may be in short supply in some areas, technological advance and the shift of existing supplies to more productive uses should provide amounts more than adequate for the future. Despite the hue and cry about the advancing tentacles of the monster called urbanization, only 2 or 3 per cent of the nation's land is or will be devoted to urban uses in the next few decades. The immediate conclusion is all too evident. Resource problems will, by and large, not be critical for economic purposes. A technological advance here or a local adjustment there will take care of the worst difficulties. From a strictly economic viewpoint, nothing much need be done.

The terrible difficulty for economists is that problems of environmental quality do not look so bad as they ought. If present modes of economic justification are used, there is no way of preserving the basic values these men hold as users of the natural environment. To have personal values done in by professional values is no fun at all. Hence, a "new economics" has emerged to get around the old. If

149

the old economics will not let you have what you know is right, it follows that a new economics is evidently needed. The term *new economics of natural resources* is used to designate an emerging trend, discernible in this volume, and permits economists to avoid direct confrontation with political problems by bringing in aesthetic factors to make economic analysis come out "right."

Since the new economists of today are the old economists of yesterday, a certain ambivalence about their enterprise might be expected. It is tempting to retain an economic vocabulary for essentially non-economic processes. The deep woods with clear lakes, white-water streams, and rare animal species may be called unique and irreplaceable, like the White House or the Liberty Bell or a man's children or his sweetheart. One could say that no price is too high for these treasures except that the concept "price" is really inapplicable. These treasures are not to be bought and sold at all. They are literally "priceless"—that is, outside any market. The usual system for determining what is allowable in the market place is political or in some sense deeply traditional or social, but in no case may it be called economic. The old economist considers it ridiculous for a society to spend $20 billion to rid itself entirely of water pollution when marginal benefits of spending the largest fraction of that sum elsewhere would be much higher. The new economist says "why not" and invents rationales. After all, at current rates of economic growth, $20 billion a year represents only a few months delay in reaching a GNP that much higher. This marginalist fallacy, a variant of the old argument that for want of a nail a war was lost, suffers from a fatal defect. We can all think of huge expenditures to accomplish highly cherished ends that could be justified if only people would wait a little while longer to become richer. All the wilderness areas and fine old buildings might be preserved for even less, and many experimental cities might be built. The wealth is here. Presumably, all that is required is the will. We undoubtedly can have some of the things some of us want, but not all the things all of us want. Otherwise, there would be no problem of scarcity, no need for allocation. This is not a new economics but a "non-economics."

The old economists cried out against the use of "finagle factors" that might in some sense be important, but that could not be measured in the market place. In preference to having such factors expanded or contracted at will, they preferred that these be brought to the attention of decision-makers who could take them into account. To do otherwise would be to compromise fatally the economic part of the analysis. The new economists are tempted to abandon this position. Maintaining the wilds may be justified, without being able to specify size or cost or conditions, on the grounds that people like to leave a legacy to their children. Outdoor recreation may be alleged to have great psychic benefits, though demonstrating its dimensions or comparing it with television or people-watching on crowded streets is another matter. Yet alternative expenditures may also serve some values people hold, and the economic problem is to justify one expenditure rather than another on something more than personal grounds. Surely economics is not to become a parody of a parody, the social-science version of Saul Bellow's *Henderson the Rain King* who plunges throughout time and continents shouting ever more loudly, "I want, I want."

No one will argue that the values of economic man in the market place are the only ones that count. Who is so vulgar and insensitive as to claim that only what is objectively demonstrable is important? Will progress be made, however, by undermining the rationale for economic analysis or by concealing intransigent political problems under an economic guise? The new economics poses for itself essentially political problems. Which decisions shall be made through the market and which not? What decision structures will best assure environmental quality? How can aesthetic feelings be translated into public policy? What happens if strong aesthetic impulses are shared by only a small minority? Consideration of the problems surrounding public preferences will help throw the many political dilemmas into sharper focus.

Let us assume, for the moment, that all problems of directly measuring public preferences in regard to the quality of the environment were solved through opinion surveys or other devices. Would our problems of allocating resources then be solved? In one sense, they would be solved all too well. The problem of the interpersonal comparison of utilities, the relative preferences among different people for shares in things like housing, transportation, space exploration, or ballet, must be solved before environmental quality may be given its place. If the results of the survey are accepted, then all allocation problems in society have been solved. Such a state of affairs is usually called utopia.

Suppose, however, that some people prefer a different mix of goods than was provided in the grand allocation mechanism. Perhaps they are among the relatively small groups that intensely desire long canoe trips through completely wild areas and have been outvoted (or "outpreferenced") by others who want skin diving near where they live or who prefer large indemnities to black people to repay them for decades of service in slavery. These minorities would certainly challenge the existing state of preferences. They might argue, as democratic theorists have through the ages, that strict majority rule should not prevail. Minorities like themselves should be given some proportionate share of good things (though it is doubtful whether they would agree that every minority, including ones opposed to their desires, should get similar consideration regardless of what they wanted). The wilderness minority might say that people should not get what they want, but what they ought to have, according to the principles of the sensitive few. Perhaps many people decide in ignorance and ought to be educated before their preferences are counted or weighed equally with those of the more knowledgeable. Things might be different if people were encouraged through subsidies to experience elementary contact with nature, which would in turn alter their previous preferences. What turns out to be crucial is not merely knowledge of preferences but a set of rules for putting them together so that policy decisions emerge. Yet we have not even mentioned the knotty problems of accounting for intensity of preferences. Should the intense minority triumph over the apathetic majority? Should we satisfy the widespread norm of equality by treating all citizens equally or only equals equally? Extraordinary difficulties arise when public preferences must be translated into public policy.

Should their sensitivities be sufficiently outraged, the wilderness minority might question the procedures through which public preferences for governmental expenditures are determined. The use of opinion polls to derive a rank order of public preferences is suspect in many ways. The process of seeking preferences may create preferences where none existed before. People may feel they have to respond to a questionnaire without ever having thought of the matter before or having any real preference. Many citizens may discover that they have preferences only after an act to which they can respond has taken place. It is difficult to get people of low education to understand the wording of questions and the complex choices involved. Highly educated people will also have trouble sorting out their feelings if they are required to make a series of comparisons leading to a ranking of some fifteen or twenty major areas of public policy. If the ranking is performed by a survey analyst, the rules for determining the hierarchy of preferences may be challenged as inadequate or controversial. Political leaders like the President are known to influence the determination of public preferences from time to time. What a President may get from a survey, therefore, is an echo of his own voice. Since opinion is mutable, the opposition can say that if they will just work harder, public preferences will come closer to their values in the future. Although the temptation is understandably great, the hard problems of making interpersonal comparisons of utility cannot be avoided by fobbing off the task on other people through an opinion survey.

For the old economics, the political system unfortunately did not produce decisions that met the strict criteria of economic rationality. It was desirable economically, for example, to take into account as many measurable consequences for others as possible. The larger the area covered, the greater is the number of externalities that can be internalized within the analysis. If economic criteria were to be followed, bargaining, horse-trading, log-rolling, or other practices that might introduce inconsistencies had to be kept to a minimum. Thus, a unitary government with highly centralized parties and powerful hierarchical leadership would appear to be preferable to a federal system with extremely decentralized parties and fragmented leadership continuously engaged in bargaining to accommodate the most diverse range of interests. But the desirability and feasibility of abolishing the federal system, the separation of powers, and decentralized parties are not usually considered because such matters go beyond economic analysis.

The new economics need not face the same problems. It is concerned, after all, with getting away from rigid economic analysis and the strict application of efficiency criteria. Its practitioners are committed to values favoring the enhancement of environmental quality. The new economists are advocates as well as scholars. For them, policy outcomes cannot simply be the result of a set of analytic procedures. They want some results and not others. They want to develop the best arguments they can for securing the results they favor. In cases of doubt and indeterminacy, the new economists want the values they favor included rather than excluded. But they are inhibited by a nostalgia for the credibility accorded to the old economists they once were. Caught between the desire to insure certain outcomes and the pull of their economist's conscience, they risk being neither economists nor effective advocates.

The new economics is in danger of misconstruing its mission. Its goals are laudatory (that is, I share them), but they cannot be achieved by self-deception. Little is to be gained and much lost by compromising the old economics. It should be perfected according to its own lights, so that at least part of the spectrum of values will be properly illuminated. What is first required is an accurate statement of the political problems involved in realizing environmental values.

There is no evidence to suggest widespread and intense support for drastically improving the quality of the environment. Most people are probably indifferent. Some care a little, but are unwilling to sacrifice much. Only a relatively small minority cares deeply enough to make significant sacrifices. The best available evidence comes from a survey of attitudes toward government programs conducted in 1961 by Eva Mueller through the Michigan Survey Research Center.[1] The survey is especially valuable because people were asked whether they would give up income in the form of higher taxes in order to pay for expenditures they

Attitudes Toward Government Programs					
Program	More	Less	Same	No opinion	Total	More even if taxes had to be raised[2]
	%	%	%	%	%	%
Help for older people	70	3	23	4	100	34
Help for needy people	60	7	28	5	100	26
Education	60	7	25	8	100	41
Slum clearance, city improvement[1]	55	9	24	12	100	[3]
Hospital and medical care	54	9	28	9	100	25
Public works[1]	48	11	31	10	100	[3]
Defense, rearmament[2]	47	6	34	13	100	30
Support for small business[1]	37	11	31	21	100	[3]
Highway construction	36	10	45	9	100	13
Unemployment benefits	29	14	45	12	100	10
Parks, recreational facilities	27	15	48	10	100	7
Space exploration[2]	26	32	28	14	100	14
Support for agriculture	20	26	34	20	100	6
Help to other countries[2]	7	53	28	12	100	2

[1] Question asked only in June, 1961.
[2] Question asked only in November, 1961.
[3] Unavailable.

believed desirable. Of fourteen types of public policy mentioned, the item called "Parks, recreation facilities" provides a fair test of public support for improving the environment. No doubt more people care about parks than about the remote backwoods, but 10 per cent of the people interviewed have no opinion on these resource programs, and 48 per cent think that existing governmental expenditure is about right. Thus, 58 per cent of the population is essentially indifferent to a change in public policy. It is true that a larger minority favors more rather than less expenditure (27 to 15 per cent), but the favorable minority declines by almost 400 per cent (27 to 7 per cent) when asked if they would pay higher taxes to support this resource policy. Larger proportions of the population are willing to pay through higher taxes for help for the old and needy, education, defense, and highways. Indeed, the number of people willing to pay to explore outer space is twice that willing to pay to improve the earthly environment (14 per cent as compared to 7 per cent).

Public sentiment may have changed since 1961. Perhaps people would now be willing to pay more to deal with water pollution. When a candidate for governor of California suggests selling part of the state's wilderness areas, however, and still receives overwhelming endorsement by the electorate, it is difficult to believe that the wilderness minority is very large. Though small, the wilderness minority is not always impotent. Yet the victories recorded here and there all appear to stem from an intense campaign run by a few dedicated individuals. When this middle- and upperclass effort fails to materialize, nothing happens, except the loss of another site of scenic splendor.

The provision of subsidies on behalf of the aesthetic minority—subsidies like the British Broadcasting Company's Third Programme —might suggest that a unitary and centralized political system would be more receptive to demands of this nature. But this result depends on the existence of a privileged minority to which great deference is accorded. The cultural conditions for this phenomenon do not exist in the United States, nor, on other grounds, would many of us prefer such a situation. In America, a centralized political system that registered immediate majority demands could well wreak havoc with the policies preferred by the aesthetic minority. Bigger and better highways might always be preferred to clean air, or parks, or refuges for wildlife.

A system like the American one that provides special opportunities for skillful and well-organized minorities would appear well suited to the characteristics of the aesthetic few. How should they go about realizing their preferences? How can they mobilize their forces? What organizational structures and strategies are best suited to translating their preferences into public policy? What kinds of administrative arrangements will help obtain favorable results in the future? Although satisfactory answers are not likely to be immediately forthcoming, these questions are foremost among the right ones to ask.

There is no reason to suppose that the most aesthetically interested members of society are politically disadvantaged. They probably do not suffer from being denied the right to vote or from low educational attainments or poor family backgrounds that would deny them the skills necessary to compete in political life. Like those with special interests in theater or ballet or sailing, the aesthetic minority is likely to be composed of middle- or upper-class people who do not have to struggle for the necessities of life and can afford to be sensitive. Their problems of political mobilization are likely to be quite different from those of the poor and downtrodden. Given a choice between political activity in behalf of their preferences for environmental quality or individual economic action, they may well choose the latter. They can move to the suburbs to get away from air pollution or travel to where the remote wilderness still exists. Things may have to get worse before they find it less costly to spend time in political activity than in raising income to satisfy their aesthetic preferences. Yet they are also capable of reasonably long-run perspectives. The leaders of this minority must first convince people who share their preferences that political action is necessary now if they want their children to be able to enjoy a natural environment of higher quality in the future.

Political elites are far more likely to share the preferences of the aesthetic minority than are the mass of people. While long-term efforts of mass education may be desirable, short-term results depend on the men in power. Since various interests oppose certain specific measures, and alternative objects of expenditures compete for existing resources, ways must be found to enable public officials to support the policies most of them would like to see implemented. The questions of who will pay and how are crucial. In the best of all possible worlds, a new process is discovered that produces a good like wood pulp more cheaply and with far less noxious waste than before. Everyone gains, and no one loses; or those who win in one transaction compensate the losers in another. In most cases, however, the questions of who will pay and how much loom large. Costs can be transferred to large industries or to those who consume their products, to general taxpayers or to specific industries, to citizens or to foreigners, from one region or class of citizens to another. Citizens with low incomes are notorious for their willingness to seek greater public benefits, and their unwillingness to pay more taxes. The wealthy are famous for the ingenuity with which they escape the full burden of the income tax. The acknowledged principles of the public-finance literature—ability to pay and benefits received—are inadequate when there are severe disagreements over the justice and applicability of each principle. The difficulties are compounded when a desired objective, say reduction of air pollution, can be accomplished if and only if an objectionable mode of assigning costs is accepted. If it turns out to be much easier to pass the burden on in the form of hidden consumer taxes than to assess the polluters or desecraters of the wilderness, difficult choices must be made.

In the past, there has been considerable public support for conservation in some western states. Mass support may now be generated in various areas in regard to water and air pollution, but the possibilities of support may be slim for a subtle policy specifying so much reduction of pollution here, a little less there, and none someplace else (the kind of policy favored by the old economics). The price of mass support may be massive programs to wipe out pollution entirely. Again, a difficult choice may have to be made between too little effort to reduce pollution and too much.

Presently we do not have the knowledge that would enable us to choose the kinds of organizational structure that would lead to decisions in favor of improving environmental quality. We can, however, identify critical choices. The number of governmental organizations concerned with natural resources is already large and growing. These agencies traditionally perform specialized functions for a particular clientele and are closely tied to local interests and their congressional advocates. To these divisive forces are then joined narrow organizational loyalties. The legitimization of new functions by society, such as desalinization, pollution abatement, and highway beautification, has been accompanied by the creation of separate organizations to devise and implement programs. For people concerned with rationalizing policy in the resource field, the rapid proliferation of autonomous organizations is alarming. It points to the need for larger units or co-ordinating structures that will presumably produce decisions which take into account a wider range of values. Leaving aside questions of the feasibility and cost of such a change, it is not clear whether it would further the cause of the aesthetic minority. New and "narrow" agencies supporting environmental quality with ever greater determination might be preferable. Sub-units within larger multipurpose agencies dealing with extensive geographical areas might be used to great advantage in the cause of the aesthetic minority. We do not know and are hardly in a position to guess.

Another critical issue involves the choice between setting-up or strengthening a regulatory agency or trying to enact legislation that contains automatic incentives making it advantageous for the affected parties to do the right thing. When outrage over pollution or destruction of forests bursts out, it is tempting to pillory the offenders and to control their future conduct by establishing a regulatory commission of some sort. But the history of regulation has not been an entirely happy one. With the best of motives, the original regulatory passion begins to wane. The people whose interests are most directly affected maintain constant vigilance, while the rest of us turn to other pursuits. The regulatory agency is surrounded by the interests it is supposed to regulate. The inevitable accommodations may leave little regulation intact. Moreover, the existence of friendly regulatory bodies is used as a rationale for avoiding the necessity of other and possibly more stringent measures. We have little evaluated experience in developing incentives in the form of tax measures, bonuses for keeping land or water in certain conditions, support for competitive products, or other devices that might accomplish the task.

If action is to be based on some knowledge, the consequences of varying institutional arrangements for major values must be specified. In different times and places, there has been considerable variety in organizational arrangements and legal patterns. Knowledge of what results ensued under different conditions might give direction to future judgments. New techniques of organizational analysis also provide splendid opportunities for current research. The development of computer simulation models is especially promising. These models view organizations as problem-solving mechanisms that use certain rules for arriving at decisions in a complex environment. These rules can be derived from interviews and observations, and programmed on computers. By recapitulating the processes of decisions on computers, it should be possible to explain how the organization works. One can then experiment with alterations in the assumptions guiding the organization, its specific rules for decisions, and its environment, and determine how these changes affect its policy outputs. Organizational changes can be experimentally produced as a better guide to action than mere guesswork.

There is, in general, an appalling lack of information on the causes and consequences of environmental deterioration. If environmental quality is broadened to include the design of urban living (and hence poverty and race relations), the absence of knowledge is even more startling. The availability of better information might reveal a wider range of choice and thus result in different political decisions. There is overwhelming need for experimentation. We could use more than one experimental city. Thus, there is an important role for the man who does not find it becoming to devote his talent to direct political questions of mobilizing support to preserve the wilderness or the cultures of the city. He may feel that his desires are not more worthy than those of other men. Such a man may be prepared to have his minority preferences overridden. But by working to improve the information base for decision-making, he may hope to make everyone wiser about the scope of their interests and the possibilities of reconciliation with others.

We do not wish to restrict ourselves to the values appropriate to economic man in the market place. (Failure to preserve superb redwoods because the economic worth of the income produced by cutting them down exceeds their presently known aesthetic value would be tragic.) Nor do we wish to become mere schemers who, so long as they can muster the political power necessary to achieve their personal objectives, do not care about other people's feelings. (Failure to alleviate the psychic deprivation suffered by people who will lose their jobs if the redwoods are protected, and whose identity is bound up with the lumber trade rather than selling souvenirs to tourists, would be cruel.) Yet, like Dostoevski's underground man, whose appreciation of the endless depths of every question rendered him unfit for any action, the cost of taking everyone's preferences into account may be paralysis. Worse, it may result in grand opportunities foregone or in irreversible damage to the environment. Weak and frail as we are, beset by doubts and anxieties, undoubtedly partial in our views, we must act. If those who love the wilderness will not save it, who will?[2]

REFERENCES

1. Eva Mueller, "Public Attitudes Toward Fiscal Programs," *The Quarterly Journal of Economics*, Vol. 77 (May, 1963), pp. 210-35. For questions, see Table 1.

2. Having come late to this symposium, I have had the opportunity of profiting from and reacting to the other papers. My obligation to the authors of these papers is gratefully acknowledged. I would like to thank Irving Fox, Jerome Milliman, Vincent Ostrom, Jeffrey Pressman, David Wentworth, and Carol Wildavsky for their valuable comments. All of these people disagree with me in significant ways and are not responsible that I often did not take their excellent advice.

JOHN V. KRUTILLA

Some Environmental Effects of Economic Development

AMERICAN CULTURE and character have been influenced profoundly by the open rural countryside and the wilderness beyond. The further we are removed from the conditions of a more primitive America, the greater is our nostalgia for the conditions of earlier times. But despite the many influential and eloquent advocates for preserving the American scene—and especially the wilderness and rural countryside—the assaults upon America's landscape and the erosion of its natural environment continue.

In the past, the degradation of the landscape has been associated principally with mining, logging, and agricultural activities. Open pits abandoned after completion of strip-mining operations seriously deface a natural landscape, but strip mining is certainly not alone, nor is it first among the mining methods that have such an adverse consequence. The dredging of stream beds and hydraulic mining, particularly in connection with the recovery of gold, create unsightly mounds of debris along streams. By its very nature, mining is inimical to natural environments. Mining operations annually produce solid wastes amounting to 3.3 billion tons.[1] The discharge into streams used in washing and in transporting wastes often degrades the water quality for miles along the watercourse. Occasionally, as in the case of zinc-recovery operations, escape of flue gases destroys the vegetation in the surrounding area. Ducktown, Tennessee, and Sudbury, Ontario, are the classic examples here, and more recent experience in the Trail, British Columbia, area reminds us that mine-mill activities threaten the maintenance of the vegetative cover and topographic equilibrium in surrounding areas.

Together, logging and agricultural activities, including livestock grazing, have most probably had a more extensive effect on nat-

161

ural environments than mining. Where soils were initially thin, or slopes so steep that clearing and converting to cropland was, at best, questionable, early ignorance of or disregard for the equilibrium of topography, soil, and vegetation transformed many an Appalachian landscape into a series of denuded slopes and gullied ridges. Clear-cutting in some private forest holdings often fails to ensure the maintenance of bases for viable biotic communities. In the western portions of North America, the pressure of grazing on the carrying capacity of the range is transforming, and in some cases has transformed, grasslands into areas of desert shrubs, forbs, and other wasteland vegetation.

Such activities are not alone in changing the character of the landscape. Highways, dams, reservoirs, railroads, and utilities all alter the landscape, and their effects on the natural environment are probably greatest in primitive or wilderness areas. Ironically, recreationists, many of whom are lovers of nature, and students of natural history pose the greatest threat to some fragile ecosystems by the intensity of recreation activities in areas of unique geologic, biotic, or recreational interest, in national parks and forests.

Rural areas that lie within easy reach of urbanites are subject to a variety of different factors. The refuse of our increasingly "containerized" society litters the landscape along the corridors between urban places. Currently the most pressing problem may be disposing of discarded automobiles—whether they are concentrated in junk yards or abandoned at random along rural roads and country woodlands. Automobile graveyards are, however, evidence of only one kind of littering. Frequently there are no sanitation departments in rural villages and counties, so that household trash gets dumped wherever convenient, without regard for appearance. Streambanks, in particular, appear to invite the disposal of refuse, doubtless with the thought that freshets will periodically remove the trash from view.

Americans often observe that the European landscape appears to be graced by reason of human habitation. Structures erected for their utility to man are often disguised ingeniously or blended into the landscape so that they do not mar the harmony of the pastoral setting. And certainly some of New England, notably the Dorset Valley, also exhibits pastoral scenes that provide a landscape aesthetically more pleasing in some respects than the original forest. But in areas of submarginal agriculture, in New England no less than elsewhere, America is strewn with the unsightly evidence of deteriorating farmsteads and dying and dilapidated communities. Derelict coal tipples and abandoned trucks further insult the landscape in areas where mines have shut down.

The opening up and development of the country has, of course, affected the natural environments for the survival and reproduction of wildlife.[2] Changes in the landscape have wrought fundamental changes in habitat, thereby altering greatly the numbers, distribution, and character of wildlife in the United States. Some species adaptable to village and farm conditions have increased in numbers since the advent of the white man in America, but these represent a small minority.

Before the Atlantic Seaboard, the Appalachian Highlands, and the Ohio Valley were settled, the eastern portion of the United States abounded with game. Most of the species that have survived are now restricted to greatly reduced ranges in the West. The American elk once roamed all the areas of the New England and Middle Atlantic states and the forest areas to the west. By 1850, no elk were left in the eastern United States, being reduced in range to the western mountain regions. The woods bison was also in evidence in great numbers throughout the forested areas along the Atlantic, the Appalachians, and the Ohio Valley as late as 1750; by 1800, however, the great herds of Pennsylvania had disappeared, and within twenty-five years, the bison were gone from West Virginia, the last refuge of the eastern herds. A half century later, the plains bison, too, had all but disappeared. Woodland caribou, found in New England until after the Civil War, persisted in Maine until 1890. Of the moose that originally ranged through New England, New York, and Pennsylvania, only remnants still survive in the Maine woods.

For the large game mammals, as well as for such fowl as turkey (which are deep-woods species), logging and, perhaps even more, the conversion of forest to cropland altered the conditions of survival beyond immediate retrieval. Not only did these practices change the character of the vegetation, they broke the continuity of the range. Even when large areas of forest land remained, the species that require conditions remote from human habitation disappeared from these areas.

Among the predators, the populations of lynx, cougar, and bobcat have diminished with the wilderness. The gray wolf, formerly found everywhere except desert areas, disappeared from the East by 1905, was still abundant in the intermountain area of the West until 1915, but had almost disappeared by the early 1940's. Only remnants continue to exist in northwestern Michigan, Minnesota, Wisconsin, and Oregon. The red wolf is still found in small numbers in portions of Louisiana, Texas, Arkansas, Missouri, and Oklahoma. The cougar, with a natural range extending throughout the continental United States, is now confined largely to the Rocky Mountains, the Sierras, the Cascades, the Olympic Mountains, and, in drastically diminished numbers, the cypress swamps and Everglades in Florida where the "panther" is threatened with extirpation.

The depredation of bird populations is partly associated with the adaptation of natural environments to the requirements of agriculture and industry. Some species have disappeared entirely; others are vastly reduced in numbers and range. An early victim was the great auk, the last of these being seen and slaughtered in 1844. Only three decades later, the Labrador or sand-shoal duck was last seen and shot on Long Island. The passenger pigeon was gone by 1900; the Guadalupe petrel and the masked bobwhite, by the second decade of the present century, although the latter may have been rediscovered as a small flock of domesticated fowl in Mexico. Of the three recognized races of prairie chicken which collectively occupied a large area of the United States from Maine to Virginia on the Atlantic Seaboard across the continent to the western Gulf states and the Great Plains of the Southwest, the heath hen is extinct, Attwater's prairie chicken is found only in a small area of Texas, and the common prairie chicken of the northern United States and Canada is still declining in numbers. As with the masked bobwhite, the conversion of grasslands to agricultural purposes and overgrazing have been responsible for the demise or decimation of these once large populations.

Among the birds of prey with the greatest geographic distribution, the kites seem to have suffered the greatest depredation. Originally seen on both continents of the Western Hemisphere, the several races now occupy only the most restricted areas—the swallow-tail kite appearing principally in the swamps of South Carolina, Florida, and Louisiana, and the white-tail in California. Only the Mississippi kite appears out of danger of extinction. Of greatest irony is the threat to the continued survival of the bald eagle, proud symbol of American freedom and power.

The condition of some species, on the other hand, has improved during the last several decades. The whitetail deer and the raccoon have made an excellent adjustment to conditions associated with rural human habitation, and the opossum has even adapted to modern urban conditions. Moreover, much of the marginal cropland in the Appalachians has gone back to forest. In New England, the reversion began with the introduction of the trans-Appalachian railroads in the last century, and some of the long abandoned cropland is now supporting forest growth approaching climax conditions. In the southern Appalachians where the shift did not begin until the turn of the century, the timber stands are in earlier stages of succession, but some have matured sufficiently to produce mast and cover hospitable to some species of woodland wildlife. Consolidation of lands into comparatively large public holdings for parks, wildlife management, and hunting, and the establishment of large national forests have made it possible to reintroduce some woodland species in a limited way. The wild turkey, for example, has been reintroduced to forested areas of the Pennsylvania and Virginia Appalachians and elsewhere in the South with the spread of new forests. Reintroduction of elk in a more limited way has also been accomplished with some success.

Except for the few species mentioned above, however, not only has the original range been reduced drastically, but the survival of the species itself is threatened. A systematic survey by the U. S. Fish and Wildlife Service has identified seventy-eight species of mammals, birds, fishes, and reptiles that are endangered, forty-four others that have become rare, and twenty-one whose occurrence in the United States represents the outer edges of their natural ranges.[3] In some instances, the threat is not necessarily to continued existence of the species itself, but to its survival in the United States. Another category includes fifty or sixty species on which there is insufficient information to warrant such classification, but among which there may be species whose survival is precarious.

The Problem in Perspective: Past and Current

Large, and in many cases, irreversible changes in the American landscape and biota have taken place, but one should not conclude that all of these changes should not have occurred. The extractive activities that have contributed to the deterioration of the natural environment have promoted in a significant way the growth of the national economy and the material well-being of human society. Without them, a modern industrial nation could not have developed.

165

Earlier in the nation's history, the level of material well-being was quite low relative to present standards, technology was in its infancy, and the wilderness was large in relation to the lands under cultivation and the domesticated varieties of plant and animal life. Under these circumstances, the reduction in the size of the wilderness and the wildlife populations represented a conversion of resources that were abundant, and hence of limited value *at the margin*, into goods and services of high marginal value for the development of the economy. Today we have a large accumulation of capital and a level of living unparalleled in other cultures and previous periods. Moreover, the sophisticated technology that has made this possible appears to have reached a stage where the rate of advance can be manipulated, within limits, by research and development. The continued advance in material well-being now seems to depend more on programming technological advance than on converting the remaining wilderness into material inputs for agricultural and industrial production. If this is so, may we now relax, satisfied that the preservation of the remaining natural environments is assured? On the contrary, there are reasons to fear that additional and unnecessary degradation of natural environments may continue. This is due partly to the imperfection in the economic organization of production and partly to the imperfection with which the governmental processes work.

The organization of industrial production by means of the free market spins off *some* consequences for natural environments that would not be accepted by members of the community were they to have a choice, even if the choice involved costs that they would be required to share. Certain economic choices threaten the continued existence of an irreplaceable asset, while others create nuisances or fail to take advantage of feasible opportunities for enhancing human welfare, primarily because there is no incentive mechanism to reward entrepreneurs for taking action.

Consider first a natural environment that is unique and non-reproducible: Let it be a landscape of commanding beauty overlying mineral deposits of commercial value. To harvest the timber, to work the mineral deposits, and to beneficiate the ores at the site of the mining activity would irreparably destroy the aesthetic quality of the landscape. Preserving the landscape would, however, have no irreversible consequence. It would provide opportunity to harvest the timber and mine the minerals in the future *were circumstances to warrant.*

A private entrepreneur could realize a return from his investment either by marketing the aesthetic features of the landscape and associate biota as a scientific resource or recreational product, or by resorting to mining and logging. In a private-enterprise system, a rational profit-motivated entrepreneur would choose the alternative from which he expected the highest returns. His choice would be based on market values, but the market would register the full value only in a competitive situation.

Under competitive conditions, the value of the output of a good or service is measured by the price of the commodity and the amount sold. There are enough sellers and buyers so that no one seller or buyer can affect the price of the good or the supply appreciably by entering or withdrawing from the market. But when there is no close substitute for a commodity, no alternative source of supply, the value of the output is greater than the product of the price and the quantity, because the price represents only the value per unit that the marginal buyer attaches to the commodity. All buyers who would be willing to pay more than the market price rather than do without receive a bonus represented by the difference between the price and their valuations. This value is not captured by the seller.[4] Thus, if a unique commodity is removed from the market, the social loss is not what the seller could have received, but the sum of the maximum each buyer would have been willing to pay rather than go without. If in our hypothetical example the receipts from mining and other extractive activities correspond to competitive returns, while the receipts from the use of the resources for scientific and recreational purposes correspond to returns from sale of rare commodities for which no adequate substitutes exist, the returns expected by the entrepreneur from the two alternatives are not comparable indices of social value. What do economic observations tell us about the two possibilities?

The continuous decline in the price of natural-resource commodities relative to prices of commodities in general suggests the existence of numerous alternative sources of supply and roughly competitive conditions in the extractive industries.[5] But conditions of extreme congestion at scenic landmarks in the national parks suggest that there are no adequate substitutes for these unique natural environments.

The market has another potential deficiency as the mechanism for allocating rare natural environments among competing uses. Individuals who have no definite plans to visit a particular natural wonder may be willing to pay some price in order to retain the option. Large sums change hands in commercial transactions trading in options of one sort or another, not all of which are ultimately exercised. This is a way of hedging against uncertainty by postponing a decision in the hopes that some of the uncertainty will be reduced with time. In the present context, there is a value associated with deferring a decision that will have an irreversible consequence potentially inimical to human welfare. A decision in favor of converting the landscape through commercial exploitation by extractive industries permanently forecloses the opportunity to use the landscape itself as an amenity that gratifies aesthetic interests or psychological needs.

A parallel rationale can be advanced for protecting species threatened with extinction or an entire ecosystem essential to the survival of a species. Such biotic communities represent banks of genetic information required by a species for survival as it competes for the finely graduated niches in nature. Such competition is absent in domestic counterparts; indeed, modern agriculture provides so highly protected an environment that the energy released from some of the genetic characteristics no longer needed for survival is redirected toward greater productivity. At the same time, the instability that results from progressive reduction of biological diversity through monoculture and the application of pesticides occasionally requires a reintroduction of some genetic materials that have been lost in the domestic strains.

Substantial use is also made of biological specimens for medicinal purposes; indeed, approximately half of the new drugs being produced have botanical sources.[6] Because only a small part of the potential medicinal value of biological sources has been realized, preserving the opportunity to examine all species among the natural biota for this purpose is a matter of no little importance.

There may be substantial commercial value in preserving wild species and natural environments, but the market cannot communicate the option demand nor can the resource owners appropriate the option value. The conventional market operation does not provide adequate information or rewards to ensure the preservation of rare and irreproducible natural phenomena.[7] If the disposition of irreproducible natural environments is determined through normal market transactions, we cannot be confident that the results will represent the most highly valued disposition—either economic or social. At the same time, it must be recognized that only a small proportion of the market allocation of resources involves rare natural environments. And the deficiencies of the market's organization of industrial production detailed above occur only when a rare and irreplaceable asset is involved.

Certain cases of resource use threaten no irreplaceable asset, but neither do the prices by which the economy responds in organizing production reflect the social costs and benefits of such use. These situations have external, offsite, or spillover effects that compromise the efficiency of the market in allocating resources to their highest socially-valued uses. External effects occur in three forms. In the first case, one consumer's behavior affects the enjoyment another may obtain from a consumption activity. If, for example, one household keeps feline pets that regularly call upon the neighbor children's sandbox, the enjoyment of the neighbor is adversely affected by the consumption behavior of the household in question. In the second case, a production activity affects the consumer's enjoyment. The discharge of mill wastes into a watercourse may, for instance, spoil a sport fishery. In the third case, the production activity of one firm directly affects another's output. The release of water from a storage facility upstream to increase the production of power at the site of the dam during the dry season may increase the power generated at some independent hydro projects downstream or make available an improved flow for irrigation or another productive purpose.

Where such external effects occur—and they appear to be concentrated in the natural resources field—benefits are enjoyed by some without cost to themselves, and uncompensated costs are inflicted on others. These costs and benefits do not get reflected in market prices of goods and services to which entrepreneurs respond in making their production decisions. Accordingly, when the spoliation of a natural environment occurs to the advantage of, but without cost to, the despoiler, the market offers no incentive to do otherwise. Without public supervision, continued assaults on the natural environment can be expected. Alternately, when a benefit is conferred on all members of an area if it is provided for any one member—for example, elimination of air pollution in the area—the conditions for a market to develop for the good do not exist. No one in the area can be excluded from benefiting by failure to pay a price. If a private entrepreneur cannot expect to appropriate enough of the value to compensate for his costs, no incentive exists for him to provide such services.

The market mechanism does not everywhere provide entrepreneurs or resource owners with appropriate information or incentives to adopt actions that are socially optimal while still privately remunerative. Thus, there are imperfections in the way the market organizes production, and the government usually intervenes in particular situations to offset this deficiency. The prime example is the need for public action to offset the absence of adequate market signals or incentives in the field of water-resources development. Development, however, almost always conflicts with the preservation of the natural environment. In such situations, the implementing of collective decisions by public agencies may itself spawn difficult problems which neither the market nor the government is yet equipped to handle adequately. Reservoirs of the Bureau of Reclamation's proposed Bridge and Marble Canyon Dams would, for example, encroach on the Grand Canyon National Park.

When a public agency undertakes a mission necessitating the resolution of conflicting interests, a decision in favor of the predominant viewpoint as a reflection of majority rule often appears to be required.[8] This reasoning does not hold, however, when public intervention is made in order to improve the allocation of resources because often it would lead to an uneconomic allocation contrary to the justification for public intervention. Nevertheless, a public agency will generally provide a good or service that appeals to many over an alternative that pleases a small minority. If such decisions come up *one at a time,* and each decision in favor of the commonly held preference pre-empts one of the remaining opportunities for indulging an esoteric taste, all of the resources or configurations of land forms and biota necessary to indulge less common tastes will be extinguished over time.[9]

No adequate mechanism exists in the public sector for automatically allocating among the qualitatively different demands in their relative proportions. Since the government is deeply involved in the resources field and dominates, to a large extent, the remaining wildlands, many of the grand panoramic landscapes, and all navigable streams, such machinery is required if we wish to safeguard rare natural environments. It is not just a question of, say, adjusting the margins between hydro-power production and more water-based recreation. Catering to the mass demand for lakes for swimming, boating, and water-skiing is not all of the problem. Provision should also be made for those who prefer to canoe in white water or to fish in free-flowing streams, even if such activities require some resources of use in the more popular water sports.

While public servants might be expected to respond to the predominant viewpoint when they consider a given case, the problem can be structured more meaningfully. We can visualize an explicit policy that takes into account the intensity of both the dominant and minority demands as well as the number of individuals nurturing each. *This procedure requires viewing resource configurations not as individual cases but as parts of systems with an appropriate allocation of resources within the system to accommodate the widest range of demands in proportion to their representation.*

If we are to have an economic assignment of resources within a system, we must have a far more discriminating ecological survey than any yet contemplated. Such a survey should identify and classify all terrestrial and aquatic communities as a basis for appropriate reservations in the interest of scientific research and education as well as recreational experiences. A great deal of research in the behavioral sciences would also need to be undertaken to enable us to distinguish between the significant constituents of demand for outdoor recreation.

Earlier I suggested that the modern industrial economy is winning its independence from the conventional resource base through advances in technology. The more optimistic students of the problem, in fact, hold that ultimately only mass and energy are relevant inputs to an ever increasing production of goods.[10] Yet even these optimists acknowledge that the quality of the environment is deteriorating.[11] Implicit in this paradox of plenty and impoverishment is the asymmetry in the implication of technological advance for manufacturing goods, on the one hand, and for producing natural environments, on the other. In spite of the remarkable advances in technology, rare natural features cannot be created. Producing a replica of the Grand Canyon or Yosemite Valley is as out of the question as the resurrection of an extinct species. Technology can make only a limited contribution to re-establishing *natural* environments. Modern earth-moving technology can help remedy the ravages of open-pit mining, but even so it takes time and the co-operation of nature to restore the landscape and its natural fauna. Technology thus promises liberation from dependence on natural environments as a source of industrial inputs, but not from dependence on natural environments for the amenities associated with personal contacts with nature.

171

The differential capability for increasing the supply of industrial goods as compared to natural amenities has important implications. As manufactured goods become more abundant and natural amenities more scarce, the trade-off between them will progressively favor the latter. Natural environments, hence, represent assets of appreciating future value.

This leads to a final comment. Modern economic research has established that heads of households are motivated by a desire not only to gain satisfaction from consumption but to leave an estate.[12] An estate may be left either as private goods (or the assets to purchase such goods and services), or as public goods. An aesthetically attractive, scientifically valuable natural endowment of appreciating future value may be an efficient way for the bulk of the population to leave its heirs an estate of maximum value. This is unlikely to occur if we rely solely on the operation of the private market. It can be done only by a policy directed toward the protection of natural environments against unjustified encroachment.

The change in the face of North America by reason of industrial man's dominance has resulted in a high standard of material well-being, but the ecological consequences may not yet be understood fully nor the ultimate cost appreciated. Some of the degradation—but certainly not all—is the necessary price of the high material standard of living achieved through industrialization. There have been unintended or socially unwarranted side effects of the organization of industrial production that we should have avoided. Yet the information on which decisions are made is not always adequate, nor are the incentives to individuals always in harmony with the larger public interest, often because the mechanisms for harmonizing private and public purposes have not been developed. Some of the environmental deterioration, although sought by no one, cannot be avoided by individual action. Thus, public authority must help to achieve collectively what cannot be attained individually. This involves, in part, the acquisition of greater knowledge in the natural as well as the behavorial sciences. Such knowledge would enable both private and public managers of natural resources to make more discriminating judgments about matters that might have adverse and irreversible consequences. It also involves a need for the creation of social institutions or mechanisms that will not produce results inimical to the preservation of natural environments simply because of the way the machine is assembled.

REFERENCES

1. I owe this estimate to Dr. Richard J. Frankel of Resources for the Future, Inc.

2. The following summary sketch of the effect of human dominance on wildlife populations is based principally on Peter Mathiessen, *Wildlife in America* (New York, 1959) and Raymond Camp, ed., *The Hunter's Encyclopedia* (Harrisburg, Pa., 1954).

3. U. S. Department of the Interior, Fish and Wildlife Service, Bureau of Sport Fisheries and Wildlife, *Survival or Surrender for Endangered Wildlife* (Washington, D. C., 1965).

4. The student of economics will recognize this as Jules Dupuit's discovery and the value in excess of the entrepreneur's receipts as Alfred Marshall's consumer surplus, a real part of the social valuation of the services of the resource in question. Of course, if there were no substitute for the services of the resources used in one way, monopoly pricing could be practiced, but this would not alter the result that pricing would not appropriate the total social value of the resources in their specialized uses.

5. Neal Potter and Francis T. Christy, Jr., *Trends in Natural Resource Commodities: Statistics of Prices, Output, Consumption, Foreign Trade, and Employment in the United States, 1870-1957* (Baltimore, 1962).

6. Margret B. Kreig, *Green Medicine—The Search for Plants That Heal* (New York, 1964).

7. John V. Krutilla, "Conservation Reconsidered," *The American Economic Review* (forthcoming).

8. For an alternative explanation, see Julius Margolis, "The Economic Evaluation of Federal Water Resource Development," *The American Economic Review*, Vol. 49, No. 1 (March, 1959), pp. 99-100. For a different view of what transpires in government decision-making, see Roland McKean, "The Unseen Hand in Government," *American Economic Review*, Vol. 55, No. 3 (June, 1965).

9. For an interesting development of a similar point, see Alfred E. Kahn, "The Tyranny of Small Decisions: Market Failures, Imperfections, and the Limits of Economics," *Kyklos*, Vol. 19-1966-Fasc. 1, pp. 23-47.

10. Harold J. Barnett and Chandler Morse, *Scarcity and Growth—The Economics of Natural Resource Availability* (Baltimore, 1963), p. 238.

11. *Ibid.*, p. 254 ff.

12. Franco Modigliani and Richard Brumberg, "Utility Analysis and the Consumption Function: An Interpretation of Cross Section Data," *Post-Keynesian Economics*, ed. Kenneth K. Kurihara (New Brunswick, N. J., 1954).

ROBERT W. PATTERSON

The Art of the Impossible

NOT MANY years ago, only a few people knew what conservation meant; today everyone is a conservationist, whether he knows what it means or not. It is the thing to believe in, to be concerned about. Power companies and bird-watchers are conservationists, as are fishermen and hunters, paper manufacturers, miners, the chemical industry, highway departments, the Army Engineers, and Congressmen. But if all the lips that serve conservation were laid end-to-end, there would be a lot of fixed smiles, for in spite of the seriousness of our environmental problems, the conservation effort still consists largely of words. Many of them are good, as are many of the intentions behind them, but accomplishment has been relatively and disturbingly small.

Despite its innumerable technical and economic complications, conservation is basically a social problem. Any accomplishment in conservation requires changes in habit and thinking, a willingness to pay both in dollars and in freedom of action. Given that willingness, technical obstacles could be overcome; without the one, the other will always hold us back, just as it is holding us back today. Social change is a slow process; perhaps we cannot change quickly enough, for we are running out of time. Yet we may already have changed more than we realize; we may, in fact, be ready, as citizens and taxpayers, to accept the regulations, restrictions, and costs of conservation. Discussions of our needs can go on forever. The longer we wait, the larger the bills will be, and the more restrictive the regulations. Americans have always accepted new principles readily. We cannot know until we ask whether Americans are now ready again, and, if they are, just how far they are prepared to go.

It seems to be a simple matter to demonstrate that it is impracti-

174

cal, if not impossible, to do much about any given environmental mess. We cannot insist on an unrealistic ten-year timetable to clean up a particular stream near Fiasco, because the town would have to close its pickle mill, which discharges effluents that can only be purified by distillation. In the metropolitan area, it has become impossible, physically and financially, to dispose of the garbage and trash. Upstate, an outbreak of clodhoppers—in part, the result of annihilating things that used to eat clodhoppers—is endangering the nutmeg industry. Although we do not know the long-run effects of DDT, we must use it to save the industry from bankruptcy. On the farms around Paperville, goats wince at the stench from the mill. Ninety-nine per cent of the smell is said to have been eliminated, but the remaining 1 per cent still blights the countryside.

All this is familiar, too familiar, to anyone who has gone beyond the stage of hand-wringing. The further one goes, the more the problems proliferate. Processes, procedures, and habits have been developed and established without thought for the environment; they now seem as immutable as the laws of nature. Most problems within what might be called the "red areas" of conservation are urgent, but they could be solved. We know, for example, that the many forms of pollution must be controlled. Nevertheless, although we like to add "at all costs," we do not yet mean it. In almost every case, the real stumbling block is cost—cost in dollars—the only measurement that we have learned to use. The cleaning-up of a river, the development of new processes, the strict control of pesticides, and the construction of omnivorous disposal plants cost money. No one wants to pay, and some are simply unable to pay, the staggering bills. Government pollutes to keep taxes down, dumping sewage into the river. Business pollutes to keep costs down and increase profits. A city's abatement costs must be paid by the taxpayer; those of a business, by the consumer. A city is not in business to make money, and taxes spent for clear air and water, for garbage and rubbish disposal pay non-monetary dividends in improved living conditions. A business, on the other hand, must make a profit in dollars, and to make one, it must sell its product. It is interested in a clean environment only when its own welfare is concerned. Heavy investment in pollution abatement may price its product out of the market.

We have begun to ease and equalize the governmental abatement load through federal aid to states and municipalities, spreading the cost among all the country's taxpayers. In relation to the need, we

175

have not done very much, but the principle has been established and accepted. We are now toying with the idea of federal aid to industry, but talk only of "incentives." Apparently we are not yet ready to make mandatory the halt of all environmental pollution.

There are always reasons for not doing something, and in this case there happen to be very good reasons. We still like to think that we live in a democracy, and we abhor regulation and governmental decrees. But even a democracy cannot afford to carry freedom of action to the point of idiocy. A report of a task force of the Department of Health, Education, and Welfare recently made the point that we are travelers in a space ship, with everything that this implies: a strictly limited supply of all the things that make life possible and worth living. We must, therefore, accept increasing regulation and stricter rules, whether we like them or not. And in the "red areas," regulation will have to come soon.

Political action in conservation is in the direction of local or regional options, since nothing else has yet seemed politically feasible. It seems doubtful that either will work. Local option often means endless competition for the too-little-too-late championship, and its success remains most dubious. There are always too many problems, too many special situations, too many extenuating circumstances. But the world is shrinking, and environmental control cannot continue much longer on a catch-as-catch-can basis. The inevitable conclusion, unpleasant though it may be, is that there must be one set of rules for all, whatever the cost.

The cost to cities and towns will be huge, but if it is shared by all taxpayers, it can be paid. What about industry? Many firms would not survive if they were forced to pay all the costs of abating the pollution they generate. Moreover, such a blanket edict would be unjust, even if it were feasible. Much industrial pollution occurs because the public has agreed that it may occur. In many cases, pollution is a long-established way of life. A corporation that has had the public's blessing on its habits for a hundred years should not be forced to pay the same percentage of its abatement costs as a newcomer who has ignored the new rules or arranged to have them changed.

Water pollution is far from being our only problem, but because we have had some experience in trying to stop it, it illustrates the difficulties encountered in all such fields. A river in southern Maine, for example, exhibits the full range of pollution horrors. Cities and towns contributing to the river's degradation will receive substantial federal aid for construction of sewage-treatment plants. But what should be done about the prime industrial polluter? A paper company has fouled the stream for generations because, until recently, no one ever suggested that it stop. Should it now be required to pay all the costs of abating its own pollution, or should it, too, receive federal aid? If equipment needed for abatement adds to the cost of the company's paper, what will happen to its competitive position in relation to companies in other states where the rules are different?

At present, the rules are different even in other parts of Maine. In recent sessions, the Maine legislature lowered or eliminated water classifications and made other concessions for the benefit of new industries. In the northern part of the state, a small city built, with federal aid but also at considerable expense to local taxpayers, a sewage-disposal plant to conform with the state's classification of a stream. When an upstream potato-processing plant, already a polluter, proposed to add the processing of sugar beets to that of potatoes—and it was said to be difficult to treat the effluent from the beet process—the state legislature under bipartisan pressure lowered the stream's classification. The Federal Government helped pay for the downstream sewage plant, which now discharges clean effluent into polluted waters. But it also put up most of the money for the beet plant, and subsequently for a cane processing addition when potato farmers proved to be largely uninterested in growing beets. The stream remains grossly polluted, and its purification, if anyone ever musters the political courage to insist on it, will be costly. Heavy investments stimulate the protective instinct. If, however, federal funds were to be made available to industry for pollution abatement, should they be equally available to the recently built beet plant and to the hundred-year-old paper company downstate?

When we finally stop bickering and are forced into agreement, perhaps by a major catastrophe, the administrators of environmental clean-up will be faced with thousands of such situations. Hardships and inequalities will be inevitable, but the job will not be impossible of accomplishment if we agree that there must be one set of antipollution rules for all, with no exceptions. Only by imposing equal requirements on everyone can we eliminate the deadly competition that tempts states, cities, business, and industry to gain an advantage by not spending money on protection of the environment.

Environmental poisons, the "red areas" of conservation, demand the most immediate and drastic action. Although we have not found the answers, the issues are comparatively clear-cut: We must stop fouling our nest or we will not be able to live in it, and we have no other. Hopefully, we will succeed in changing our suicidal habits and eliminate poisons as an immediate threat to life. Even with this in prospect—if, indeed, it is in prospect—we will still have other habits to change, and these may be more difficult to break.

Up to now, our ever expanding economy has been supported by our ever expanding population, and we like to think that the first can continue to provide the second with more and more of everything. Perhaps it can, but it is hard to see how. We continue to treat nonrenewable resources as we have treated the renewable. When it becomes profitable to mine, mining must begin, and, if necessary, the rules are changed to make this possible. While we hold that it is admirable and fiscally sound to accumulate dollars for a rainy day and to pass them along to succeeding generations, we deem it unnecessary, if not actually silly, to pass along the resources that generate dollars—a strangely selfish and improvident point of view.

The world could go on, no doubt, without copper, oil, iron, or gold, but man cannot go on without space, the most important nonrenewable resource. Fumblings toward population control have come too late, and much more space will be used before we stop increasing our numbers. Although we have begun to understand what overcrowding can do, we will have to continue to use more and more of the world for the plain mechanics of living. Crowded living can be borne only if there is uncrowded space to which people can escape, and the upsurge of interest in outdoor recreation is one of the striking phenomena of the last decade. So eager are we to set up recreation areas and to use them that we are in danger, as we always seem to be when a thing offers both pleasure and profit, of going too far too fast. Some forms of outdoor recreation cease to be recreation at all if too many people participate at the same time. In our determination to provide something for everybody, we are simply moving the crowds from the cities to the country. And as the quality of recreation deteriorates, so does the quality of life.

America was founded on the principle that the rights of minorities must be protected, but today the public-opinion survey has taken the place of thought. In many respects, we live by a mindless majority rule, with the minorities lost somewhere in the shuffle. Our slogan is "The greatest good for the greatest number"; since we cannot decide what the greatest good really is, we like to ask the greatest number to tell us. In the field of recreation, we often get such answers as "driving for pleasure." The good life is a simpler matter than we had thought.

Unfortunately, most of the people polled are not able to make sound judgments. They head their lists with familiar things—the things they have done and known how to do. Most recreation polls are local in character, conducted by state or municipal agencies, and the pollee checks, in order of preference, a list of the common kinds of recreation that happen to be available. It might be more productive to include in the list such things as sitting on a log surrounded by silence, looking at the Grand Canyon or the Hudson River Gorge as they are today, or walking or canoeing in wild country, and to ask the pollee not just what he likes to do, but what he hopes his grandchildren will be able to do.

The planning we accomplish in the next decade—the principles we adopt and the legislation that is enacted—will affect the country for countless years to come. We should try not to be influenced too much by polls, surveys, systems analysis, and the rest. It is hard to learn much that is worth knowing from people who do not understand the question. When their answers are fed to the analysts, the numbers game takes over: In the year X, with a population A, we will need B more miles of highways, C more Ferris wheels, D more acres of wilderness. No one seems to dare to look very far ahead; the year 2000 is about the limit of popular statistical prophecy. You cannot multiply forever both people and the things that people want unless you plan to take over more territory than the sterile moon represents.

Since there are obvious limits to expansion, we must assume that population will someday be stabilized. This will not happen in this decade. Even in America, where the birth rate is declining faster than it is in most parts of the world, the population, when it levels off, will number a great many more million than it now does. Our planning must try to provide the necessities of life for those millions—water, air, food, a clean environment. But what about the quality of life?

The task of preserving the quality of life necessary to maintain a sound, ethical, and productive society cannot be completed by employing economics and systems analysis alone. If we assume, as we must, that our descendants will be able to stave off catastrophe, the only logical course is to muster every effort and every dollar for the preservation and protection of space. Carried to the point to which it should be carried, this process would be painful and, in some respects, undemocratic. Most people will have to live in a kind of national cluster development in more or less crowded conditions—more rather than less, as time goes on—with the carefully protected spaces reserved for re-creation. That is somewhat the way we live now, by accident rather than by design; but without design in the future, accident, greed, what we term economic necessity will expand development everywhere to the point where irreplaceable space will be gone forever. Statistically, there is still a lot of space left, but only because most of it cannot yet be developed profitably since it is not within reasonable reach of most of the population. The immediate danger points are near the clusters where development is a growing threat. A good deal is being said and a little done about this threat, but accomplishment is still pitifully small. Much of the effective work has been done by conservationists, but they cannot undertake the large-scale planning and enforcement that are necessary. Only government can do this. We need not only parks and reservations, but a system of zoning and easements that will permanently protect extensive areas of seacoast, lakes and streams, mountains, plains, forests, and fields from development. In no other way can we realistically hope to preserve the space that will be needed by coming generations.

This is an expensive procedure, since taxes will have to be reduced or compensation paid where there is no productive land use other than development. In terms of potential profits and business activity, we must pay for lost economic opportunity. This is an undemocratic procedure, perhaps, but is it so undemocratic for one generation to try to ensure the welfare of those still to come? (If we really care about their welfare, we should perhaps go even further and prohibit development in many of the arid sections of the country until our water supply problems have been solved. Unless water precedes development, national sprawl will necessitate massive transfers of water from wet regions to dry, and there will be a permanent water shortage for all.)

Whether or not this kind of action is taken (and the prospects are dim), all space destined for recreation in the higher sense needs protection not only from inappropriate development and use, but from *over*-use. Already some of our national parks are at times more crowded than the cities from which the crowds escaped, and overcrowding inevitably leads to pressures for more facilities, which in turn attract more crowds. Such pressures cannot be resisted easily, particularly by the National Park Service, which is financially dependent on Congress. It has become increasingly difficult to stand up to ski-resort promoters, tote-goat clubs, outboard motor associations, and all the rest. They, too, like to move into undeveloped country, but where do we stop? Do we say that our only course is to keep up with the demand? Or do we admit that to try to keep up with it is to destroy for our descendents the quality of life that so concerns us?

The point beyond which we must not go should be defined, and effective restraints set up. These rules will have to limit not only the kind and extent of development, but the number of people who may use an area at the same time. This would be a most unpopular proposal, for every taxpayer considers himself part-owner of public areas, with the right to use and visit his property at any time he sees fit. We readily accept the principle of reservations, waiting one's turn, and the payment of entrance fees in innumerable instances; there seems to be no alternative but to apply this principle to many of our recreation areas. It is a measure of our troubles that an American will soon have to buy a reserved ticket for a seat in the woods; if he will not accept that fact, he might not have a woods to sit in.

The climate for conservation appears to be improving, but the problems have never been more serious. While there has been some progress, we are naturally much concerned with what seem to many to be more immediate problems, at home and abroad, and with considerably less immediate but more glamorous affairs, such as moon shots and supersonic transports. Even in vital areas like pollution control, conservation is still far down the line when the cash is handed out, in spite of all the talk. Unfortunately, much of what is called conservation does not pay off in immediate and tangible returns, measurable in dollars, and it is unpopular—indeed suspect— in the business world. Conservationists are often looked upon as obstructers of economic progress, odd-balls who advocate programs that bring them no personal profit. It is to the credit of private conservation organizations that enough of this natural suspicion has been overcome to enable them to accomplish what they have. These organizations must, in the next few years, make themselves so large, so representative of all the people, and so well-spoken that practical politics will come to mean the implementation of much that is now thought to be impractical. These organizations, many and varied in their immediate goals, serve as the collective voice of millions of people who have nonmercenary interests in the protection and wise use of natural resources. They are beginning to be heard, but they would be heard and heeded much more were they on a more nearly equal footing with those organizations that profit from our resources.

Conservationists do not band together to make money, but even nonprofit organizations must have money to carry out their purposes. To encourage donations to legitimate nonprofit corporations that are working in one way or another for the public welfare, the Internal Revenue Code provides that contributions to eligible corporations may be deducted from the donor's Federal Income Tax, and it is this provision that makes existence possible for many conservation organizations. The Code further stipulates, however, that where donations have been ruled deductible, the donee may not use any "substantial part" of its income in efforts to influence legislation. For many organizations, this is no hardship, but because resource use is regulated by legislation, the form of that legislation is a legitimate concern of conservationists. Here is the inequity: Those who do gain profit have ample funds to spend in attempts to influence legislation for their own ends, and they pay no tax on income so spent. The nonprofiters, on the other hand—those with different but equally legitimate interests in the same resources—are penniless by comparison. Moreover, if no tax is to be paid on money given to them to promote their cause, they are forbidden to promote it.

On equal amounts of money, the government's tax loss is equal, but the rights of those who spend the money are not. For example, a nonprofit, tax-deductible conservation organization may oppose the construction of a hydroelectric dam, believing that other uses of the river and lands would bring greater long-range public benefits. One thousand citizens with similar beliefs, but no organized voice to speak for them, contribute one hundred dollars each to the conservation group, and deduct the gifts from their income taxes. The government loses the tax on $100,000, but the organized voice is not allowed to speak. On the other hand, the corporation that wants to build the dam spends $100,000 in the same year in direct attempts to push through legislation that will permit its construction. Under a specific provision of the Internal Revenue Code (Sec. 162[e] 1[A]), the money so spent is a deductible business expense, and again the government loses the tax on $100,000. The conservationists and those citizens for whom they speak should have an equal right to be heard on the subject of resource use, but under the present law they obviously do not. The final irony is that the law protects itself; they cannot fight to have it changed.

Conservationists are not anti-business, for they know as well as anyone else that business feeds, clothes, and houses us, moves us about, pays a very large part of our taxes, and generally supports us in the manner to which we have become accustomed. But business is by necessity competitive, ambitious, and single-minded. We have already learned what unregulated and unchecked competition can do. As we approach the end of our resources, insupportable overcrowding, and the loss of space and all wildness, more and more people realize that economic activity cannot provide certain necessities of life and that it can, in fact, destroy them. As citizens, these people have the same right as the potential destroyers to be heard. They deserve equal treatment, and at present they are not getting it. Their individual voices are lost in the wind, and they are heard only when they join together. Their organizations, being nonprofit, can never hope for war chests that come even close to matching the apparently limitless funds available to the opposition. But an even break on taxes and the right to promote legislation while maintaining their tax-deductible status would move them at least one step closer to equality. Such a step could be taken by amending the Code so that nonprofit, tax-deductible corporations with bona fide interests in our environment and natural resources could work to influence legislation that affects those resources.

But who can work for the amendment?

The country's private conservation organizations, diverse and fragmented though they are, are the rallying points for all who are concerned about our environment, the only semblance of a united voice for restraint and planning. And there must be a united voice. We will not control our environment until we control ourselves, through legislation at all levels of government, and the legislation will not come without public demand. It is the conservationists who will create the demand and provide the support, but their organizations must be more than social clubs, groups of like-minded people talking to one another, or militant associations fighting only for their own narrow interests. They must be broad in purpose and interest, thoroughly informed, and a great deal more unified than they are now.

In a sense we are all conservationists, but most of us become seriously concerned only when we are directly affected by what we think is a wrong use. When we are really concerned, we organize—to work for zoning ordinances, for or against dams, or whatever it may be that affects our pleasures or our pocketbooks. There are hundreds of organizations of this sort, with comparatively limited objectives, and while many of them have been effective, the narrow approach is not the answer. Some of the more responsible private organizations, aware of the complexities of resource use and management, have, therefore, joined forces to inform their members and the public and to be prepared to speak both more forcefully and more intelligently. These joinings have many forms, from small associations of local clubs to national organizations, the largest of which represents two million Americans. Inevitably, most of them continue to reflect the particular interests that originally brought their memberships together. But the majority profess a broad conservation interest, and perhaps the first responsibility of their leadership is to see to it that their interest is indeed broad, and more important, intelligently informed. This is in many ways the most difficult task that faces these conservation groups—first to assemble full, accurate, and unbiased information on which sound judgments can be based; and second, to educate their memberships and the public, to lead them to accept these judgments even when they conflict with immediate personal interests.

Few membership organizations are equipped to carry on the continuing study and research that are needed if we hope to evolve intelligent, long-range conservation policies—to determine what, in fact, constitutes wise use, use that will not just produce economic growth, aesthetic pleasure, physical satisfaction, or spiritual peace, but, over the decades, enhance the quality of the American environment and of American life. There are, however, a few private conservation organizations, supported largely by foundation grants and gifts from individuals, that were formed to carry on study and research on resource problems. They are not open to general membership, they have no particular axes to grind, and they can maintain a disinterested and unbiased viewpoint. Because of their character and purposes, they could be of great help to the membership groups. There could well be closer, and perhaps more formal, cooperation between the two types of organization.

But interested and informed leadership is one thing, and interested and informed membership is something else. It is not difficult to enlist a thousand members in a fight to preserve a wild river, but it is extremely difficult to get those same thousand interested in informing themselves about the political and economic factors that brought about the threat of the river's destruction.

Without the excitement of battle, attention wanders, and with the battle won, perhaps 10 per cent of the thousand will continue an active interest in the organization. But the important point is that there were a thousand who wanted the river saved. It was the organization that alerted and informed them, and only through the organization could they be effectively heard.

The state of our resources being what it is, there is no shortage of battles, and the temptation is great to keep the membership alive by blowing the bugle; but conservation organizations must be something more than shock troops. The real fight is against habit, indifference, and ignorance, and these will not be overcome by sporadic skirmishes, however spectacular and successful—and necessary— they may be. They will be overcome, in the end, by political action; but it has already been pointed out that while conservation organizations may educate and inform, if they are tax-deductible, they may not legally promote legislation. If they are not tax-deductible, they have great difficulty in raising even enough money to maintain themselves.

Some organizations with narrow aims and interests have allied themselves to some extent with business and industry, accepting substantial contributions and other forms of financial aid. But those that work for conservation in its broadest sense hesitate to accept this kind of help from those with whom they may find themselves in conflict. Most maintain their independence, get their incomes from tax-deductible memberships and gifts, and work only indirectly for the things they believe in. They must find ways to free themselves, so that they can work on a more nearly equal footing with political and industrial profit interest.

Whether or not conservationists are ever able to work directly for environmental legislation, their principal weapon will continue to be education. Up to now, publications aimed at adults are probably the most effective way of educating the general public, and in the last few years some national conservation magazines have shown marked improvement in quality and sophistication. Others continue to concern themselves almost entirely with a single phase of conservation, although some carry brief paragraphs of general conservation interest. All could be more educationally effective were they to broaden their coverage and write more frequently about underlying causes and possible long-range solutions. There is no conservation organization that does not need to raise the sights of its members.

There is much talk about conservation education in the schools, and some organizations have made considerable efforts to persuade local and state school systems to make conservation a regular part of the curriculum. So far, school administrators seem to have shown a notable lack of interest. With schedules over-full, conservation generally gets into the primary grades only, if at all, where it consists of sporadic nature study and occasional field trips. The primary school is the place to begin, but environmental study should continue in secondary school and college. The biggest obstacle is perhaps a lack of properly designed courses, and conservationists should work with qualified educators to remedy the situation and to make the study of our environment a regular part of all curricula. The universities, which should lead the way, seem to have been slow to realize the need, particularly at the undergraduate level; but there are some encouraging signs of progress in the graduate schools. Students of landscape architecture and city planning at the Harvard Graduate School of Design, for example, are working on environmental problems at the instigation and with the assistance of The Conservation Foundation and Resources for the Future, two examples of the nonmembership conservation organizations already referred to; and other schools are beginning to work along similar lines. With this kind of interest at the upper levels, conservationists can hope—and work—for increasing interest and activity down the educational line.

A united demand would speed action in this as in all other areas, but conservation is not yet a united movement. It should not be expected that all conservation organizations will join as one, but they must at least speak to one another. At present, their diverse interests and, in some cases, a kind of pointless rivalry keep many of them apart. Their educational efforts need to be directed not only at others, but at themselves, to convince their memberships that they must join forces to some extent and work more effectively for the higher goals of conservation. Co-operation of this sort is succeeding in a few states, where federations or councils bring together the majority of all conservation interests. But in many instances the state organizations represent only a narrow segment of the conservation population. Truly representative, active councils are needed in all states. Beyond this, one national organization has had notable success in bringing together its state affiliates on the national level. This kind of unity need not stifle individual interests, nor suppress differences of opinion; on the contrary, it can provide an opportunity for differences to be expressed and resolved. At its best, it could give every conservationist, of whatever stripe, a strong central organization to which to turn for information and support and, most important, a strong voice to speak for him on important issues. Leaders of national conservation organizations would do well to explore together the possibilities of more constructive moves in the direction of unity and co-operation.

It is commonplace to say that the next decade will bring answers to this, that, or the other problem. But decades are not what they once were, and in conservation the next will be shorter and more important than any that have gone before. The answers it brings will come from free expression of public opinion, speaking largely through private conservation groups. In them lies our best hope for the protection of our environment and the preservation of its quality. If the public can make itself heard, perhaps in the politics of the next ten years, the art of the possible will at last find it to its advantage to embrace conservation—until now, the art of the impossible.

THE HUMANE CITY

FREDERICK GUTHEIM

New Towns?

THE NEW TOWN was offered earlier as a utopia and as a solution to the problems of nineteenth-century urbanization, housing, and metropolitan growth. Now it is pressed as a solution to the contemporary problems of inner cities and as an alternative to sprawling suburbia. There is even the "new-town-in-town." As a panacea, the new town has defied criticism by avoiding definition. Just possibly it is all things to all men. But more likely it is the basic element in a new and more widely distributed form of city.

Before the counting of new towns was given up for lack of an acceptable definition, the more optimistic observers thought such developments in the United States exceeded two hundred. As early as 1964, the Housing and Home Finance Agency (now the Department of Housing and Urban Development) identified nearly fifty "new communities" in California alone, and over one hundred and sixty of more than one thousand acres in over thirty states.[1] Data are given for fifty-four developments in sixteen states by Edward Eichler and Marshall Kaplan's survey.[2] While the scale of such development is impressive, involving perhaps a total of 250,000 acres, the experience thus far is both meager and obscure. Documentation is limited to not more than ten major ventures, of which the two most highly visible are both in the Washington-Baltimore metropolitan area—Reston, Virginia, and Columbia, Maryland. Some typical characteristics of new towns are suggested in Table 1.

The recent crest of popularity has resulted in new towns being recognized in the 1968 federal housing and urban development legislation as an object of particular solicitude.[3] Prompted by recommendations of a Presidential Task Force, Congress has strengthened its earlier rather mild support of a new-town policy by offering a federally guaranteed cash-flow debenture, which assures financial

TABLE 1. Representative New Towns

New Town Name, Location	Developer	Size	Notes
Foster City, California S. San Francisco	T. Jack Foster & Sons	2,600 A	Built on reclaimed land
Reston, Va. W. Washington, D.C.	Robert E. Simon, Jr./Gulf-Reston	7,100 A	Most advanced planning
Lake Havasu City, Ariz. 150 mi. W. Phoenix	McCulloch Properties Inc.	16,250 A	Industry, recreation, lots
Irvine Ranch, Calif. S. Los Angeles	The Irvine Company	88,256 A	Largest new town
Palm Beach Gardens, Fla. W. Palm Beach	John D. MacArthur	7,680 A	Industry; retirement
Clear Lake City, Texas Houston-Galveston	Friendswood Development Corp. (Humble Oil Subsidiary)	15,234 A	NASA's Manned Spacecraft Center, Ellington Air Base; Bayport Industrial Area
Laguna Niguel, Calif. Orange Co.	Cabot, Cabot & Forbes	7,100 A	Publicly owned Corporation
Elk Grove Village, Ill. NW. Chicago	Centex Construction Corp.	6,000 A	Industry

Source: Practical Builder, July 1966

underwriters of suitably planned new-town developments that they will not suffer from the slow rate of return experienced in such pioneer ventures as Reston and Columbia. As a result of this experience, Robert E. Simon, Jr., who conceived Reston, lost out to Gulf Oil in a corporate takeover, which cast doubt on the community's intention to realize earlier plans. The principal lesson to be learned from Simon's experience was the critical year he lost pursuing more than seventy prospective investors before Gulf Oil put up its initial $15,000,000 and John Hancock a further $20,000,000. Private investors are needed if the large capital demands of new-town building are to be met on any large scale other than by the federal budget.

Columbia is about one year behind according to the timetable it projected for its major investors: the Connecticut General Insurance Company and the Teachers Insurance and Annuity Association. But the new legislation ought to reassure timid institutional investors in the future. Rising land prices have meant that few investors have ever faced the real possibility of losing their equity, but the slow pace of such complex large-scale developments and public acceptance of a novel way of living have left them without a sufficiently competitive yield on their investments. In practice it has been the entrepreneurs, not the investors, who have lost.

This new legislative encouragement raises more problems than it is likely to solve. It will probably not release a flood of new activity. It will not help present new towns that are struggling against the handicaps of the tight money market. Nor does it provide new directions or guidelines for public policy that new-town developers should recognize. But it does reaffirm a growing federal commitment to this type of development and allows the accumulation of further experience as the basis for future and larger programs. There is hope, in short, for a truly national program in which a comprehensive settlement and urbanization policy can be enunciated to guide new-town development. Many public policy issues must be resolved before new towns can make their potential contribution to the future urban environment.[4]

New-town builders with the vision to undertake such developments, the skill to put together difficult and novel combinations of interests, and the boldness to venture into new paths are rare but urgently required if this building technique is to be used to offer new types of multiracial and mixed-income communities or persuasive alternatives to the enticements and momentum of conventional suburbia. To use a simpler illustration, no successful carbon copy of William J. Levitt has appeared during the nearly thirty years in which his style of low-cost, high-volume housing has succeeded. Perhaps the major question faced by any federal program of new-town development is whether it can swell the still-thin ranks of such individuals as Philip Klutznick, James Rouse, Robert E. Simon, Jr., and the Janss brothers. Whatever measures of corporate involvement may be induced, under present conditions in the United States there is no substitute for highly motivated individual leadership. Anyone who doubts this can ask what success new towns might have under the direction of municipal housing authorities, the U.S. Corps of Engineers, or similar bureaucracies.

Builders as usual will not do. The FHA (Federal Housing Authority) is no training ground. The constraints new-town developers must overcome include small-bore politics, usually expressed in local government zoning, building codes, and development regulations; bureaucratic inertia and fragmentation at the federal and state levels; and financial conservatism. After clearing those fences the developer must face the real problems: new kinds of planning (notably social planning), urban design, and housing technology; new forms of community organization, local government, and management; new strategies of marketing and ways of charging for community amenities and services.

The experiences of new-town developers are still under study.[5] Without accepting the classification of "expansionists" and "non-expansionists" used by Marshall Kaplan to distinguish Rouse and Simon from the West Coast firms (Janss Corporation, Sunset International Petroleum Company, and others), a fundamental distinction exists between the two groups of developers.[6] The West Coast firms are less innovating as well as more expansionist. They are concerned with continuous operation in the fashion of large-scale homebuilders. Rouse and Simon, with significant differences between them, have been engaged in accomplishing fundamental changes both in the community-building process and in the physical and social planning of new communities. Each has regarded his task as sufficiently large and difficult not to look beyond it to other enterprises. (The creation of a large, effective business organization to plan, design, build and manage Columbia later generated pressures to find other work for this organization, and once the success of Columbia had been assured the Rouse Company has been seeking new business.) Both Rouse and Simon had considerable success; in their results as well as the further gains promised, they have taken a large forward step toward the future urban environment. These gains lie in both the socioeconomic character of the communities being developed and in their physical design, as well as in the interaction between the social and physical environments.

Only exceptionally motivated individuals would have incurred the risks and enormous labors required to innovate in the field of new-community development. Rouse has characterized Columbia as a "garden for people, God-centered," and Simon's evident high-mindedness caused a highly placed British observer to note: "It sounds like Hampstead Garden Suburb," rather than a government new town. Either man could have comfortably refrained from the ardors of building a new town.

James W. Rouse was born to good expectations in Baltimore, but was scarred by the Depression. Following an interrupted undergraduate program, he went to work in the FHA's Baltimore office at age twenty in 1934. Concurrently he earned a law degree at the University of Maryland. After a further brief apprenticeship in the mortgage and title business, Rouse opened his own office and commenced trading in FHA paper, gradually broadening to include other types of mortgages. It was a rapidly expanding field, and Rouse's operations expanded with it through the later recovery, the war housing program, and the postwar boom in veterans' housing. In the postwar period, he was extensively involved in developing regional shopping centers, a significant school in which to study decentralization and other aspects of urban change. A liberal Republican, he backed Eisenhower and in 1953 served on the President's housing advisory committee, which urged great efforts by private enterprise in housing and community building. He was a leader in forming the national organization ACTION (the American Council To Improve Our Neighborhoods, today Urban America, Inc.) and later served as president and board chairman. This organization was intended to further the program offered by the Eisenhower housing advisers, and it occasioned Rouse's first considerable recognition outside the city of Baltimore and the mortgage banking field. Thereafter Rouse's voice was a respected and frequently heard one in housing, although his optimism stumbled with the publication "No Slums in Ten Years." His leadership in Baltimore was impressive, yielding first Charles Center (a major and highly successful downtown redevelopment program) and then in 1963 the beginnings of Columbia.

Columbia is strongly marked by this individual—a self-made,

deeply religious man, a Presbyterian elder, a convinced environmentalist, a liberal capitalist, and an experienced and shrewd development entrepreneur. Most of all, Rouse is a man determined to leave his mark in lasting public works of humane significance. In his determination to excel, he enlisted an impressively rounded group of highly qualified planning advisers.[7] Five years after the land was first assembled for the new town of Columbia, with its planning accomplishment strengthened by successes in financing and the location of a quarter-billion-dollar General Electric appliance plant, one might regard as an understatement the estimate of Edward P. Eichler and Marshall Kaplan that "Columbia has been essentially the story of one man's skill and dedication."[8]

While the deliberations of the developer and his planning staff have not been disclosed, and there is some doubt that all of the advice proffered was taken or that much of it prevailed against other more business-like judgments, their attitude is commendable.

Rouse's success with Columbia has been evidenced in economic and political terms. Land sales in the most recent annual report amounted to $14.7 for the year, with annual income up $4 million from the previous year for a total of $11.5 million. The community of 4000 was expected to grow to 12,000 population by mid-1970. Howard County Commissioners changed zoning laws to facilitate building of the General Electric plant, with 12,000 employees, which is the key industrial development at Columbia. Can this success be duplicated? Can others do it? President Nixon, advised in this instance by Vice President Agnew, appears convinced it is possible, and such endorsement is included in his 1970 State of the Union speech. Rouse's ideas have also been successfully exported and now appear to have been embraced by the British Tories.

Robert E. Simon, Jr., was graduated from Harvard in 1935 at the age of twenty-one. His well-to-do New York background and lighthearted career as a popular, piano-playing undergraduate had scarcely prepared him for the responsibility he abruptly assumed, on the occasion of his father's death in the fall of 1935, as head of the family real-estate business. This responsibility left little scope for imagination or enterprise, concerned as it was with a relatively narrow range of building management and investment activities, mainly in the New York area. His first tentative steps toward business diversification and expansion came in the mid-1950's when he developed shopping centers in Dallas, Philadelphia, and other locations. In 1960 Simon faced a major business decision: how to invest between three and four million dollars in capital gains from the sale of Carnegie Hall, a family holding, in order to minimize its tax impact. At this point, he was offered and bought a tract of 6750 acres of land (later enlarged to 7400 acres) in Fairfax County, Virginia, eighteen miles west of Washington. The development of such a large tract for diversified uses rapidly assumed the form of a new town, under the advice of A. D. Little, Inc., and other consultants, within the then progressive planning policies of Fairfax County, which had enunciated a policy of concentrated development in the western part adjacent to Dulles Airport, but always with a highly significant input from Simon himself. In appraising this decision, it should be recognized that Simon's father had been a member of the board of the City Housing Corporation, builder of Sunnyside and Radburn, the two most important housing communities of the 1920's, and that his principal planning advisers, Whittlesey and Conklin (now Conklin and Rossant) were heirs to the same community planning tradition stemming from Clarence S. Stein and Henry Wright. With its social emphasis and its stress on green space and concentrated housing development, Reston was set squarely in the mainstream of American housing and community planning.[9]

Buoyed by these circumstances, Simon prepared himself for the great new tasks by assembling an elaborate group of consultants and advisers to develop in greater detail his concept of the new town. He was determined to overlook no chance to improve the community through the application of knowledge and research. Through his A. D. Little advisers, he established contact in 1960 with the Washington Center for Metropolitan Studies and through it contact with others in urban and regional planning, especially in the Washington area. Simon's concept of the incremental building of a series of residential communities was designed to allow the feedback of early experience into later planning through a process of research and evaluation. To guide this process, Dr. Carol Lubin joined the Reston staff as director of social planning, coordinating extensive studies and planning activities by the developer, Fairfax County, and others. Under her direction and with a supporting grant from the Ford Foundation, a new decentralized cluster-plan school was developed for Reston. This plan represented a real architectural breakthrough for the Fairfax County school system. A youth activities center, a nursery school, a church, a public library, and other services were incorporated into the community shopping center; an activity-oriented program for nature study was organized to explore

the wealth of Reston's natural setting; and the developing community was encouraged to participate in planning for its future. A
Reston Foundation for Community Programs was organized and
funded to develop the community's programs in the arts, education,
and philanthropy, directed not only by resident civic leaders and
representatives of Reston's rapidly growing industrial base, but also
by such eminent Virginians as Armistead Booth, Leslie Cheek,
Marshall Hahn, and Robert Porterfield, and national figures like
August Heckscher and Michael Straight. And, from the background,
Robert Simon was devising festive and urbane occasions to match
the mood of Washington in the Kennedy years. In scarcely four
years Reston was off and running, with high visibility and increasing
public acceptance as hundreds of thousands of visitors streamed
through its handsome Washington Plaza on Lake Anne.[10]

Both Reston and Columbia inescapably became vehicles for
expressing large bodies of contemporary technology and professional
judgment. As is clear in the statements of both men and their firms,
they are striving for the same objectives, and these have been determined mainly by real-estate market analysis. And the similarity is
still more evident in the general plans for the two communities—
with their abundant and wooded green space, ornamental water,
busy and interesting community centers, diversified housing, emphasis upon community social and cultural life, new types of schools,
churches, parks, and other community institutions and services, industrial development, efforts toward low-rent housing and open-
occupancy, careful attention to the needs of children, and progressive health programs and other innovations. Certainly the similarities
are more important than the differences. The analogy that comes to
mind is of two America's Cup racing yachts, each built in jealously
guarded secrecy, but emerging almost identical in dimensions, specifications, and appearance. The two towns have also responded to
"the rules of the game" as set down in local ordinances and federal
housing directives, to the conventional wisdom of designers, architects, planners, and other advisers, as well as competition with each
other. Finally, the two communities—about an hour's drive apart—
have learned from each other and have grown more alike than
different.

Differences there are, however, and these are most evident in
Rouse's superlative skill in his own field as a mortgage banker, in his
masterful and persuasive sales presentations to investors, purchasers
of land, associated developers, and industry. While his activities

have assured the commercial success of the enterprise, without doubt the plans for the community itself have been severely tailored to the requirements of the market. The price of this concession is the visual suburban blandness of Columbia and the evidence of compromise with every institutional restraint. Simon's openness to design innovation and his willingness to seek and use the best designers are evidenced in the powerful, clear, and far-reaching image Reston has achieved. When Simon lost control of the town, Gulf-Reston promptly disavowed publicly its advanced architecture and emphasis on town houses, but two years of the new administration have led to a reaffirmation of the original planning and design policies, not least because of the vociferous demands of the Restonians themselves. This has been demonstrated both in the decisions of the Gulf-Reston management to follow Simon's original plans and architectural standards, and the Fairfax County Board's insistence that this be done. Simon's downfall, by contrast, appears due mainly to the exhausting periods of time required to overcome inertia—the objections of government at all levels to innovation and the unwillingness of business and investors to accept new risks in an experimental operation. The result was lost opportunity, lost momentum, and—for the moment—the loss of a talented and irreplaceable innovator and promoter. Except for a small new town development near Rochester, N.Y., Simon now appears active primarily in more conventional real estate developments.

As a pioneer Simon suffered from the failure of federal officials to give the private developer specific goals he must meet in order to receive federal aid and to coordinate the many discretionary powers that collectively could have induced compliance with such goals. Instead, the developer was led on a wild goose chase in and around federal offices, left to his own devices as a private entrepreneur, and deprived of any responsible guidance. That Congress in 1964 backed away from accepting administration recommendations on new towns did not leave federal officials so powerless as they pretended, as was demonstrated in another context by the subsequent action of Interior Secretary Udall in locating the U.S. Geological Survey in Reston.

Reston and Columbia are not—like the twenty-eight new towns of Britain or the municipal new towns of Stockholm—government projects, supported by tax funds and subsidized to accomplish public purposes.[11] They are undertakings of private entrepreneurs, who work with private capital and compete with other private ventures, whether they be conventional suburban housing or other new towns.

(In the Washington-Baltimore area, about twenty-five other new town developments have been reported.) Public-spirited as the developers are, their awareness of a relationship between the problems of central cities and of urban America can be recognized in their new towns but only within certain limits. Both developments aspire to a domestic community of modest scale and reasonable definition; to social balance of income, class, and race; to a diversity of housing choice; to a mixture of residential, commercial, industrial, and public land uses; to a richly textured and integrated community life, with high cultural standards and a strong emphasis on recreation and leisure time opportunities; to efficient and often novel local public services, and active participation in community decisions, (although neither town has an organized local government, each being managed by private corporations and serviced by counties).[12] Both communities are trying with some success to become centers for higher education and training. Both Reston and Columbia already have flourishing industrial areas. Reston provides more jobs than there are families living there (Table 2). While it is expected that jobs and housing will approximately balance, and that many residents will also work in the town, this relationship must be largely coincidental.[13] Both towns have clearly stated their objective of providing housing for all who may be employed in the community. As a first step in support of this policy, with which the residents have declared themselves to be in agreement, Reston has commenced to develop a novel application of a product of the mobile home industry in a stacked form.[14] Recent amendments to the federal housing laws have also introduced greater flexibility into housing subsidies, increasing the potential for low-rent housing in private developments.[15]

The practical appearance of middle-income housing in the two towns is evidenced by the leasing of initial units of a 198-dwelling apartment complex in Reston by the Fairfax County Redevelopment and Housing Authority. Families with incomes of $6000 to $11,000 are eligible. At Columbia the Interfaith Housing Corporation has sponsored a 300-unit apartment project in which subsidies will allow families with incomes of $5500 to $10,000 to find housing. In both communities management proposes to disperse low-income families widely.

No new town as yet has commenced to exploit the great potential economies of the Habitat-like building systems that are just around the corner and will comprise one of the major competitive advantages of new towns.[16]

TABLE 2. Industries at Reston, Va.

Name of Firm	Type of Industry	Moved From	Element at Reston	Date
HRB Singer	Electronics, R&D	State College, Pa.	Washington Branch	1964
Bowser Inc.	Pumps, filtration	Chicago	Research Center	1965
GM Kinetics	Ultrasonic Devices; Research	Arlington		1967
Hazelton Labs	Life Sciences R&D	Fairfax Co.	Four Divisions	1965
Air Survey Corp.	Photogrammetry	Beltway		1966
Scope Inc.	Electronics	Falls Church	Expansion	1967
General Technology Corp.	Research on Fibres for Aerospace	Alexandria		1967
Motorola	Regional Marketing Electronics	Moved from Washington; now moved back due to change in corporate marketing policy.		
Philco	Electronics Development	Fairfax Co.	Office; lab	1967
Sanders Assoc., Inc.	International Ground	Nashua, N.H.	Systems Div.	1967
Schonstedt Instruments	Mfgr. Magnetic Devices	Silver Spring, Md.	Expansion	1968
Hunter Assoc. Labs	Color spectrum Research			Future
Human Sciences Research Inc.	Ergonomics			Future
Transportation Consultants Inc.	R&D	Washington	Branch of Commonwealth Services	Future
U.S. Geological Survey	Government Science	Washington and area	Headquarters	Future

Source: Robert Barker, Industrial Division, Gulf-Reston, Inc., Interview, March 1, 1968.

These may be encouraged by the still-dubious results of HUD's "Operation Breakthrough" and by the large business corporations that are being attracted to this new field of enterprise by dwindling demands from military and aero-space clients. Thus far, however, the record of corporate activity in this field is not impressive, and its future seems more likely to have been foreshadowed by take-overs of existing building firms, as International Telegraph and Telephone Corporation acquired Levitt and Sons Inc.

However one evaluates such efforts, Reston and Columbia are not designed as solutions to the problems of anguished central cities and particularly of their ghettos. With an average net return of 6.4 percent, new-town developers cannot be expected to assume many risks.[17] They do offer solutions to the problems of metropolitan areas, to sprawling suburbia, to environmental pollution, to urban transportation—or, rather, they offer communities in which these problems and many others have been dealt with more rationally. A large body of thought has developed, predictably in California, that regards such planning as politically irresponsible and economically hopeless. Such critics regard community planning and design as the product of professional ignorance and arrogance.[18] But to another body of thought, modern cities are an accident and California cities a catastrophe. It is now necessary to recognize that something new and apparently successful has appeared in the large-scale physical development of cities. This new approach presents an alternative to the concentric growth of older cities or to the urban field apparent in the corridor metropolis as found in California, for example. The advantages of new towns are so compelling that they will drain off the best people and the cream of the market from both central cities and suburbs. If cities are to compete, they will have to change.

New towns in the United States thus far have resulted from the limited interaction of developers, designers, and other consultants and decision-makers with local public agencies. New towns have also been criticized for failing to reflect either fundamental problems of existing cities or human aspirations. It has been difficult to broaden the basis for new-town planning simply because no way has been found to represent the interest of the future population of such communities. Overcoming this gap is not impossible. A shadow community could be developed that would provide a social model with realistic possibilities for interaction and response in the planning process. The machinery now being employed to plan "model cities" might with considerable validity be used to plan a new town on raw land—perhaps something like Oakland East (discussed below). The strategy of incremental building employed at Reston also recommends itself as the early population (hopefully more representative of the later, more complete community) participates in planning further stages of the town. Parochialism has no place in new-town decisions. The ability of state and federal governments to speak for the future community is certainly greater than the capacity of any immediate locality, and they should have a stronger voice.

If central cities want their problems recognized in new towns, they should participate in planning them. This step is both logical and desirable since many of the people who will live in such new communities will come from the central cities. One useful precedent for this involvement took place in the heyday of British national planning for new towns. Dissatisfied with the pace of such development and its recognition of London problems, the then London County Council recognized that new towns have "made a notable contribution to human happiness and are highly successful ventures." Its design for the new town also recognized that a community of one hundred thousand people had to be more than a suburb. In particular, it needed a strong central area to provide structure and urbanity; a transportation system other than the private car; good provision for open space for recreational use, amenity, and natural balance; and a population mix of different age groups, family structure, and employment that would be diversified from the start.[19]

Interest in new towns has been stimulated in Canada by experiences in the Don Mills Valley near Toronto, where industrial development and new housing have been successfully coordinated, and the Aluminum Company of Canada's town of Kitimat, British Columbia. The major Canadian cities are seen as strong candidates to sponsor new towns. As Humphrey Carver has written:

The task of converting raw land into the form of a city has commonly been imposed upon a bordering municipality that is in a state of shock, its population half rural and half suburban, neither part having financial resources or any real motives for such a formidable undertaking. Why, say the farmers, should we pay to provide schools and services for an incoming urban population with expensive city tastes? And why, say the newly arrived, newly married suburbanites, should we pay for the next migration of similar suburbanites? The situation invites a disintegration of farming operations and encourages creative interest in the important decisions that have to be made for building a city. As a general principle, the Mother

City, which attracts population, creates employment, and spawns the new suburbs, should be responsible for city-building. This zone of urban shadow should be within the jurisdiction of the metropolitan community and, as new daughter communities are settled and become established, new junior municipalities should be formed to take over local affairs.[20]

There is no reason why such new towns cannot be developed in the United States to the great advantage of central cities. Such development would not only help solve many immediate problems of housing and employment, but would also prevent them from getting worse with cities growing along older obsolete patterns. While the advantages of "skip annexation" may have been exaggerated, such new towns could indeed be organic parts of central cities.[21]

The potentials of new towns and of the new experimental cities are discussed elsewhere in this volume by Dr. Athelstan Spilhaus. One of the most compelling is the opportunity to apply new urban technologies. Such technologies encounter formidable obstacles when introduced in existing cities, where local public regulations, union restraints, and other institutional barriers must be overcome.[22] Innovation on new sites would be less disturbing to both existing interests and values. Among the major areas of promise is total climate control. (Reston offers central air conditioning, as other communities have offered centralized district heating, but total climate control would allow urban development in regions of climatic extremes.) New technologies are available for water supply and disposal, achieving major economies as well as conservation objectives; lower utility costs, based on new techniques in power generation and distribution, including the amenity of less wirescape; new methods of communication; and—probably of most immediate application—new developments in transportation, both for local services and interurban mass transportation.[23] On a small scale, Columbia has introduced a mini-bus service for local travel, as well as special arrangements for getting children to school. Commuter transportation innovations have been developed at Reston—significantly, by the Restonians themselves. The Phoenix new town of Litchfield Park has provided special routes for electric vehicles resembling golf carts (also used for that purpose) for many forms of localized travel.

Innovation in education, health, local public administration, urban economics, and other spheres would also appear to be less difficult in the framework of new development. Such experimentation would be a high public purpose, whatever its further application may amount to.

The temptation for an experimental city is to reflect chiefly the present ills of cities—environmental pollution, for example. Instead, the potential of urban technology for fundamentally new forms of urban environments and living should be tested.

A rapidly increasing interest in the social-psychological and behavioral factors in the physical environment has brought this aspect of new community development, in both new towns and cities, to the threshold of experimental application. These efforts, both alone and in conjunction with the design of new physical environments, are quite as significant as the technological elements of new communities.[24] This potential has been suggested by Marshall McLuhan:

We have now become aware of the possibility of arranging the entire human environment as a work of art, as a teaching machine designed to maximize perception and to make everyday learning a process of discovery. Application of this knowledge would be the equivalent of a thermostat controlling room temperature. It would seem only reasonable to extend such controls to all the sensory thresholds of our being. We have no reason to be grateful to those who juggle these thresholds in the name of haphazard innovation.[25]

Finally, the complex interrelationship of so many elements of the social and physical community makes it impossible to deal with them piecemeal with much success or as an experience from which to learn. Widespread awareness of national urban growth and of the new urban potential as well as the capability to experiment on a large scale in this area have combined today to make the construction of experimental new towns and cities a national imperative. A call has been heard "to create communities that are products of late-twentieth-century technology and social ideas and not merely shinier versions of early-twentieth-century cities."[26] Such a task— with all the lessons to be learned from it—could be the decisive event in the search for a new American urban environment.

While the fundamental plans were being developed for Reston and Columbia, both Simon and Rouse were alert for signals from Washington that would influence their operations. They were vitally concerned with specific public decisions. Both wanted a major federal installation located in their towns. Simon succeeded in securing the U.S. Geological Survey headquarters, but Rouse lost the Patent Office. Both were interested in seeing federal housing officials back their endorsement of new towns in principle with some practical steps toward coordinating the many federal development aids that would recognize and reward the larger scale and greater risks of new-town development. President Kennedy's endorsement of the "radial corridor" policies plan for Washington, which explicitly showed Reston as a development objective, was interpreted by Simon as promising a measure of federal support that never materialized. To these and other expectations there was little response. Both developments faced specific issues, perhaps the most significant being whether the Dulles Airport access road, a superhighway offering speedy connection to downtown Washington, would be opened to local traffic—a possibility still denied the Virginia town. In this vast range of possibility, it was abundantly clear that many steps, entirely apart from new legislation and funds, could be taken within the administrative discretion of high public officials to aid new towns. Few of them were. Secretary of Housing and Urban Development Robert C. Weaver frequently asked the rhetorical question as to why he should help a development like Reston which appeared to him indistinguishable from a conventional middle-class suburb; but he did not appear to consider how he might influence the objectives of such development toward more public ends.

Observers of these paradoxical difficulties began to ask what the federal government could do that would influence the goals, plans, and operations of new-town developers. Perhaps the most important answer lay not in the area of housing and urban development, but in that of transportation. Transportation, particularly highway building, has an enormous potential to change time-space relations, to open newly accessible land, to effect dramatic changes in land use and value.[27]

The profound influence of transportation upon the location and character of urban development has been carefully studied by geographers and economists.[28] So has the more specific effect of interstate system expressways, particularly the location of their interchanges in metropolitan areas.[29] With the advent of federal interest in urban mass-transportation programs, the structuring effect of rapid transit on urban development has been studied anew. (It had been fruitfully examined in the period 1900–1915, particularly in the New York area.) Most recently, the possibility has been recognized that urban development should be a major objective of transportation policies and planning.[30] With the transfer of the urban transportation grants program from the Department of Housing and

Urban Development (HUD) to the Department of Transportation in mid-1968, HUD retained important powers that could be effectively employed to influence urban development.

A second but less immediately significant step that the federal government could take would make surplus federal land available as the sites for new towns and cities. As consultant to Interior Secretary Stewart Udall, Robert E. Simon, Jr., has been studying the possible use of some Indian tribal lands in this fashion. The Public Land Law Review Commission has included such urbanization possibilities among the new uses of the public domain that it contemplates. More than a score of federal surplus sites, most of them from the military, have already been identified and turned over to municipalities for use as housing, but without much apparent thought of systematic new-town development. Important machinery has been created, however, that could be used for such purposes.

Using federal surplus land is probably the most immediate assistance that could be given a socially worthy development like Floyd B. McKissick's "Soul City," a new town in the North Carolina "black belt." A series of more complicated financial aids have been explored since this development was first announced. Such a use of Steward Air Force Base, near Newburgh, N.Y., has been proposed by Urban Ventures, a New York City black business organization. But as a practical matter, few surplus tracts are likely to conform to the essential criteria of a new town in which specific employment for lower income families might be created, to say nothing of many other environmental and economic considerations.

The potential of new towns as a vehicle for public policy should be examined against the experience of Reston and Columbia, both private developments responding fundamentally to market factors. The creative input of the private developer should not be underestimated. Nevertheless, that talent might be combined with the powers and resources of a public agency to yield a stronger and more responsive new-town effort than has yet been seen. Previous experience suggests a federal new-town building program on the model of the earlier Resettlement Administration, with its "Greenbelt Towns" of the mid-1930's. The present urban crisis might be considered a sufficient national emergency to countenance such employment of federal powers, as was the case during the Depression years. While the idea of converting the U.S. Corps of Engineers, the Bureau of Reclamation, or some other superfluous federal engineering bureaucracy into a new-town building agency has a certain attraction, it is hardly feasible politically. The federal role is likely to be that of financing and rendering technical assistance to other agencies.

Activity by states is an interesting possibility, particularly in a period of revived interest in state power and its more progressive employment (as evidenced in the current reform of state constitutions). New-town building is well suited to the geographical jurisdiction and powers of a state, if not to its financial resources. Some progressive states like New York and New Jersey exhibit a growing interest in new-town building, usually for reasons of better urban balance or more efficient state planning and economic development. In some interstate areas, new-town building could also be a significant competitive activity. States should probably charter public or Comsat-type semipublic corporations for such enterprises. The result in the end, as with some forms of federal activity, might not be greatly different from the British new-town corporation. At best, however, one might realistically expect only a few of the largest and most resourceful states to respond to such opportunities.

The New York State Urban Development Corporation has commenced work on two new towns near Buffalo and Syracuse, but these appear subject to many of the constraints earlier mentioned in this article. Inherently, however, this is a more promising framework in which to innovate. New Jersey, with its state housing program and the prospective development of the Hackensack Meadows; Pennsylvania, which has recently commenced to move in this direction; Minnesota, which has recognized the new town of Jonathan; and the always-beckoning California are the most promising states in the new towns field. Unfortunately, this demonstration of state capabilities does not lead to the conclusion that many other states are ready, willing and likely to follow their example.

The major possibility would appear to be direct action by a municipality or perhaps an urban county, working within its own metropolitan area or housing market along the lines suggested above. The present climate of opinion appears to favor such action, particularly as cities rid themselves of the earlier notion that somehow new towns would further complicate rather than ease their problems. Even former President Eisenhower endorsed the idea that new towns can mitigate central-city problems.[31] The recently enacted federal programs enhance the feasibility of such local efforts. And fortunately there is the example of one such development planned by the city of Oakland, California.

Oakland East was the creation of Oakland's former city manager Wayne Thompson, who advanced it as a solution to the problems of unemployment, housing, urban renewal, industrial development, and congestion his city faced. Using a tract of surplus federal land seventeen miles east of Oakland, his plan proposed the development of an enclave of the city based on an industrial park with its associated employment opportunities. Related to such employment, Thompson proposed an extensive manpower development and training program, enlisting large numbers of Oakland's poor and unemployed. Invoking public powers and subsidies where necessary, housing was to be built to match the rent-paying ability of the new town's population. Schools and other public services equal to those in Oakland would be provided. The new town would be linked to the parent city by high-speed transportation. Social development, economic growth, and a contributory physical environment with new types of housing were the ingredients for the new town. It is not difficult to see in such a sketch the beginnings of a more realistic and contemporary idea of a new town that would make a fruitful contribution to the solution of the problems of the urban ghetto and not merely offer a new way of sweeping them under the rug.[32]

By contrast, it is hard to imagine that the difficulties of new town building are likely to be overcome by the well-intentioned efforts of Floyd McKissick's "Soul City" (already rejected by the Department of Housing and Urban Development as contrary to national desegregation efforts), or the New York sponsors of a similar development, "City of Man" in the mid-Hudson locality. Although the important recently perceived advantage of new towns is their potential to assist in dispersing the ghetto and providing an alternative goal to rural-urban migration, they can represent a fundamentally new approach to the problem of city growth. Paul Ylvisaker, Commissioner of the New Jersey Department of Community Affairs, has warned, "We may have reached a dead end in evolving an urban culture." He sees new towns as offering a break with the past and the opportunity to invent new forms of urban life. "We cannot rely entirely on the incremental method to achieve the full measure of progress that is now necessary. Radical departures are called for, both in reshaping our old communities and in designing the new. Certainly the new town in this sense is a healthy concept and I am among those who welcome it." New towns in metropolitan areas and entirely new cities may also comprise the greatest hope for a new American environment. New towns might range from 15,000 to 100,000 population, while new cities would probably be in the 250,000 to 600,000 scale. New towns would have to be conceived as integral parts of the metropolitan areas in which they are located and the central cities of which they are satellites. In contrast, new cities are freestanding, responsive to larger regional factors and new technological developments that trigger urban growth. Either type of development will involve planning as well as action on an unprecedented scale. Past obstructions have been imposed by central cities fearing new towns as competitors for population and jobs, by small builders with larger competitors, by interregional rivalries in Congress, and by the apprehensions of many areas, especially in the South, that federal standards of integrated housing and schools would be strengthened by federally sponsored new towns.[33] These objections have not been overcome, and compromises will probably be found in future as well as present federal action.

Such past difficulties have tested political resolve, but greater efforts are justified simply because nothing smaller will meet the problems of congestion, slum housing, segregation, and environmental obsolescence that are fundamental characteristics of the present urban ghettos of large cities.

While the report of the National Advisory Commission on Civil Disorders recommended reorienting federal housing programs to place more low- and moderate-income housing programs outside ghetto areas, it said nothing explicit about new towns.[34] In its report on the hearings held on the Kerner Commission report, the Joint Economic Committee summarized the advantages of dispersion. It cited industrial dispersion particularly because of lower land costs outside the city, developments in transportation, the demand for more space for single-story plants, general suburbanization of housing, and the growth of commuting. This analysis constituted an elaboration of the problem presented by the two worlds of city and suburb, rather than an attempt to reconcile such differences. The significance of new towns in this situation was hardly mentioned. Yet in earlier testimony before the Kerner Commission, dispersal of the ghetto was identified as one of five policies that might cope with civil disorders.[35] While acknowledging that dispersal probably has the fewest advocates of any of the measures perceived, it was contended that "this is the only program that promises a long-range solution." Without dispersal, it was argued, metropolitan area imbalance will intensify as ghettos expand. Furthermore, not only would dispersal cost less than "gilding the ghetto" with new industries and housing, but it is more "consistent with stated goals of American society." Allied with dispersing the present ghetto are proposals to redirect the present streams of rural-urban migration to avoid further concentration in a limited number of large metropolitan centers. This was proposed to the Kerner Commission in a major rural redevelopment program that would create jobs in areas where agricultural decline or rationalization was creating massive unemployment and where only one job in agriculture could be foreseen for every ten boys born on the farm. The nine others, it was predicted, would be "in the cities tomorrow, burning our buildings because we have been unable to develop a better rural-urban balance of economic opportunities and population patterns."[36]

Neither proposals for ghetto dispersal nor those for redirecting urbanward migration to new rural industrial opportunities have dealt specifically with new-town development, although this is clearly one of the principal means that might be employed to achieve such results.

Experience thus far does not show that new towns like Reston and Columbia are in themselves important contributors to the solution of the major urban problems, especially poverty, segregation, and civil disorder. They do demonstrate, however, that the capability to develop such new towns now exists, that significant public as well as economic advantages lie with such developments, and that they will be appearing in increasing numbers, particularly in the large and rapidly growing metropolitan regional housing markets. As such development increases, the problems of central cities will probably worsen as the division of population and environment becomes sharper between central city and outlying new towns. The further advantages of new towns as alternatives to conventional suburbs are too compelling to make it likely that they can be nipped in the bud. They yield more attractive, healthier environments and are compatible with other measures of urban dispersal. The alternative, therefore, is to examine how these important economic growth points can be made to contribute to greater social usefulness. This is particularly the case if new towns are to be encouraged by public powers, subsidies, and discretionary administrative efforts.

The crux of the matter is jobs and housing. Many new towns have been closely oriented to heavy industry and the diverse range of jobs it offers. Levittown, Pennsylvania—with its primary orientation to the Fairless Works—is an outstanding example. But given the present character of industrial expansion, especially in the larger metropolitan areas, and despite Columbia's success with its General Electric appliance assembly plant, it will be neither easy nor automatic to assure such employment. The experience of Reston given in the table on page 201 is perhaps an extreme example, but it illustrates what may happen. These industries, with their strong scientific complexion and job requirements, are typical of the Washington area. Although few of the highly volatile firms that moved to the new town had ever been located in a central city and few would have been attracted to any location there, they do not offer much in the way of employment to the central-city jobless. The industrial mix of new towns must be carefully regulated if the employment mix and the housing mix are to be related to the central city and its people.

Housing is equally important, but may prove easier than controlling industrial location and development. Arriving at a proper mix of housing, a sufficiently diversified range of rents and tenure as well as building type is the problem. Unlike the Swedish towns that direct the distribution of tenants according to their educational or social status as well as their income, family size, age, and other characteristics, American communities cannot billet families, but they can provide powerful if less direct inducements to secure many of the same results, as experience in urban renewal has amply demonstrated. Housing is also on the threshold of important technological developments, seen most dramatically in the use of Fiberglas, plastics, and other new materials, and these are most easily applied in new towns. Although these developments promise significant cost savings, they are not enough, by themselves, to yield new housing for low-income families. Subsidies will be necessary.

"It is self-deception to talk of socially balanced new neighborhoods or new towns when one-third of the population cannot possibly afford to live in them," wrote Hans Blumenfeld.[37] New building technology, coupled with gains in land utilization and other possible cost savings can go far in a new town to produce low rents, but public subsidy will still be required before really low-income families can be reached. The question is not whether to extend such subsidies, but where to place them to get the greatest social benefit as well as the greatest economic advantage. Among such alternatives the new towns have a strong competitive position.

Whether or not such public objectives are incompatible with the private new-town developer's freedom, as has been suggested, they should be attempted.[38] The best of the European new towns,

212

Tapiola, is a private development that illustrates the feasibility of such a conjunction of purposes as well as their compatibility. This characteristic of Tapiola as well as its fine design makes it highly relevant to the American situation. The resources of the cooperative movement and other "middle ground" forms of enterprise in the United States are not exceptionally strong, but they can be reinforced to comprise essential elements in a total new-towns package. Difficult as such forms of mixed enterprise are, difficulties compounded by the creaking machinery of government in which they have to work, the best course open appears to be to work experimentally and resourcefully toward new solutions.[39]

Perhaps we can strengthen our confidence and resolve by looking at the not inconsiderable history of experience with new towns in America. There is a widespread but somewhat unfounded impression that the principal experience with this form of development has been in other nations. The utopian dreams, the pioneer visions, of the European examples of new-community development appeal today as never before as an answer to the acute problems of an urbanizing nation. Through the centuries the prospect of a fresh start on raw land has lured those increasingly appalled by the manifold evils of industrial cities—among them, Charles Fourier, Robert Owen, James Silk Buckingham, and Ebenezer Howard. Others, particularly in the United States, sought to create more than a hundred deliberately planned frontier settlements whose physical outlines reflected their determination to build a new world responsive to communitarian ideals. The religious ideology of radical Protestant sects fused with ideas of political egalitarianism, social betterment, and collective economics in a pioneer setting of immigrants. Paternalistic industry —as in New England mill villages, manufacturing centers like Pullman, Kohler, or Torrance, or mining towns like Tyrone—often exhibited its own idealization of the industrial urban environment. These forces were all recognized in the ultimately successful realizations of Ebenezer Howard and his followers in Letchworth, Welwyn, and twenty-eight postwar British new towns, and in Radburn, the Greenbelt towns, Kittimat, Reston, and contemporary developments in the United States. To neglect the international character and impressive continuity of the new-town movement would be a serious omission.

With all their primary concern throughout history with religious, social, and economic goals, the physical expression of new communities was always a major distinguishing element. New towns recommended themselves because they promised to improve the environment. Most readily the physical design of the new towns also reveals their origins.

When America listened to Robert Owen, or to the disciples of Charles Fourier, [it] reshaped the new doctrines to conform to a communitarian ideal that the religious communities had already made familiar. In effect, what these men and women thought they discovered in Owenism or Fourierism was a way of achieving the prosperity, the security, and the peace of a Shaker village without subjecting themselves to the celibacy and the narrow social conformity exacted by Shaker theology.[40]

Not simply new social institutions but highly abstract physical images of Owen's "parallelograms" or Fourier's "phalansteries" were transformed by the immediate conditions facing the community builders. In the most famous of these communities—Harmony and Economy, Pennsylvania—people moved into buildings earlier constructed and used by the Rappites. It would be difficult to find a more convincing illustration that American life, rather than imported theories, assured the continuity of experience that, in the end, defined the new communities. The new towns built in the United States will certainly be our own rather than a copy of the solutions arrived at elsewhere.

American experiments with new-community development have not yielded any models nor processes of urban development that are applicable today. This argues the difficulty of the job, but in making the effort, new potentialities are opened for further development and for the eventual solution of what at the outset appear insoluble problems. Past experiments surely justify the present effort to invent the future, to build our present ideals of social equality, freedom, and technological efficiency into new towns.

REFERENCES

1. Thomas McDade, Director of Urban Studies, Housing and Home Finance Agency, "New Communities in America: A New Context for Institutional Innovation," a talk to the Eighth Annual Organization of Cornell Planners Conference, Cornell University, October 17, 1964. A good introduction to the garden city in history is Peter Batchelor, "The Origin of the Garden City Concept of Urban Form," *Journal of the Society of Architectural Historians*, vol. xxviii, no. 3 (October, 1969), pp. 184-200. British new towns are explored in greater detail by Walter L. Creese, *The Search for Environment* (New Haven: Yale University Press, 1966).

2. Edward P. Eichler and Marshall Kaplan, *The Community Builders* (Berkeley, 1967), pp. 185-86. For a summary of basic data for a representative

214

group of new towns, see *Practical Builder* (July, 1966), pp. 72-83. See also *New Communities: A Selected, Annotated Reading List,* compiled by Library, Housing and Home Finance Agency (January, 1965, with additions May, 1967).

3. Public Law 90-448 of 1968, particularly Title IV. This follows earlier endorsement with some encouragement to new-town developers beginning in 1964 with federal aid for land development. Significant opposition developed to federal loans to new-town developers that the present legislation was able to overcome. More detailed guidelines and regulations under which this legislation is to be administered will be found in *Federal Register,* Vol. 34, No. 242, December 18, 1969 (Washington, 1969).

4. Muriel I. Allen (ed.), *New Communities: Challenge for Today,* an American Institute of Planners Background Paper, No. 2 (Washington, 1968). This is the major effort to raise such questions in the light of the 1968 legislation for new towns.

5. Reston has been under continuous study since 1963 by the Washington Center for Metropolitan Studies. Elements of this work are currently being prepared for publication by Kathryn H. Stone of the Center's staff. A continuing historical report of the development of Columbia has been a significant feature of this project since its inception. A veritable library of technical planning documents, consultants' reports, descriptions, and special studies by social scientists and planners has been produced on the two neighboring projects, although thus far no comparative study appears to have been undertaken. Nor do the present studies appear likely to yield biographies of the new-town builders. A related publication with valuable comments on the Restonians is Henry Bain, *The Reston Express Bus: A Case History of Citizen Action to Improve Urban Transportation,* Washington Center for Metropolitan Studies, Washington, 1969.

6. Marshall Kaplan, "The Role of Planner and Developer in the New Community," *Washington University Law Quarterly* (February, 1965), pp. 91-92.

7. These activities are detailed in Eichler and Kaplan, *The Community Builders,* pp. 63 ff.

8. *Ibid.,* p. 78. The description of Columbia, pp. 54-79, remains the best analysis of this development, although necessarily limited by its termination in 1965. The description of Reston (*ibid.,* pp. 79-87) appears limited by a lack of information. One would welcome Eichler's conclusions following his experience on Simon's staff for a few months prior to the Gulf Oil corporate take-over in 1967. On the personal role of developers, see also Marshall Kaplan, "The Roles of Planner and Developer in the New Community," *Washington University Law Quarterly* (February, 1965), pp. 88-104.

9. Roy W. Lubove, *Community Planning in the 1920's* (Pittsburgh, 1962); Clarence S. Stein, *Toward New Towns for America* (New York, 1957); Frederick Gutheim, "Greenbelt Revisited," *Magazine of Art* (January, 1947), pp. 16-20.

10. Three hundred thousand in 1968.

11. Frederic J. Osborn and Arnold Whittick, *The New Towns, the Answer to Megalopolis* (London, 1964). For a more current appraisal see Frank Schaffer, *The New Town Story* (London, 1970). The Tory view of new towns appears in *Private Capital for New Towns* (Institute for Economic Affairs, London, 1969).

12. As of the end of 1968, Reston and Columbia had about sixty black families each.

13. As Table 2 suggests, industries currently locating in new towns are unlikely to offer great employment opportunities to the presently unemployed. For a good appraisal of this situation and its consequences in human terms, see "Columbia, Reston or 'Soul City'" by Susan Jacoby, *Washington Post*, February 14, 1969.

14. Margaret Drury, *Mobile Homes* (Ithaca: Cornell University Press, 1968), offers a recent evaluation of similar developments in housing. A federally-aided research project at Reston has yielded encouraging first-stage reports on mobile home technology transfer, but this alone is no answer to housing needs of low-income families.

15. While Americans have reacted against the socioeconomic layering of suburbia, the British have just been advised to end the predominantly proletarian character of their new towns and increase the amount of home ownership they offer.

16. Plans developed for the Scottish new town of Livingston initially explored the possibilities of "element building" both to create the buildings of the town and provide a continuing industry there. Unluckily these ideas of Peter Daniel, the town's original planner, were abandoned by the developing corporation.

17. Eichler and Kaplan, *The Community Builders*, p. 151. This early analysis of new town building did not reckon with their educational effect upon hundreds of thousands of visitors and the widespread publicity they generated. This has been shrewdly appraised by Howard County planners in a persuasive statement on "value image dynamics." They argue that the combined impact of Columbia, Reston and other new towns being developed will be one of the major educational contributions of recent times, a tremendous impact on the future direction of urban-suburban development, and will strengthen awareness of the inherent advantages of planned development. *General Plan Technical Report No. 1, Howard County 1985*, Howard County Planning Commission (Ellicott City, Md., 1967).

18. Melvin Webber, "The Urban Place and the Nonplace Urban Realm" in Melvin Webber, John W. Dyckman, *et al.*, *Explorations into Urban Structure* (Philadelphia, 1964), pp. 79-153. Another presumed critic of new towns is Jane Jacobs, but a careful reading of *The Death and Life of Great American Cities* (New York, 1961) shows that the object of her criticism

was the Garden City, and few of these objections apply to the current movement.

19. *The Planning of a New Town, Data and Design Based on a Study for a New Town of 100,000 at Hook, Hampshire* (London, 1961).

20. Humphrey Carver, *Cities in the Suburbs* (Toronto, 1962), pp. 55-56.

21. Kent Matthewson, "A Challenging New Concept: Skip Annexation," *Nation's Cities* (October, 1967), pp. 41-44.

22. Burnham Kelly and Associates, *Design and the Production of Houses* (New York, 1959), pp. 302-47, deals with land-use controls. Former Senator Paul H. Douglas's National Commission on Urban Problems is already producing background reports that detail such obstacles to low-cost housing.

23. Victor Gruen Associates, *New Cities USA* (privately printed by Victor Gruen Associates, Los Angeles, 1966), pp. 21-28.

24. A working group to exchange information and explore mutual interests in this field has been organized as the Conference on Socio-physical Environment, which first met with the American Institute of Architects in 1967 and meets concurrently with the American Association for the Advancement of Science.

25. Marshall McLuhan and Quentin Fiore, *The Medium Is the Massage* (New York, 1967).

26. Harvey S. Perloff, "Modernizing Urban Development," this volume.

27. The coordinated development of rapid transit and the new towns of Vällingby, Fårsta, and Årsta by the city of Stockholm, operating on municipal land reserves, is the outstanding example of such policy. In a more enterprising framework, the Finnish new town of Tapiola was buoyed to eventual success by the fortunate purchase of a tract of land soon linked to the central city by new bridge and highway developments.

28. Edward L. Ullman, "The Role of Transportation and the Bases of Interaction," in William L. Thomas, Jr. (ed.), *Man's Role in Changing the Face of the Earth* (Chicago, 1956), pp. 862-80.

29. Wilfred Owen, *The Metropolitan Transportation Problem,* rev. ed. (Washington, 1966).

30. *Tomorrow's Transportation: New Systems for the Urban Future,* Department of Housing and Urban Development (U.S. Government Printing Office, Washington, 1968), p. 779.

31. In the *Reader's Digest* (May, 1968); also *The New York Times,* editorial page, April 29, 1968.

32. A more elaborate but less specific plan of this sort has been proposed by Joseph P. Lyford, *The Airtight Cage* (Santa Barbara, 1966). Bernard Weissbourd and Herbert Channick, in a further study for the Fund for the Republic's Center for the Study of Democratic Institutions (1968), have

217

proposed a massive new-town building program as the first step toward relieving growth pressures in central cities, and concentrating in them virtually all new public housing and related public facilities. Legal questions implicit in Oakland East are explored by Kent Matthewson in "Skip Annexation," *Nation's Cities* (October, 1967).

33. See Wolf Von Eckardt, "The Case for Building 350 New Towns," *Harper's Magazine* (December, 1965), pp. 85-94.

34. *Report of the National Advisory Commission on Civil Disorders* (Washington, 1968), p. 263.

35. John F. Kain and Joseph J. Persky, "Alternative Strategies for Metropolitan Ghettos," excerpts from Statements Before the National Advisory Commission on Civil Disorders, November 2, 1967 (mimeo).

36. John A. Baker, Assistant Secretary, U.S. Department of Agriculture, before the National Commission on Civil Disorders, November 2, 1967 (mimeo). A somewhat different view is conveyed in *The People Left Behind*, Report of the President's Commission on Rural Poverty. These earlier and rather impressionistic views have been followed by the deeper and more searching inquiry of the Advisory Commission on Intergovernmental Relations, *Urban and Rural America: Policies for Future Growth* (Washington, 1968). This report is about as close to the needed statement of national urban policy as we have been given, and it appears to have encouraged those in the Nixon administration who believe a national settlement and urbanization policy is fundamental both to the problems of cities and of the environment. It is the first serious questioning of those too-easily accepted trends towards metropolitan concentration, and the beginnings in the United States of a debate that is far advanced in such other countries as Israel, the Netherlands, Sweden, Great Britain and in the United Nations. See also, Hans Blumenfeld, "Trend to the Metropolis," *Urban Research Bulletin* (Canadian Council on Urban and Regional Research, Vol. 1, No. 4, Ottawa, 1969).

37. Paul D. Spreiregen (ed.), *The Modern Metropolis, Selected Essays by Hans Blumenfeld* (Cambridge, 1967), p. 60. The context is an essay, pp. 38-60, examining a 1948 proposal of the New York Regional Plan Association to direct metropolitan growth into a network of forty "self-contained towns."

38. Daniel R. Mandelker, "A Legal Strategy for Urban Development," in Sam Bass Warner (ed.), *Planning for a Nation of Cities* (Cambridge, 1966), pp. 217 ff.

39. United Nations, Department of Economic and Social Affairs, *Planning of Metropolitan Areas and New Towns* (United Nations, New York, 1967), especially pp. 149-252. Also *Urbanization: Development Policies and Planning, International Social Development Review*, No. 1 (United Nations, New York, 1968).

40. Arthur E. Bestor, *Backwards Utopia* (Philadelphia, 1950), p. 59.

ATHELSTAN SPILHAUS

The Experimental City

THE EXPERIMENTAL City suggested some years ago is now being planned. Started from scratch, the-Experimental City will be unlike other cities or towns that have been built in this way. It will not be a bedroom satellite of an existing city, as some of the New Towns in England have become; nor will it attempt to be an instant utopia. It will be neither a single company town—Hershey, Pennsylvania—nor a single occupation town—Oak Ridge, Manned Space Center, Los Alamos, Chandrigar, Brazilia, Washington, D. C. The Experimental City should not be confused with "demonstration" or "model" cities that attempt to show what can be done temporarily to renew old cities. Yet it will experiment with extensions of many of the assets and experiences of these. It will attempt to be a city representing a true cross section of people, income, business and industry, recreation, education, health care, and cultural opportunities that are representative of the United States.

The Experimental City will be carefully planned for the specific purpose of people's living and working, but, like a machine, it will be planned for an optimum population size. When it reaches this capacity, its growth will be stopped, just as machines are not overloaded when they reach their capacity. Even bacterial cultures stop growing when their size is such that they can no longer get rid of their waste metabolites. Man has not only the products of his own metabolism but what James Lodge calls the metabolites of his labor-saving slaves. Buckminster Fuller estimates that each of us has the equivalent of four hundred slaves. As technology proceeds, more and more of these mechanical slaves are used. In turn, waste metabolites increase, and cities should decrease proportionally in size.

For the experiment to be real, the city must be large enough to offer a variety of job opportunities and recreational, educational, and cultural choices. Fortunately, as technology moves forward, it affords a variety of choices without needing great numbers of people. For example, television can bring to a small community a variety in education, recreation, and information that in the past would have been possible only in large urban areas.

Three million people—the annual population increase in the United States—is equivalent to a dozen cities of 250,000 people. No engineer nor industry would build a dozen of anything so costly and complicated as a city without having an experimental prototype. The three million new citizens must be housed anyway, and the experience of many industries tells us that it is often cheaper to build a new modern plant than to patch an old one. To allow our presently overgrown cities, burdened as they are with complex problems, to take care of an unplanned bulge is costly.

Cities grow unplanned; they just spread haphazardly. By planning now, the advantages of high-density living can be preserved without the ugliness, filth, congestion, and noise that presently accompany city living. The urban mess is due to unplanned growth —too many students for the schools, too much sludge for the sewers, too many cars for the highways, too many sick for the hospitals, too much crime for the police, too many commuters for the transport system, too many fumes for the atmosphere to bear, too many chemicals for the water to carry.

The immediate threat must be met as we would meet the threat of war—by the mobilization of people, industry, and government. The potential gains are so great that we should take correspondingly calculated experimental risks. Curiously, we only take great risks and tolerate great mistakes in war. Up to now, government's efforts have been ineffective, concentrating on measuring what is happening, then viewing with alarm, and making industry the scapegoat in what are often essentially punitive measures. Instead, government should provide incentives to industry to encourage control of waste at its source.

Imaginative things are being done to control waste at its source. Fly ash from smokestacks is collected for use in making cement and bricks, but, so far only one sixteenth of the total has a market; a plant in Florida uses a city's garbage to make fertilizer; dust from grain elevators is made into pellets for cattle feed; iron-ore dust from steel plants is fed back to make steel; sulfur dioxide from factory chimneys and sulfur from oil refineries is made into sulfuric acid. There are examples of industrial symbiosis where one industry feeds off, or at least neutralizes, the wastes of another—inorganic wastes from a chemical plant may neutralize the over-abundance of organic nutrients from sewage and prevent uncontrollable growth of algae.

In many of these cases, the cost of recovery far exceeds the value of the recovered material. But if a clean environment is our aim, it costs the nation less to recover wastes where they are generated, even if they have no value, than to clean them up after they have been dispersed. Costs resultant from control at the source must be passed on in the cost of the product, but the total increase in manufacturing costs would not compare to the amount the nation would have to spend for cleaning up after the filth is dispersed in rivers, in the air, or on the land.

But what about the manufactured goods themselves once they are in the consumer's hands? We call him a consumer, but he consumes nothing. Eventually he must discard the same mass of material that he uses. Just as the iron-ore dust is recycled into the steel mill, manufactured hardware articles must be recycled after use. This process would close the loop from manufacture, to user, back to the factory. Total recycling is the ultimate goal, for it would eliminate waste and pollution. The automobile, for example, should be designed at the start with its eventual reclamation in mind. The automobile industry serves the public magnificently by mass-producing, mass-marketing, and mass-distributing a highly complex and useful machine. The industry could equally well apply its imagination and use its farflung network of operations to collect, disassemble, and reuse used cars.

In recycling, the *consumer* becomes a *user* which he has, in fact, always been. He essentially "rents" everything. If the automobile were designed with reclamation in mind, the widespread distribution network could double as the collection network. The same applies to refrigerators, washing machines, vacuum cleaners, and every piece of hardware that we use and throw away via the euphemistic "trade-in" process. Complete recycling makes "trade-in" real and meaningful.

In the water-pollution problem, recycling—the multiple use of water of different qualities—is the ultimate goal. We never use up any water; it just carries nutrients and flushes wastes and heat from our systems. One simple example is a totally enclosed greenhouse in the desert. Water with dissolved plant foods flows into hydroponic gardens, is transpired by the plants in the hot part of the greenhouse, sucked to a cooled part where it recondenses and acquires more dissolved nutrients to repeat the cycle. The only water needed is a cupful now and then to offset leakage.

The emotional prophets of doom and the sanitary engineers provide us with a dismal picture of how fast we must run using conventional methods merely to prevent the situation from getting worse. We commend Los Angeles for taking a legislative step toward controlling the automobile emissions that cause smog, but if they achieve this control of the unburned hydrocarbons, they will blissfully go on, the automobiles will increase, and by 1980 the oxides of nitrogen, an inevitable result of burning air with anything, may reach dangerous proportions.

We need total recycling, control at the source, symbiosis of industry, and experiments with entirely new technologies toward this end. Often new technologies cannot be tried in the older cities because they are incompatible with existing systems and obsolete legal, labor, and taxation codes. The new subway in New York is not new; it is merely an extension of the old.

Some economists maintain that total recycling is too expensive, but neither they nor anyone else knows the staggering cost of present waste mismanagement. Other economists, with commendable confidence in the abilities of scientists and engineers, say "why worry to recycle"—we can invent substitutes for anything we may run out of. But recycling conserves not only what we ordinarily think of as natural resources, but also the one God-given resource that we cannot reinvent once we destroy it—our natural environment.

To preserve the total quality of the natural environment, we must think of pollution in a broad sense. Pollution would then embrace all the ills of a city. Using *disease* as an antonym of *ease*, Dr. R. K. Cannan has spoken of a different kind of disease from environmental pollution. In this context, "dis-ease" embraces the psychological insult to aesthetic sensitivity that even a perfectly sanitized junk yard presents. Filthy environments may make us mentally ill before they make us physically sick.

A pollutant often neglected is noise. Environmental noise in cities is rapidly reaching levels that industry has long considered harmful to the ears. Even lower levels of the continuously irritating noises of a concentrated civilization may make serious contributions to mental sickness. Noise is a product of the cities: Jet airplanes land near cities, trucks bring goods into cities, machines are concentrated in cities, and noisy pavement breakers are always digging up city streets. Cutting down noise costs money too; silencing a jet engine reduces its power, and a quiet machine is usually overpowered.

People concentrate in cities to escape the rigors of climate and to maximize social, business, and cultural contacts with others with a minimum of travel. But when cities grow too large, the urban climate deteriorates to such an extent that people flee. Like the nomadic peoples of primitive times who moved with the seasons, they travel far to live in the uneasy compromise of suburbia. In the summer, the power stations of the cities exude waste heat, the buildings prevent breezes from carrying off fumes and heat, and air conditioning pumps heat from the buildings to the streets to aggravate the situation further.

We need a mathematical computer model study of where waste should be taken, where it could do the most good in the insulating belt around the city. We should plan our cities on the basis of maps of pollution proneness. The industrialization of Appalachia with dirty industry is ridiculous. Those mountains were called the Smokies by the first men who saw them because they were so prone to pollution due to stagnant anticyclones that even the natural turpentines hung in a haze.

Pollution comes from concentration: Half our national population crowds onto 1 per cent of the land. People flock to the cities because they like high-density living. Fortunately, high-density living can give better and cheaper public service. It is a well-known axiom that the bigger the lots, the lower the caliber of public service. High-density living *per se* has not caused the filth in the cities; the assemblages have simply grown too large. If the one hundred million people that represent half the population of the U. S. today lived in the same high density as they do now, but were dispersed in eight hundred smaller concentrations of one-quarter million apiece, there would probably be no serious pollution problem. We need urban *dispersal,* not urban renewal.

Politicians are now stressing the need for industry and the private sector to take part in the rebuilding of slums in old, overgrown cities. Why should they? What bank would make a long-term loan to rebuild a slum in a city so overgrown that it would be a slum again before the mortgage was paid off? Moreover, what good would it do for people in the long run? Part of the problem is that our elected officials, particularly since reapportionment, represent districts. Politicians are most numerous where the population is most dense. There is little incentive for an elected official to suggest dispersal of his own thickly populated and easily covered district. Consequently, we hear little of urban dispersal, but a good deal about renewal, which usually means going faster the wrong way and bringing more people into already overcrowded precincts.

Such considerations led me to urge the Experimental City project. This will provide a laboratory for experimentation and a prototype for future dispersed systems with separated cities of high concentration and controlled size. As yet, no one has studied what the best size for a city is, nor attempted to keep a city to a certain size. Chambers of Commerce uniformly believe that bigger is better. We must get away from this conventional thinking and realize that bigger than an undetermined optimum size is not better.

A city of one hundred thousand may be too small for the diversity of cultural, recreational, educational, health-care, and work opportunities that make for a virile self-contained community. Eight or ten million has, however, been amply proved to be too big. Somewhere in between lies an optimum number.

Once we have decided on a city's optimum size, how do we prevent the uncontrolled growth that leads to many of today's urban problems? The answer is *not* to control individuals, but to design a mix of industrial, commercial, and other employment opportunities that keeps the population in a healthy equilibrium. In the absence of better information on the proportion in a healthy mix, perhaps we should start with a cross section of the United States. But what about regional differences? A healthy mix in the Northwest might be quite different from the comfortable mix in the Southeast. Social scientists have a challenge to define these mixes. The whole concept behind the Experimental City begins and ends with people. Profiles of employees in various enterprises can be studied by wage level, group preferences, and any other factors important to a healthy representative sample, including the right quota of those dependent on welfare, the very young, and the old and retired. Here again, regional differences of employee preferences must be considered in relation to the industrial mix.

A city grows because business and industry concentrate there, providing people with diverse opportunities for work and a variety of life styles. If an Experimental City is to be built to preserve a better quality of urban environment, industry and business must build it, but in a planned way.

Although the Experimental City would be planned as much as possible, it would be designed and built so that it could change easily. In a way, the city would be designed backwards, starting with innovations in the newest engineering systems conceived for a certain number of people and no more. It would be designed to remove the burdens of chores and filth, which modern technology can do. It goes without saying that one designs for man and his society and, in general, the planning of transportation, communication, feeding, and other networks comes later. In this case, one would use technological innovation to reduce physical restraints, which would hopefully allow man and his society more freedom to thrive. The crux is to remove the pollutants of chores, filth, noise, and congestion from the city in the hope that this will free the city dweller for a greater choice and diversity of individual human activities.

People congregate in the city because it is a gathering place for work and social interaction. Thus, working and living must be compatible, but often the factories for work make the environment for living unpleasant or unbearable. Clearly the most dramatic role of industry in the Experimental City is to show that places of work need not pollute the environment with congestion, fumes, dirty water, and noise. If living and working conditions are compatible, then people will not have to travel so much. Because of pollutants, cities are divided into separate residential and industrial areas. With the pollutants removed, industrial, commercial, residential, and educational institutions could exist side by side, reducing the human waste of commuting to and fro. If the technology of the Experimental City succeeds, there will be no need for zoning. In the interim, we should recognize four-dimensional zoning which adds a time dimension to space zoning. An example of this is the control of noise at airports, where planes are prevented from taking off during the night.

Improved communications also reduce the need for travel. As a start, an information utility could be devised that would link by broad-band coaxial cables all points now connected by telephone wires. The information utility, possibly with two-way, point-to-point video and other broad-band communication, would remove much of the obvious waste in the present conduct of business and commerce, banking and shopping. (Housewives would have bedside shopping and banking, and tele-baby-sitting when they went to visit a neighbor.) City-wide improved communications with access to the central hospital open up the possibility of less costly, less intense services and better, more abundant home care. These, of course, are not radical ideas—but extensions. (Pediatricians today ask mothers to have their children breathe into the telephone receiver.) Los Angeles is already planning emergency helicopter-lifted hospital units that go to the scene of an accident, drop the hospital pod, and then lift the wreckage out of the way so that traffic can resume.

As a total experiment in social science, human ecology, environmental biology, and environmental engineering, the Experimental City would lend itself to a totally new concept of modern preventive medicine. Instead of healing the sick, doctors would contribute to the public-health concept that emphasizes the building up and banking of a capital of health and vigor while young, and the prudent spending of this capital over a lifetime without deficits of ill health. They would concentrate on eliminating ailments in early life rather than on repairing later ills. Their dedication, somewhat less personal in public health, would be, in a sense, what Dr. Walsh McDermott calls "statistical compassion."

Moreover, broad-band interconnections with other cities would provide smaller areas with wider access to national medical centers. Also, the educational, scientific, artistic, and entertainment opportunities would be far greater than a city of limited size would be able to offer otherwise. Point-to-point video, providing improved surveillance, should enable police to spend less time catching criminals after the event and more time preventing crimes.

Due to the present furor over the use of bugging and wire tapping, the information utility immediately invokes the specter of Big Brother and a Brave New World. In their best use, such devices can preserve and improve the quality of the urban environment, but like any other device they can also be misused by unscrupulous people. If the masses of information filed in our necessary public bureaus—the Internal Revenue Service, the National Institutes of Health, the Census Bureau, and the F.B.I.—were combined by an unscrupulous dictator, they would provide a potent coercive weapon against any individual. We cannot *not* use such devices, although we must set up adequate safeguards against their misuse. On the other hand, the information utility provides survey mechanisms for an instantaneous city census and flexible city management exactly analogous to methods of data collection used in weather forecasting.

The information utility and the mixing of living and working areas would reduce transportation needs, but it would still be necessary to experiment with new forms of mass transportation. People like automobiles because the automobile respects their desire to go directly from where they are to where they want to be without stopping where others want to stop. But the automobile produces polluting fumes and occupies parking space when the owner is not in it—which is about 90 per cent of the time.

Many suggestions have been made for a mass transportation system that retains the automobile's advantages without incorporating its disadvantages. One such scheme calls for pneumatically or electrically driven small pods with propulsion in the track. The pods may be computer-controlled to the common destination of a few people. After indicating your destination to the computer on entering the turnstile, you would wait X minutes or until, let us say, the six-person pod fills up—whichever is shorter—and then go nonstop to your destination. The pods would be small enough to pass noiselessly through buildings with normal ceiling heights. There are no motors in the pods, and because they are inexpensive small shells, we could afford many of them.

In order for there to be no air-burning machines within the city limits, connections to intercity and existing national transportation systems might be made at the city's periphery. Alternatively, air-burning machines might come into the city in underground tunnels with fume sewers. These would also provide connections to the Experimental City's airport, located at a distance and in a direction so that landing patterns are over not the city, but the noninhabited insulating belt.

The main public utilities could be accessible in the vehicular and other underground tunnels, thereby abating the noisy digging up and remaking of streets common to all American cities. The interconnecting utility tunnels would double or multiplex as traffic tunnels and utility trenches for the transport of heavy freight, for telephone lines, for power and gas lines, water and sewer mains, and for the rapid transit of emergency vehicles—police, fire, and medical rescue. All would be below the city for increased mobility and less noise.

The sewers, with a view to conserving water, might be pneumatic as in the English and French systems. To save the immense areas occupied by present sewage-treatment plants, we might treat the sewage in transit in the sewer. All this presupposes that we can throw away the old-fashioned codes stipulating that telephone and power lines, and water mains and sewers be separate. Modern technology permits messages to be sent over power lines, and pure water pipes to be concentric with sewer mains. Just as garages can be housed under parks, all services can be underground, even to the extent of going hundreds of feet down for heavy manufacturing, storage of storm water, and snow and waste heat.

The Experimental City could also provide opportunities for test-marketing new products, building materials, and postal systems. New materials would give architects a tremendous scope in developing new forms. No traffic at ground level and no land owned by individuals or individual corporations would offer a degree of freedom not possible in cities where ownership of property delimits plots. Even the materials used in the buildings themselves would be such that they could be taken down and reused if found to be obsolete or inferior. Architecture, with its emphasis on form and the visual environment, is fundamental to the success of the Experimental City. Architects would be freer to exploit the mutuality of function and form in producing a visual environment *with* other improved qualities. In Philadelphia, for example, the planners have done a magnificent job improving the visual environment, but their work is mitigated by the stench of oil refineries.

In the Experimental City, we will seek a total optimum environment without hampering diversity of architectural forms and combinations. We will experiment with enclosing portions of the city within domes that will be conditioned as to temperature, humidity, fumes, and light. It is, of course, not at all certain that people want a perfectly controlled climate. The sense of beauty and well-being involves exposure to some degree of variation. Artists know this in their play with light and shade and with colors that clash. Slight breezes and variations of temperature might be necessary to transform even clean air into the fresh air that stimulates our sense of health.

The advantages of leasing and not owning land, combined with those of the new technologies, would free architects from rectilinear or stereotype ground plans that ownership of plots dictates. Space might be leased in a three-dimensional sense, and the forms the architects use in three dimensions might be emphasized by paths and foot thoroughfares, there being no wheeled traffic at ground level. Today, streets and plot plans too often predefine form. In the Experimental City, the architect will face the challenge of providing new ways for people to find face-to-face relationships in an environment that does not *require* wasteful movement.

Ralph Burgard has suggested that creative artists today are not so much concerned with the fixed audience-performer relationship. Many artists feel that art centers, now so much in fashion, are already outmoded, and that the newest forms of music, art, theater, and dance have very little to do with exhibit galleries, proscenium stages, and conventional auditoriums. Increased leisure should lead to active participation in all the arts instead of passive exposure. For this is needed an arts-recreation space completely flexible in lighting, sound, television, film, and electronic devices and in physical dimensions.

Where does one locate an Experimental City? It should be far enough away from urban areas so that it can develop self-sufficiency and not be hampered by the restrictive practices of a dominant neighboring community. Extremes of climate, far from being a disadvantage, would provide the kind of all-weather test facility needed for experimenting with technological innovations. There must be enough land for an insulating belt around the city; otherwise, conventional uncontrolled encroachments and developments would soon nullify the experiment. A density of one hundred people per acre in the city proper would mean a city area of 2,500 acres. To preserve its identity, character, cleanliness, and experimental freedom, it might need a hundred times this area as an insulating belt.

Federal and state governments are presently acquiring large tracts of unspoiled forests and lands for conservation. This is a worthy objective if done for some purpose. What better purpose is there than providing open space around cities? Such lands would be most suitable for the insulating belts between controlled-size, dispersed cities. The insulating belt would include forests, lakes, farms, outdoor museums, arboretums, and zoos. Such a mixture would make the enjoyment of the open surroundings not only attractive aesthetically and physically, but intellectually profitable. Part of the insulating belt might be devoted to hobby farms and gardens—the system so enjoyed by the Germans, who leave the city and camp in little gardens. This minimum rustic setting enables them to retain the smell and touch of the soil. There might also be high-intensity food farming and high-rise finishing farms. Fresh foods might be brought to farms in the insulating belt from starting farms farther out, and dairy cows could be fed in high-rise sterile buildings at the edge of the city to ensure the freshest, purest milk.

The legal codes and governmental structures of a city built with private funds on ground leased by a nonprofit corporation will be different from those of existing cities. Revenues to manage the city will come from leases rather than real-estate taxes. The laws and controls in the Experimental City will center on the new recognition of an individual's right to a clean environment. Though regulations will be different, there may be fewer of them because many of our laws evolved to protect us from the evil and nuisances precipitated by urban overgrowth. As the stresses of dirt, noise, and congestion are removed, other origins of antisocial behavior may be clarified.

Do people want dirt, noise, and congestion removed? Most of us assume so. But, like everything else in the Experimental City, we will have to see. The ideas and directions that have been suggested here are merely possible pieces of the total experiment, any one of which is likely to change and develop as the experiment itself develops.

About $330,000 have been allocated for defining the Experimental City project—three fourths from three departments of the Federal Government (Department of Commerce; Department of Health, Education, and Welfare; Department of Housing and Urban Development) and one fourth from local industries. This is to be used for surveys of literature and experience, conferences and workshops, and development of a structure for the program's next five phases. Laboratory evaluations of new concepts and systems will then be made and experimentation done with small-scale models. After a pilot model has been constructed so that a choice can be made among the various alternatives, the city will be designed, constructed, and occupied. Finally, the actual Experimental City will be studied further, changed, and developed.

The first year's work will be carried out with the University of Minnesota serving as the host and organizer of group discussions on a series of special topics. To these conferences we will invite interested national experts from many disciplines. A distinguished group of individuals has agreed to serve as a national steering committee for the Experimental City. After the year of definition, a suitable nonprofit corporation will be formed to carry through the later phases. Then a quasi-governmental, quasi-private corporation, following the experience of the Communications Satellite Corporation, will be formed to complete the building of the Experimental City and to oversee its subsequent operation.

Clearly, we cannot continue to experiment in bits: Each new technology affects others; better communications change patterns of travel, medical care, and education; methods of cleaning and noise-proofing make zoning unnecessary. The city is a completely interacting system, and, thus, the experiment must be a total system. Nobody knows the answers to city living in the future, and when answers are unknown, experiment is essential.

PLAYGROUNDS FOR PEOPLE

ALEXIS PAPAGEORGIOU

Architectural Schemata for Outdoor Recreation Areas of Tomorrow

I

THE INCREASING pressures from urbanites fleeing to the countryside are multiplying in both extent and complexity the demand for new parks. Open areas will be transformed by needs for transportation, parking, and outdoor sports and games. In the coming decade, thousands of buildings will be erected in parks and forests, at seashore and historic sites. The visual problems encountered can only increase, for the new structures will have to fulfill a wide variety of functions encompassing a long list of building types—picnic shelters, stables, bathhouses, comfort stations, camping accommodations, vacation cabins, lodges, food concessions, commissary and administrative buildings, maintenance and utility buildings. One can even add a few more: marinas, sportsman's buildings, game buildings, clubhouses, information centers, outdoor theaters, and museums of natural history. These structures will be as small as a one-foot pole carrying an electric outlet and as large as an airport. None will fulfill its function if it upsets the visual atmosphere of the park for which it was erected.

Ten years ago, Conrad L. Wirth, former director of the National Park Service, estimated that eighty million people would visit American parks in 1966. To anticipate the needs of this estimate, he quadrupled the 1945-55 yearly park expenditures of $25,000,000 for the 1956-66 period. Demand nevertheless surpassed estimates. New York's Adirondack State Park alone received two million visitors last year. Many parks have already developed temporary villages for campers. One of these, the Grand's Village in Yellowstone, reported 140,000 camper days in 1965.

The massive exodus from cities relates directly to increases in leisure time, income, and mobility. In 1900, an American worker had two months "off" each year, but by 1960 he had accumulated four months' vacation. According to one estimate, by the year 2000 he will have six months "off"—with a probable three-day weekend and a month's vacation. Moreover, leisure-time activity today differs not only in quantity, but also in character from that of the past. In view of these developments, it is doubtful that the future needs and expectations of travelers, tourists, and vacationists can be met by a mere quantitative increase of familiar types of park construction. On the contrary, the difference in life style will most probably create a new ecological situation in the natural landscape.

During certain other periods in history, broad masses of people had at their disposal an excessive amount of leisure time. The working days of the Romans barely covered half of the calendar year. In the reign of Claudius, ninety-three of the 159 days marked as holidays were devoted to games at the public's expense. In the middle of the fourth century, there were 175 days of games among the two hundred public holidays. No doubt this allocation of time and public money had a powerful effect on the articulation of the public spaces of Rome—baths, circuses, forums, and stoae. Today, the disposition of time and money parallels that of Rome, although the average individual's present potential for mobility finds no parallel in history. Such a combination will most certainly bring about an unprecedented ecological change in the countryside.

It is questionable if planning for recreation acknowledges the importance of this new ecological situation. The National Recreation Survey states its objectives in a rather general question: "What are the recreation wants and needs of American people now and what will [they] be in the years 1976 and 2000?" The people interviewed related their statements to specific questions on athletic activities and were unable to orient their needs and wants to a future situation. The result was a program for increasing quantitatively the present types of athletic recreation facilities.

Certain elements of the new ecological situation demand not a quantitative increase in park facilities but a reframing of questionnaires and of future policies. The population of future recreation areas will be anonymous, heterogeneous, and transient, consisting mainly of young people. A gross approximation raises the proportion of children to 30 per cent and of teen-agers to another 30 per cent, while that of adults remains as low as 40 per cent. These young people will have an excessive amount of leisure time at their disposal. How can they properly exploit this time if they are not organized to do so? Planning propositions are based extensively on demands for athletic activities; other possible activities —summer education, informal exchange of ideas, organized lectures, artistic exhibitions, training in audiovisual means of communication, and community activities—have not yet been evaluated. Facilities for educational opportunities are not included in present programs.

Lewis Mumford draws a rather pessimistic parallel between Roman and American civilization in *The City in History*. If Mumford's conception is realized, it will find its first manifestation in those places where leisure time is spent—in the outdoor recreation areas of tomorrow.

II

What will be the image of an architectural structure—a shelter, for instance—built in a park sometime in the coming decade? Is such an image completely inconceivable? Or can it be approximated in schematic form as an expected average, since scores of these structures will go up in parks in the immediate future. To try to approximate in advance an original architectural solution is an aim contradictory in terms. But how many park buildings of the past decade can claim originality? How many were merely copies from graphic standards of "standard" publications like *Park Practice and Design*?

It is a gloomy task to approach the future with an average, particularly an architectural average and particularly for a park. Such an approach has the danger of imposing on the future the mediocrity of the past. It may propagate clichés rather than restrain them, and must be used with care. In this paper, it is employed only as a means to a limited goal: to test the visual effects of forecasted trends in parks and recreation areas and to examine the means of and processes for the creation of necessary preconditions that will promote more creative solutions.

The architectural form of recreation areas will be conditioned, of course, by developments of "free time" pursuits and habits in the United States. This factor is as important architecturally as it is pedagogically, but its architectural significance is apparent only in the quantitative and organizational aspects of design. Quality is more directly conditioned by established planning controls and design processes. Through them, recreational needs are converted to concrete architectural forms. Unfortunately, visual criteria are only loosely used in these processes.

It is a common practice in architecture to present a future image abstractly as an architectural scheme. By its very abstraction, the scheme can avoid elements of the image that are irrelevant to its objectives. Rarely does a blueprint of an architectural scheme make reference to the form of existing backgrounds. This is, of course, an unfortunate practice. If things were otherwise, the many conflicts of form in the city might have been avoided.

The role of architecture in the natural setting is even more serious, for the architectural theme is not the main element of the future image of these areas. One does not go to a park to see architecture. Not only must common practices of schematic representations be reviewed, but visual criteria—for example, "figure-background relationship"—must be clearly defined so that they can motivate better park design. At present, planning reports avoid stating observations based on generalized uses of visual criteria. In order to be instrumental for planning purposes, visual criteria must be conveyed in a generalized form; they can be drawn from studies of architectural volumes and spaces in the landscape, aerial and land photographs, graphic representations of present and future situations, and studies of light and shadow, texture and color (See illustrations.).

The numerous publications of the Outdoor Recreation Resources Review Commission and the Regional Plans for Outdoor Recreation in the various states make no reference to such visual criteria, although the policies they introduce bear direct visual reference to the landscape. These policies are supported by large samplings of socio-economic conditions, land-use and recreation demands, but lacking visual evaluation, they offer no secure protection to the image of the landscape.

Public-service institutions like the National Park Service, the Department of Natural Resources, and the Bureau of Outdoor Recreation have a direct need for a systematic inquiry into visual problems. Demands for new recreation developments are pressing, and state engineers are little equipped to cope with their visual implications. These pressures could be greatly released by establishing a service that would specialize in visual matters. This service would compile data from collective experience in, for example, form-background relationship, visual structure, concentration and dispersion of facilities, visual effects of population densities, and human scale.

Without giving any direction to specific architectural problems, such a service would be able to apply both professional judgment and factual knowledge to the visual problems of parks.

Although there is little insight into the generalized use of visual criteria, the effects and limitations of such criteria are commonly known from their applications in specific architectural projects. The design of any single construction is the result of a sequence of visual decisions that create alternative schemes. This process does not imply that the final form is subject to visual criteria alone. Four other categories of criteria enter into the picture: function, structure, construction, and economy; their effects give substance to the architectural solution. These effects, however, are not sufficient in themselves to articulate a visually coherent and aesthetically communicable whole. The finished product is understood through the senses and the empathetic state of mind (*einfühlung*) that transforms sensory messages into a coherent image.

Nonvisual factors play only a casual role in the quality of this image. If quality is a real objective, nonvisual factors must reach their formal manifestation through proportion, scale, articulation of structure, and tectonics, which are essentially visual methods. Because nonvisual factors undergo this transformation, the architectural form can be articulated in the same spirit of *empathy* by which the finished product is visually understood.

A proposal for a bathhouse in Paradise Pond, Leominster, Massachusetts (See illustrations.), demonstrates this point. Covered corridors linking the three main units (bathing facilities for men and women, and an administration building) are arranged so that they afford separate circulation for the various activities and define an open yard in the middle of the complex and a service area on the side of the administration building. They are wide enough to provide space for outdoor shelter and are furnished with wood benches, which enable visitors to sit there and enjoy a view of the pond. The units are covered with shed roofs that slope toward the main yard. The roofs are shaped like hoods and have louvered openings at their high points from which hot and humid air can escape. The form of the roofs, the distribution of open corridors, and the articulation of the building's volume in three components are functional requirements that found expression in the architectural form.

Requirements of economy, structure, and construction are also manifest in the architectural composition. By using the same struc-

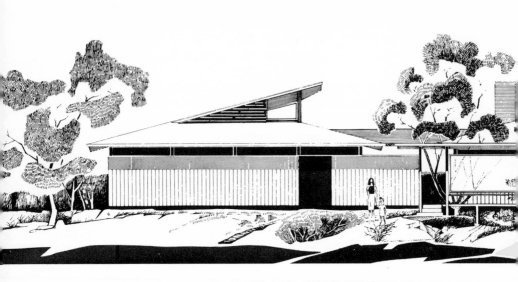

Proposal for a Bathhouse, Paradise Pond, Leominster, Massachusetts. Elevation. Designed by the author.

Natural form and architecture: House of Professor R. Demos in Athens. Architect: A. Papageorgiou.

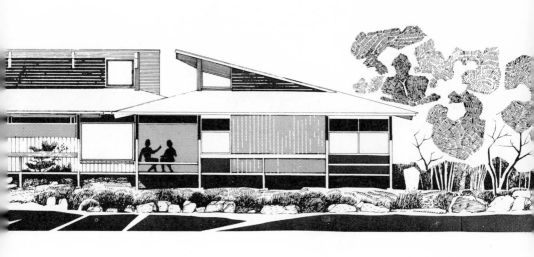

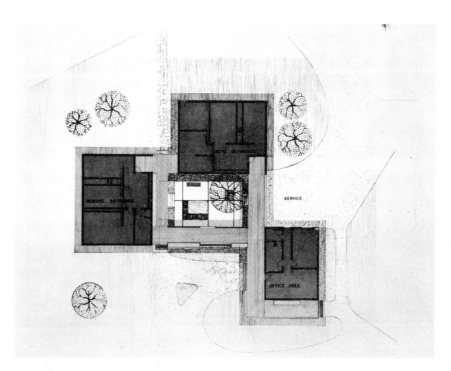

Bathhouse, Paradise Pond. Plan.

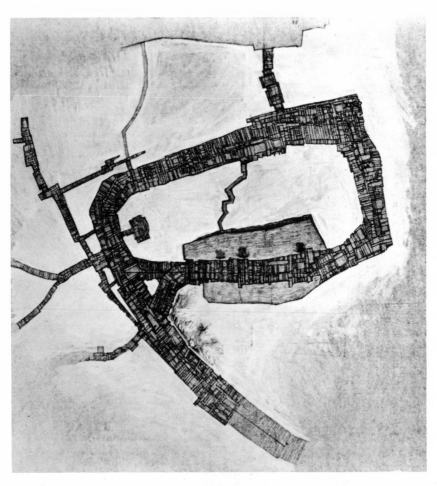

Shape: Plan of the modern road of access to the Propylaea of Athens. The shape of the road deviates from conventional parallelism of boundaries to follow the natural topography.
Architects: D. Pikionis and Alexis Papageorgiou.

Texture: To complement the roughly textured environment, the road is paved with stone, concrete, and strips of mar
Space: two olive trees form the entrance of a path. Structure: a road of the Hill of Muses.

Professor R. Demos' house. West elevation.

Professor R. Demos' house. Atrium.

tural unit for the three sections of the bathhouse, the cost is reduced. The placement of the three units varies the form of the
bathhouse; moreover, the units are perpendicular to one another
and are not perfect squares. This variety articulates the unity of the
bathhouse, which is reinforced by the structural repetition. The
shape of the shed roof enhances the feeling of "variety" for its as-
symmetrical form allows a differentiation of roof line that would not
have been possible with a hip, gable, or flat roof.

The construction is rather inexpensive, the structural members
being simple and readily available (cedar deck of 2-1/2 nominal
thickness, supported by post and beams on an 8 x 16 modular base,
and vertical redwood siding). Since wood material bears a certain
uniformity due to repetitive manufacturing processes, the wood is
treated texturally and the proportions of the wood panels as well
as their relative position in the over-all building are varied.

From a distance, the horizontal line of the building is broken
up by the silhouette of the trees in the central courtyard. Thus, the
visual theme of the building is blended with the image of the
environment that is created by the rhythmical repetition of the
shape of a tree. The big lines of the natural image—those separating
land, water, and sky—are left intact. By placing the building off
the road leading to the beach, the image of the landscape remains
open to the incomer.

The visual structure of the building differs, of course, from that
of the natural environment. It aims, however, to be humanly organic
and follows the unity and variety observed in the natural form.
Its focal point, the atrium, is a microcosm of the natural image
from which the building derives its shape.

It is difficult to transfer visual criteria from one architectural
theme to another, because architecture is a continuous experimentation with form. But the evolution of architectural forms in the
natural landscape is not a problem touching only the architectural
disciplines; it also involves the preservation of the natural image.
The architectural schemata of the future have yet to be formulated,
but the image of the landscape exists today and, however vast, can
be observed, described, and evaluated. This work has not begun,
and the projection of demands for park construction yields a rather
gloomy picture of the future.

III

The problem of maintaining the image of the landscape for the

sake of an increasing number of travelers and vacationists intensifies
the friction between planning for conservation and planning for
recreation. This friction was foreshadowed in the minds of the park
protagonists of the past. Freeman Tilden, author of *National Parks
and State Parks,* cites their controversy, which started with a meeting of preservationists in 1921 in Des Moines, Iowa, where the Park
Movement took shape. At that meeting, Stephen Mather, first director of the National Park Service, introduced a policy encouraging
the recreational use of parks.

I believe we should have comfortable camps all over the country, so
that the motorist could camp each night in a good scenic spot, preferably
a state park. . . . I hope some day the motorist will be able to round up
his family each night on some kind of public land.

Colonel Richard Lieber of Indiana attacked Mather's liberal views:

Our parks and preserves are not merely picnicking places. They are
rich storehouses of memories and reveries. . . . A state park cannot be
planned until it is found. . . . Speaking for myself I would not be at all
interested if the function of parks and recreation would merely be to
provide shallow amusement for bored and boring people.

Today, the conflicting goals of preservation and recreation continue to be the subject of rigorous discussion, but methods of planning and statistical research have brought the mood of the traditional discussion to an end. The new arguments are more technical
and the new ends more specific. The Outdoor Recreation Resources
Review Commission, established by Congress in 1958 to investigate
trends in recreation, has formulated a classification system for open
land, based on data it collected on the country's outdoor recreation activities.

The classification is as follows:

1. *High Density Recreation Areas.* Located close to big cities,
these areas assume intensive use and high investment exclusively
for recreation purposes. Two typical examples are the Patapsco
State Park in Maryland and the Palisades Park in New York and
New Jersey.[1]

2. *General Outdoor Recreation Areas.* More extensive and rather
remote from big population centers, these areas lack distinguished
natural features or historical importance. They remain anonymous
to the public but are suitable for camping, picnicking, fishing,
water sports, trailer parks, and winter sports. Many areas of this

category—for example, Massasoit State Park in Massachusetts—are now in the development stage, and they are expected to receive extensive use in the immediate future.[2]

3. *Natural Environment Areas.* A transition category between "General Outdoor" and "Primitive" areas, this is a larger class of preservation areas that commonly supports grazing, lumbering, and mining. It includes such areas as Allagash County in Maine, Grand Teton National Park in Wyoming, and Superior National Forest in Minnesota.

4. *Unique Natural Areas.* These comprise large portions of famous parks like Yosemite Valley, Grand Canyon, Yellowstone, and parts of Cape Cod.[3]

5. *Primitive Areas.* Comprising a total area of fifty million acres, including parts of Grand Canyon and Alaska, the Jewel Basin in Montana, and the Lake Mead region in Arizona, this is primarily a class of conservancies and wildlife refuges. These areas, administered by the Forest Service, the National Park Service, and the Bureau of Sports Fisheries and Wildlife, are now being surveyed and classified by various federal agencies. The classification is expected to be completed by 1974.[4]

6. *Historic and Culture Sites.* Several historic and cultural sites are found in parks—the Pueblo Indian dwellings, for example, in Mesa Verde, Colorado; others, like Old Sturbridge Village and Concord Battlefield in Massachusetts, are found on the outskirts of cities. Most, however, are found within the cities, where they are directly affected by urban growth and must be protected.[5]

Many areas of Classes 5 and 6 are overused, while adjacent areas of Classes 2 and 3 are virtually not used. By developing further Classes 2 and 3, a national policy may release pressures on Classes 4 and 6, whose outstanding features require preservation. Many areas of Class 3 have potential for further recreation development, but unlike the areas of Class 2, they maintain their original natural structure, and recreational uses must be regulated by protective means of preservation. The emphasis on preservation increases within the classification of outdoor space, the maximum stress falling on "Primitive Areas" and "Historic and Cultural Sites" listed last.

As a comprehensive means of control, the system will have extensive visual effects both in maintaining existing facilities and in creating new ones. The location of new recreation areas will depend not only upon land uses and demands, but also upon the classes in which land is arranged. Thus, land will be allocated only for its proper use. The zoning of land implicit in the system will affect the formal character of many locations since it qualifies them for a predetermined use. On the other hand, the visual effects of the system are beyond control, since the system is conceived not to control changes in the visual structure, but to arrange purposeful use of land. Thus, while the system bears extensive visual effects, it offers no provisions for visual controls.

This deficiency plagues any system whose objectives are verbal and whose responsibilities extend to the visual sector. In essence, it leads to a more general question that is related to all courses of action for preservation and for growth: How can visual values be secured by verbal means alone? We have already observed that visual criteria are barely taken into consideration in planning for recreation. Visual values are equally underestimated in planning for conservation.

IV

By 1974, when the classification system is expected to be completed, it will be possible to sort into categories and subcategories all public land to be used in conservation and recreation. The assumption that a program for preservation should not be performed without its complementary program for growth is the inherent merit of this system of classification. As we have seen, there was a long history of friction between planning for preservation and planning for recreation before this complementarity was realized.

On the other hand, the conflict of values between the verbal and the visual does not have a parallel in the history of space preservation, even though the system covers areas of obvious significance to both. The assumption that the protection of the former will secure that of the latter is false. Such a policy has harmful effects in many cases of space preservation. To substantiate this statement, one should draw upon previous case studies in which this policy has brought unfavorable results. Unfortunately, this is not easy for all categories of preservation, because preservation of areas of natural beauty is a relatively new field. One can, however, explore for these purposes the history of the preservation of historic buildings, for the preservation of areas of natural beauty follows much the same pattern.

Programs for the preservation of historic buildings have their roots in Europe (in England, in particular) where experience in problems of preservation, development, and control was gained initially in the struggle to maintain historic buildings in the cities. In Europe, old structures that had ceased to perform their original function were thought to merit preservation by virtue of their historic, archaeological, and ethnological contents as well as their aesthetic value. Erwin Panofsky, emphasizing content rather than visual values, calls these ancient buildings "documents of history." The consideration of buildings as documents did not start until the middle of the eighteenth century when archaeology became established as a scholarly discipline. The nineteenth century, with its romantic spirit, reinforced the content of the old structures with new meanings, poetic in essence, that the buildings originally did not have. Near the turn of the century, William Morris established the Society for the Protection of Ancient Buildings—the oldest group of this sort in England. When the Ancient Monument Act passed in England in 1912, the same spirit prevailed: that a preserved building is primarily a document of historic import. Visual values were recognized, of course, but conservationists were reluctant to acknowledge that the visual image of buildings is concrete enough to substantiate additional means of control. While architectural proportion was a favored subject of aesthetics, programs of preservation underestimated the importance of the relationship of the preserved buildings to the structure of the environmental space. Recognized only symbolically, the buildings were treated like specimens kept in the abstract space of a cage. Thus, legislation and other means of control insured the survival of ancient buildings, but the buildings remained divorced from their environmental space.

This error came to be censured later. The structure of space around historic buildings changed considerably during the rapid growth of cities after World War II. The visual relationship of the buildings to their changing environment, unplanned as it was, turned out to be chaotic. John Summerson, English author and historian, drew particular attention to this point in his notes on preservation written in 1947.

Preservation must be selective, co-ordinated. And one of the things I would stress is that preservation in general is only valuable when it is co-ordinated and related to a play of positive development. The planned survival of old structures can enrich a town enormously. An unplanned snatching of isolated buildings from unplanned development will result in pathetic patchworks of obsolescence.

In place of the traditionally established priority of literary values over visual values, John Summerson proposed a new policy of preservation that assigned maximum priority to visual criteria. Describing his method, he noted:

Literary values (by which I mean those associated with history and sense of continuity) are never absent from an old building. Neither are aesthetic values. But aesthetic values, unlike literary values, are not enhanced with the passage of time. They can only be accurately assessed in relation to their time and through their time in relation to all time. They are susceptive to strict comparative analysis. More precious and concrete, therefore, I have placed them at the head of my list of valid grounds for preserving buildings.

Today, trends of urban growth and their effects on the structure of the urban space around ancient buildings receive more attention. The concepts of "the Historic Center" and "the Historic District" are already common in the literature of preservation, but the application of these methods is very limited. Apart from cases of "prestige rehabilitation" like Georgetown in Washington, D. C., and Rittenhouse or Filter Square in Philadelphia, the examples of the preservation of "Historic Districts" in the United States are limited to a number of experimental cases in Rhode Island. Most areas still suffer from the anachronistic divorce of preservation and development; co-ordination does not exist, and the solution to the visual problem of "changing and steady forms in space" remains obscure.

The history of preservation in cities offers insight into the visual problem of preservation that should not be underestimated when formulating new policies for the countryside. Systems of classification of outdoor space and outdoor recreation activities are useful tools for the co-ordination of preservation and growth. Both are regulatory means that cannot alone control the changing visual image of the parks. The zoning systems that they imply can moderate extremes of disorder, but in no case can a zoning system by itself secure a humane image of environmental space. Zoning systems carry their own visual weight and may cause undesirable visual effects if they are applied blindly.

Of all the considerations that come into play in the design of parks and recreation areas, the most weakly recognized are the visual. Yet the visual experience of a hiker who reaches a shelter at the crest of a hill is so direct that he could never understand such apathy. Only a small shelter and a background are involved. Technically, it is a simple task to build a shelter and preserve a background, but in the complexity of today's living it becomes a challenging problem. The processes of design and planning required for this purpose are meaningless to the hiker, but their visual results are open to his criticism. He will resent a building that blocks the view or appears out of scale or out of proportion.

These experiences, common to all, are visual. What is recommended here is a reinforcement of the use of visual criteria in all planning considerations and design processes. A new governmental office specializing in visual matters should be established which could utilize the artistic ingenuity of young architects, landscape architects, and sculptors and undertake the much needed research on visual criteria. Finally, the public should be encouraged to criticize new projects freely.

REFERENCES

1. Although recreation areas of this class are found mostly in the northeastern region of the country, which has few parks and forests, they are also scattered in the West, Midwest, and South. Their image varies, but in places like Atlantic City, Jones Beach, and Huntington Beach State Park, it often reaches extremes of urbanity. Although urbanites familiar with this kind of outdoor space often see it as an unsatisfactory symbol of mass recreation, the High-Density Recreation areas came out of necessity. Their actuality is a result not merely of high demand but of the hard labor of public officials, planners, and conservationists to save many of their natural features from commercial exploitation. Jones Beach and Palisades Park are among the most commonly acknowledged examples of dedicated work in development and preservation.

2. The State of Ohio has purchased twenty-five thousand acres of rolling hills and farmlands east of Zanesville and plans to convert the land into an organized place for recreation with a total capacity for 25,000 vacationists. This Salt Fork project is an example of the changing ecological pattern previously mentioned. After the completion of the dam now under construction, the area will acquire a nine-mile-long artificial lake. Many facilities for vacationists, including a day-use area for eight thousand persons, will be built along the shores of this lake. Although this area is about one hundred miles distant from Cleveland, Columbus, and Pittsburgh, most of the visitors to Salt Fork are expected to come from these urban centers because of its strategic location near the circulation intersection of two major arteries (Route 70 running east-west and its perpendicular Route 77). Parks in the immediate vicinity of these cities are already overcrowded.

Salt Fork will be an economic incentive for its region, which suffers from an incipient decline in population and low rate of income—particularly when compared with the prosperous northeast (Cleveland-Akron), the central region (Columbus), and the southwest (Cincinnati). Open areas like Salt Fork abound in this country. Such land is inexpensive, and its development by the states will not only fulfill a functional necessity but will also utilize new natural assets.

3. People are always eager to see an exciting spectacle like the Yosemite firefall in the Glacier's point. Yet, activities that can be permitted in these areas must be measured not in terms of public demand but in terms of preservation. A general policy of preservation can be reinforced by practical measures that do not necessarily restrict the use of these areas, but rather call for specialization of the type of activities in them.

Facilities that encourage a prolonged stay at the point of interest must be removed. Such a measure prevents both the direct effects and the cumulative effects of secondary functions that prolonged stays inevitably create. A successful example is the removal of the old Grand Canyon Hotel and its replacement by a motor lodge one mile away from the Canyon's rim. Future projects must be drawn in the same spirit, restricting facilities near the point of interest to the minimum required for a simple visit.

4. In 1964, the Federal Government passed the Protective Wilderness Act. According to this Act, severe restrictions can be enforced. In large conservancies of wildlife, the opening of roads for public transportation, the use of power saws and motorboats, and the flying of helicopters can be forbidden. Private enterprises with vested interests in mining, lumbering, transportation, and recreation debate the enforcement of the law. Conservation associations, led by the Wilderness Society and the National Parks Association, announced their particular concern about the future of these areas at the Tenth Biennial Wilderness Conference held April 8, 1967, in San Francisco. The debate still remains open, since classification is not yet complete and restrictions cannot be enforced in many primitive areas and wildlife refuges.

5. Buildings of outstanding architectural value have been demolished, and old districts have lost their articulation by the spotty erection of new constructions. H. H. Richardson's Marshall Field Warehouse in Chicago was torn down to be replaced by a parking lot. Preservation is as urgent a need in this class as it is in the "Primitive Areas."

In many cases of intown preservation, a variety of regulatory means controls the forces of urban growth. Restrictive covenants agreed upon by the inhabitants protect Boston's Louisburg Square and Beacon Hill. This English method of control requires the consensus of the inhabitants and assumes a well-organized community. Old buildings with low economic returns are saved from demolition by tax abatements; repair and maintenance upgrade their facilities and adjust their function to the demands of contemporary life. Bulk zoning is effectively applied in districts. In Greenwich Village, New York, it helps not only to maintain the Village's urban structure but also to preserve the special character of its life. After successful application in France, the concept of "Historic Districts" has been introduced in the United States. A Historic District Commission has the responsibility of control. New structures can be erected within the boundaries of the district only after the approval of the Commission. This method offers the advantage of flexibility, but the quality of its results depends very much upon the decisions of the Commission.

BIBLIOGRAPHY

Rudolf Arnheim, *Art and Visual Perception* (Los Angeles, 1957).

James J. Gibson, *The Perception of the Visual World* (Boston, 1950).

George Hartzog, "Parkscape U.S.A.," *National Geographic* (July, 1966), pp. 48-60.

Gyorgy Kepes, *Language of Vision* (Chicago, 1959).

Martin Meyerson, Barbara Terrett, and William L. C. Wheaton, *Housing, People, and Cities* (New York, 1962); see, in particular, "Prestige Rehabilitation," pp. 183–86.

Lewis Mumford, *The City in History: Its Origins, Its Transformations, and Its Prospects* (New York, 1961), pp. 205-35.

National Park Service, *Parks for America: A Survey of Park and Related Resources in the Fifty States* (Washington, D.C., 1964).

Outdoor Recreation Resources Review Commission, *National Recreation Survey* (Washington, D. C., 1962), and *Outdoor Recreation for America* (Washington, D. C., 1962).

Erwin Panofsky, *Meaning in the Visual Arts* (New York, 1957); see, in particular, "The History of Art as a Humanistic Discipline," pp. 1-25.

E. Papanoutsos, *Aesthetiki* (Athens, 1948).

State of Ohio, *A Statewide Plan for Outdoor Recreation*, Vol. 1 (Columbus, 1966).

John Summerson, *Heavenly Mansions* (New York, 1963); see, in particular, "The Past in the Future," pp. 219-42.

Freeman Tilden, *The State Parks: Their Meaning in American Life* (New York, 1962).

Christopher Tunnard and Boris Pushkarev, *Man-Made America: Chaos or Control?* (New Haven, 1963); see, in particular, pp. 326-448.

Conrad Wirth, "The Mission Called 66," *National Geographic* (July, 1966), pp. 7-47.

Wilhelm Worringer, *Abstraction and Empathy*, trans. Michael Bullock (New York, 1963).

ROGER REVELLE

Outdoor Recreation in a Hyper-Productive Society

Problems of Need and Demand

ALL MAMMALS play when they are young, and some, particularly those we like to think of as most intelligent (seals, porpoises, dogs, bears, monkeys, and men) play off and on throughout their lives. Other species are more serious-minded, although some birds seem to play some of the time. Our fellow mammals appear to play to vent their sheer exuberance or to satisfy their curiosity. Human beings share these drives, but the sense of beauty and mystery and the urge to fulfill or forget ourselves also enter into our play.

Lewis Mumford has pointed out that early man was more than *Homo faber*—man the tool-maker: He was also man the dancer and singer, the artist and inventor of ritual, the entertainer and decorator who used not only the environment, but his own wonderfully plastic body as a medium of joy and art.[1]

Man the tool-maker, the mammoth-chaser, and the fire-builder learned that he could observe, analyze, and predict events, and act on the basis of his predictions. To maintain himself, to attain security and power, he had to be rational (even though the rationale consisted partly of casting magical spells) and to be concerned with the future. But the cave painters, the body painters and scarifiers, the trance dancers and singers looked inward into imagination and mystery. They were concerned with the unseen and with memory, rather than with the rational future.

Their spirits persist deep within us, their descendants, and they rise to the surface in our play, which today, as in the

Many of the ideas herein came from discussions at Woods Hole, and later memoranda prepared by Dan Ogden, Ann Satterthwaite, Andrew Scheffey, Robert Teeters, and Nathaniel Wollman. I must accept responsibility for the general viewpoint expressed in the paper, and, of course, for any errors and inconsistencies.

253

ineffably remote past, is still largely irrational, existential, non-teleological. Even an intellectual game like chess is basically irrational. And our play, like that of our ancestors, must also be memorable, as the prevalence of postcards, Polaroid cameras, souvenir shops, and home movies testifies.

In traditional societies, with the possible exception of such dour types as those anthropologists' pets the Trobriand Islanders, work and play are closely related. The Ibans of Sarawak start and end the rice-growing season with a week of festivals in which dancing and impromptu acting alternate with much drinking of strong beer.[2] But as men become more sophisticated, they begin to think of work and play as opposites and to give them different moral values. Aristotle said, "we labor in order to have leisure," meaning that we must work not only to gain the extra resources needed for leisure, but also to deserve it and to be able to appreciate it by contrast with work.[3]

In the Middle Ages, the sweet reasonableness of Aristotle was superseded by the harshness of organized Christianity, with its asceticism and indifference to nature, its rejection of sacred groves and the spirits in brooks and trees. Cassian's dictum "All the ulcers that spring from idleness are healed by work"[4] ultimately led to Max Weber's Protestant dogma that "one does not work to live, one lives to work."[5]

Beneath ecclesiastical thunders, however, the ancestral demons of play survived pretty well. In the thirteenth century, there were eight weeks of church holy days, besides Sundays, leaving forty-four work weeks in the year, and it was said that the common people spent more time at dancing and games than at Mass. The demons have survived into modern times; even in the puritanical United States, professional baseball used to be played every afternoon during its five-month season, and it was attended by thousands of spectators who should have been working.

Yet most middle-class Americans still believe Calvin Coolidge was right when he said America should be "a land of work, of sincere striving for the good," even though all Americans should "have a reasonable amount of leisure." Coolidge made this statement to the National Conference on Outdoor Recreation in 1924, the first gathering ever called to consider anything resembling a national policy for recreation. The Conference resolved that "outdoor recreation, . . . above all, has a direct beneficial influence on the formation of sturdy character by developing those qualities of self-control, endurance under hardship, reliance on self, and co-operation with others in team work, which are so necessary to good citizenship." We still tell ourselves that the proper use of leisure is to prepare ourselves for work, to stay or become physically fit and mentally alert so that we can outwork and out-think the competition.

Until the recent advent of the "Hippies," few middle-class Americans subscribed to Aristotle's view that the object of work is leisure. Instead, work had "practical" objectives: the obtaining of material possessions, status, and power—a bigger automobile, a house in a higher-class neighborhood, better clothes, fancier food, more education for the children (so they could look forward to higher paying jobs), more "labor-saving" devices in the house. Recreation was an adjunct to work, necessary only for physical and mental health, economic stimulation, or improved social behavior, a kind of patent medicine to cure juvenile delinquency and other mysterious social diseases.[6]

These attitudes were understandable, and possibly desirable, when there was a continent to be won and a Gross National Product to be multiplied. But they are less justifiable, and maybe even nonsensical, in the new hyper-productive society. In a time of service industries, when most people make a living by selling things to one another or have jobs in which they are faceless components of superhuman organizations, recreation may represent the only chance many have to find themselves as unique individuals.

Under these circumstances, recreation becomes a human need and must be recognized as a human right in the same sense that we have recognized needs and rights to health, education, and welfare. To help the individual find uniqueness, his recreation may have to include challenges, demand skills, and provide a sense of risk and excitement, a feeling of adventure, a chance to gain individual excellence. That this is already clear to many Europeans is shown by their emphasis on individual accomplishments in sports and their range of individual recreational activities.

Do human beings need outdoor recreation? What values are there for modern man in the world of nature outside the cities? These questions cannot be answered scientifically, because of the irrational nature of play as it comes to us from our remote ancestors, and because man is the most adaptable of animals. If the rat and the sparrow can learn to live for endless generations in the cities, why cannot man? The scientist cannot give us answers, but the prophets and poets can. Moses talked to God in the solitude of the mountains. Jesus found his mission in the wilderness and taught his disciples to look at the lilies of the field. Guatama sought peace and became the Buddha under a spreading Peepul tree. St. Francis preached to the little birds, and "in spiritual ecstasy they flapped their wings and chirped rejoicing."[7] Walt Whitman said, "The passionate tenacity of hunters, woodsmen, early risers, cultivators of gardens and fields—all is a residence of the poetic in an outdoor people. . . . Now I see the secret of the making of the best persons. It is to grow in the open air and sleep with the earth. . . . I think all heroic deeds were conceiv'd in the open air."[8]

The provision of places for outdoor recreation was long dominated by conservationists and nature lovers, individuals more concerned with the enhancement of the resources than with the needs of people. People were necessary of course, because they paid the bills, but there should not be too many of them, and they must be as inconspicuous as possible. Recently, it has occurred to some of the more advanced thinkers on these matters to ask about demand as well as supply. What do people want and need in outdoor recreational facilities? In an attempt to find out, both the Outdoor Recreation Resources Review Commission appointed by President Eisenhower and the new Bureau of Outdoor Recreation of the Department of the Interior have circulated questionnaires.[9] While the answers obtained undoubtedly give an indication of "felt" needs, they may not be a very satisfactory means of uncovering actual or potential demand.

Many people are inarticulate about their recreational needs; others do not know what possibilities exist or could exist. Karl Mannheim has put it more extremely: "The average citizen is unable to invent new uses for his leisure."[10] Hence, the public taste and preferences can be changed by providing the "right" kind of recreational opportunities. Several other things besides asking people what they want can be done. In the cities, studies of the use of existing recreational facilities will give quantitative indications of present demands. Experimentation with new kinds of activities in different environmental settings, like those now being carried out in parts of New York City, will yield valuable insights. The requirements of different groups of city-dwellers should be considered—children, teen-agers, old people, students, young unmarried persons, married couples with and without children, various income groups, people at various levels of education, persons who work at night or in the daytime, manual workers, sedentary workers, and so forth. Many of the techniques of sociological and anthropological investigation should be utilized.

University curricula for park managers are usually in departments of landscape architecture or physical education. Whatever the merits of these two fields, they are not experimental disciplines. But experimentation is needed both to give people new experiences and to help them discover what they would like if they had a choice. University curricula should have an infusion of such experimental sciences as psychology, sociology, and anthropology.

Open Spaces in the City

Numerous kinds of open spaces exist in American cities, and all could have recreational uses. In addition to formally recognized parks, we think of rooftops, private back yards, school playgrounds, river banks, city lakes and reservoirs, beaches and bays in coastal and Great Lakes cities, shopping centers and commercial recreation facilities, sanitary land-fill areas, and the city streets themselves.

In the United States, city streets and alleys are the traditional playgrounds of the poor. During the long hot summers, slum children in New York and Chicago cool off by dousing themselves in water from the fire hydrants. In some European cities, the streets are more widely used. A broad and long street in the heart of Barcelona is dedicated to pedestrians and is used as a promenade by all classes. Outdoor cafés and eating places line its sidewalks. In many American cities, traffic congestion would hardly be worsened and the happiness of city-dwellers might be much increased, if some of the widest streets were closed to automobiles and trucks during daylight or evening hours and used for a variety of fun and games.

Even the most crowded American cities contain many small parcels of empty land. The ownership is sometimes inextricably tangled; in other cases, title has reverted to the city through nonpayment of taxes. Both kinds of undeveloped land merit more consideration for outdoor recreational uses.

In utilizing existing open spaces in the city and in making new ones, we need to think of linkages between them that can provide a continuous open strip for walking, bicycle riding, and equestrian trails and create an illusion of openness and distance. Abandoned streetcar rights of way, drainage channels, and old canals are all useful for this purpose, but riverbanks are best.

American cities have usually turned their backs on their rivers. A high flood wall hides the Connecticut River from the citizens of Hartford. Until recently, the Chicago River was little more than an open sewer and was understandably avoided by the people of Chicago. In New York, access to the rivers is cut off by roaring freeways. In other cities, factories and warehouses line the riverbanks and dump their wastes into the waters.

Boston was one of the first cities to realize that rivers are priceless civic assets. Following Frederick Law Olmstead's original plan, Boston has laid out along the Charles miles of grassy slopes, interspersed with boathouses, marinas, playgrounds, and walks. On a sunny summer day, thousands of young lovers and sun worshipers can be seen on the green banks, and the white sails of small boats dot the water. Chicago is also starting to use its river as a source of recreation and enjoyment. These trends toward the human use of the rivers in our cities should be encouraged in every possible way. In many cases, full public ownership is not essential. Scenic easements, zoning, and other devices can be used to preserve the beauty of the riverbanks and other natural places in the cities.

Today many city parks are almost empty: some because they are dull and poorly equipped, and others because they are unsafe. The very word *park* raises in most minds the image of a formal area, nearly empty or partly filled with rather disreputable characters, and adorned by walks, benches, and "Keep Off the Grass" signs. These ills can be cured only by imaginative, sophisticated, and well-supported park management. The image of a park should be one of variety, informality and happy activity. As a first step, the removal of the "Keep Off the Grass" signs would be symbolic of other actions to come. Programmed recreational activities—guided tours, organized games, concerts, special exhibitions, festivals, "happenings"—should be more numerous and more varied. These could be produced by the city or by private groups subsidized for that purpose. New kinds of recreational facilities—various sorts of rides, things to climb, and things to see—should be provided. Children should be given opportunities to make things out of simple materials; the residents of a neighborhood should be encouraged to take responsibility for maintaining and modifying their own open spaces. Park managers should encourage and devise, rather than discourage, a multiplicity of uses for open spaces. Even the safety of a park will be enhanced if it is filled with people who are doing many things.

A Variety of Activities: An Essential

The primary objective of city parks should be to encompass a variety of activities. We can categorize some of these as follows:

Athletics: golf, tennis, horseback riding, swimming, surfing, sunbathing, scuba-diving, sailing, skin diving, rowing, hiking, bicycling, shuffle board, croquet, and bowling

Eating: restaurants, coffee bars, picnic grounds, and barbecue pits

Cultural Activities: concerts, indoor and outdoor art exhibitions, lectures, formal discussion groups, and informal conversations

Love-Making: for this purpose, benches and movable chairs should be provided, as well as privacy and protection against criminals

Exhibitions: zoos, gardens, herbariums, arboretums, aquariums, "climatrons," planetariums, demonstration farms, mills, and "Disneylands"

Do-It-Yourself Opportunities: small individual vegetable gardens like those found outside Copenhagen, materials for pop-art structures, and "adventure" playgrounds

Winter Activities: ice skating, skiing on artificial snow or plastic strips, swimming in heated pools, protected picnic areas under transparent plastic covers, restaurants with beautiful outdoor views, and winter fishing.

Modern city playgrounds illustrate the age-old problem that things designed for children by grown-ups fit adult ideas better than child needs. The molded concrete turtles, horses, and ducks that adorn the new playgrounds are attractive, at least to adults, but are they good to play with? What can a child do but climb or sit on them? *The Washington Post* recently published a photograph of a fallen tree in a "modern design" playground in an urban-renewal area of southwest Washington. The tree was covered with children, but the adjacent concrete horses were empty. The traditional playground is not much better. Its swings, jungle gyms, slides, and seesaws are all fixed objects to be played on or with. Only in the sandbox do the children have an opportunity to change or move things. The suburban child can build a tree house or dig a tunnel, but the city child in the orthodox playground has only prefabricated structures. Playground equipment is needed that will give children a sense of exploration and discovery, the experience of moving and building things, a consciousness of being identified with their "own thing."

Successful experiments with "adventure" or "junk" playgrounds have been conducted in Scandinavia and England. In London and Copenhagen, one can see small open spaces (sometimes only one quarter of an acre) containing pieces of used wood, old car bodies and chassis, mattresses, furniture, and miscellaneous junk. Under the eyes of a single supervisor, neighborhood children build and re-build these materials into houses, go-carts, tracks, and "pop-art" structures. Despite the seeming safety hazards, the adventure playgrounds have very low accident rates. In this country, much will have to be overcome before they can be reconciled with municipal health and safety standards. Although playgrounds of this kind are mainly interesting to four- to twelve-year-olds, their implications for self-expression in recreation go far beyond that age group.

From these implications, Karl Linn, a landscape architect and psychologist, has developed his idea of "neighborhood commons"—parks designed and built by the residents of a city neighborhood to fit their needs and desires. Several of these commons were created, with the aid of local design students, on tax-delinquent lots in the heart of ghetto areas in Philadelphia. The people built what they wanted; there were no packaged plans or equipment. Neighborhood people—retired carpenters, energetic teen-agers, and skillful house-wives—constructed dance areas for teen-agers, sitting areas for the elderly, and play areas for toddlers, buildings that can be used six-teen hours a day.[11] Artificial mountains and caves may also provide self-testing recreation in the heart of the city. In downtown Tokyo, an artificial rock for climbing, erected by a department store, has proved to be extremely popular.

The Suburbs and Surrounding Country

The recreational needs of the suburbs differ significantly from those of the center city and its ring of slums. Nevertheless, the preservation of open spaces is clearly important to them. Natural areas in the countryside are equally important to the city-dwellers, but to be useful to them, easy and well-marked access to and in-formation about interesting or pleasant spots must be available.

Outdoor Recreation in a Hyper-Productive Society

The existence of large empty areas characterizes modern urban and suburban sprawl. These areas can be prime assets for human enjoyment. A system of trails and winding scenic roads should be built, but these should lead to a goal—a place to get something to eat or drink or to spend the night, a beautiful overlook, a historic house. Many such goals could be provided by private individuals or firms, but perhaps only if they are publicly subsidized, at least at first. Something like a *Michelin Guide* to the countryside surrounding our cities—with maps showing trails, "curiosities," picnic places, areas of public access, inns, restaurants, and pubs—should be invaluable. It could be a source of revenue and advertising for oil companies and other businesses interested in persuading people to drive their automobiles for pleasure. Recognizing the economic values of tourism in its countryside, Vermont is preserving its old dirt roads and bringing up to date the WPA Country Guides of the 1930's.

How to Even Out the Loads

Public recreational facilities are subject to an extreme variation of use. The strain on a beach or a scenic picnic area during the Fourth of July weekend may be one hundred times greater than it is during the middle of the week in May or September. If the attempt were made to construct sufficient facilities to meet these peak loads, funds would be spent that could be used more effectively elsewhere. This problem can be attacked in several ways. Especially important are a careful economic and social analysis of the maximum number of persons who can be accommodated at any one time and the employment of various devices to reduce peak loads. The following devices have been suggested:

1. The educational schedules of primary and secondary schools could be changed in much the same way that university and college schedules are now being modified by the adoption of the quarter system. By freeing families to take their vacations at different times throughout the year, a new educational rhythm would reduce summer peak loads. Such scheduling would also increase the efficiency of use of all sorts of educational structures. Summer disturbances in the crowded cities might be lessened if the public schools were air-conditioned and used in the summertime.

2. A greater diversity of activities could be provided for such

overpowering holidays as the Fourth of July weekend or the Labor Day weekend. Stores, restaurants, and amusement places in the cities might benefit considerably were they to organize and support city festivals on these occasions.

3. A system of variable entrance and user fees could be devised that would tend to price people out of recreation areas at peak periods and encourage off-peak visits. In an effort to induce a more even flow of visitors, fees could be reduced on days or hours when the load is light. Variable charges could also be employed to induce people to go to little-used areas in preference to areas of overuse. Thus, in a state park, it might cost considerably more to park near a popular feature than near the boundary.

America the Beautiful

In city parks and in the suburbs, we ask for variety, novelty, and change. Just the opposite is true for the national parks. Although these treasures of the continent are, in part, sites for active recreation, skiing, mountain climbing, fishing, and camping, they are in essence great natural wonders, things of joy and beauty, places for an individual to lose himself in contemplation. While their values cannot be enhanced by human action, they can easily be destroyed by it. They are the heritage of a people, for which each living generation is the trustee. Our aim must be to keep Yosemite close to what it was when John Muir first visited it and Yellowstone as nearly as possible like the "national park and pleasuring ground" that Congress established in 1872.

National park attendance has exploded from the three million visits a year of 1930 to the 137 million of 1966. More people came to Yellowstone from June to September, 1966, than visited the nearly two hundred national parks, monuments, and historic areas thirty-five years ago. The heights of experience in the national parks are incompatible with crowds, and many of their wonders are too fragile to withstand much trampling. But within the next few decades, the number of Americans will increase by 30 to 40 per cent, and the average personal income will double, while the average working week will probably decline. Some people will work less hours per day, others fewer days per week, and almost all wage-earners will have a paid vacation. From an average of one week per year, vacations may well lengthen to four weeks or more. The average person will travel about twice as many miles each year; perhaps half this travel, about five thousand miles, will be in search of recreation.

These changes will combine to produce an enormous increase in the demand for outdoor recreation facilities at a distance from people's houses. The effects will probably be almost multiplicative: more people, times twice as much income per person, times twice as much travel, times a fourfold lengthening of vacations. If suitable accommodations were available in national parks, forests, and wildlife refuges, the annual number of visitor-days could grow to more than half a billion by the end of the century. Excluding Alaska, the present area of federal recreational preserves is somewhat over forty million acres. If these preserves are not extended, there could be more than twelve visitor-days per acre in the year 2000.

At first thought, this would seem to be a low number. But the natural wonders of the parks occupy only a small fraction of the total park area. In Yosemite, the Mariposa Grove and the Valley can be measured in tens of square miles, while the entire park covers twelve hundred square miles. Yellowstone is more than 90 per cent wilderness. Its sights can all be seen on a 150-mile drive (along which nearly a million automobiles now travel during the summer season).

The federal lands dedicated to recreational uses should, in principle, be greatly expanded. Many of the outstanding park sites are, however, already in the federal system. Should we then seek merely to multiply facilities to accommodate the growing crowds? More parking lots, more camp sites, more picnic tables, and wider roads mean more crowding and the progressive destruction of the parks' most cherished values. New patterns of use must be developed that will allow the number of visitors to be increased without serious damage. One step is to diversify the environments and the uses. Some areas can be kept inviolate, except to the lonely few who are willing to work hard for solitude. These are the "wilderness" or "roadless" regions where John Muir found "a good practical sort of immortality."[12] In other areas, we must preserve secluded spots where visitors will be able to find those "frogs in springly places . . . elysian springs and aromatic groves" that once delighted the naturalist, William Bartram.[13] Other areas can be toughened with wear-resistant paths and various guidance devices, so that they can accommodate fair-sized crowds. A desperate but perhaps necessary step would be to ration visits among applicants and to stagger visiting times, but the broadening of the base of national recreation lands through development of national seashores, riverways, wildlife refuges, "wild rivers," undersea parks, and other special environments is more hopeful.

The areas of lesser scenic value in or near a national park could be developed for camping and overnight lodging, auto parks, picnic sites, and other services. The camp sites could be well spaced to afford privacy and cleanliness. Souvenir, restaurant, and other commercial facilities, as well as ample parking space, could be installed. A variable fee system might encourage visitors to use such areas.

To reduce the use of private automobiles in the parks, a system of buses might be introduced. If necessary, this service could be offered free of charge, but it might be possible to recover capital and operating costs through fees. These buses could have glass or plastic tops to permit wide-ranging vision and a sense of being out-of-doors. Multiple doors would enable people to get in and out easily. Tours could be scheduled at frequent intervals, and stops would be planned so that visitors could see the principal scenic and historic attractions. Drivers could point out unexpected sights such as flowering plants or a bear and her cubs. Tape-recorded commentaries on the park's geology, animal and plant life, history, and other interesting aspects could be an important part of the bus ride, and the drivers could provide additional explanations for unusual attractions. Monorails or narrow-gauge railways should also be considered as a means of transportation in scenic areas. These would make it possible to keep automobiles out altogether.

Some Suggestions About Diversification

During this century, the United States has been transformed from a predominantly rural society into a predominantly urban one. As a result, we are becoming, even more than in the past, a land-surplus nation. More than half the counties in the United States have lost population during the last twenty years. In the future, much of our land area will find its greatest use as recreational space. Land taken out of agriculture can be employed in this way; obvious candidates for such use are marshy islands of the Mississippi Delta and the rocky barrens of the Nevada desert.

Guided tours of working mines, automated refineries and chem-

ical works, wineries, breweries, distilleries, and scrap-metal processing works could provide another source of programmed recreation.
Many obsolescent modes of transportation could find new use as
recreational facilities. Riding something is one of the favorite activities of most human beings. Old railroad passenger cars, municipal trolleys, and ferry boats could become as popular as the San
Francisco cable cars. Mass-transit access to mountain peaks by
aerial tramways and funiculars could be greatly expanded. Hydro-
foils and hover-craft are examples of new technology applied to
recreation.

Exciting possibilities exist for underwater transportation. Recreational submarines of all sizes with viewing ports and automatic
manipulating arms can be envisioned. Perhaps more promising are
metal tubes leading to an underwater chamber, one to two hundred
feet deep, off steeply sloping coast lines.

In outdoor recreation, as elsewhere, there should be a happy
combination of activities for both mind and body. One of the best
features of nineteenth-century America was the tented chautauquas
that sprang up across the country in the summer time. Centers like
Aspen are the modern version. A hundred Aspens scattered throughout the country would provide places where people could talk to
one another about exciting things in the morning and climb the
local mountains in the afternoon.

The Shore Line: A One-Dimensional Resource

One resource must be given special consideration: the shore
line. This essentially one-dimensional boundary zone between the
land and the sea is one of the most limited and yet heavily used
parts of our environment. Nearly half of all Americans live within a
hundred miles of the ocean or the Great Lakes; this proportion will
probably increase in future decades. By the end of the century, some
150 to 200 million people may be struggling for places on the beaches
and in the narrow coastal waters. Even if the country's entire coastal
strip were converted into public beaches, this would mean about
two people per foot. Actually only a fraction of the shore line is
available for public recreation. Long stretches are too polluted to
be safe for swimming or water sports, and much of it is owned by
either industrial, shipping, and military interests, or private individuals. For existing shore lines, two sorts of action are urgent. First,
the areas available for recreation must be retained, improved, and

extended. Second, the routes of public access to these areas must be increased. The shore line can be stretched by building spits and peninsulas, offshore bars and islands, and by dredging or improving estuaries. Chicago has already led the way by constructing a series of curving peninsulas along its lake front. Mission Bay, a great aquatic park near the heart of San Diego, was created by radical modification of a previously marshy estuary, but elsewhere in California low freeway bridges and earth-filled ramps have permanently spoiled many estuaries.

Many coastal areas are too cold for comfortable swimming. We should explore the possibility of using the waste heat from thermal power plants or other similar sources to warm these waters. Offshore barriers to retard the mixing of cold and warm water might be required to achieve a satisfactory increase in temperature. The power plants do not need to be built on the coastline, where they might spoil the view, but inland. The necessary pipelines could be constructed.

New Rivers

Man-made lakes find some of their best uses in human recreation. New "rivers" might also be created for recreational and scenic purposes. Irrigation canals, which are, in effect, man-made rivers, are commonplace. What modifications would have to be introduced if waterways were to be built not just for irrigation but for their recreation and scenic qualities? The new rivers could be designed to intersect natural watercourses that now carry too little water—arroyos or streams in suburban areas where flow has been reduced by changes in land use. The scale of the projects could extend over a wide range, and they could be designed for multipurpose use. For example, if the water were carried through several channels instead of one, the new rivers would serve as flood-control devices. The range of possibilities would become vastly greater if water supplies in Canada could be tapped. New rivers would be an asset to the eastern as well as the western parts of the country, although they are likely to be most feasible along the eastern slopes of the Rockies and in the Great Plains.

The Pitfalls of Multiple Use

In recent years, multiple-use planning and management of

land areas and development projects have been increasingly employed as a means of stretching resources to meet growing recreation demands. Ideally, a variety of activities can be made compatible with the primary purpose of a development, and relatively small changes can produce large recreation opportunities. Multiple-use planning and management have required substantial alterations in the traditional outlook of engineers and managers accustomed to single-purpose developments.

Continued progress along these lines is essential, and today it is almost taken for granted. But, like other valuable concepts, multiple use has limitations and pitfalls. Some uses are not possible in a multiple-use area. Allowing multiple use everywhere is ultimately equivalent to denying beautiful, lonely places to lovers of undisturbed nature. The danger is most serious, of course, where the supply of resources for such "fragile" use is limited, and where multiple use will destroy the resources irreversibly. Such pre-emptive uses as hunting and water skiing prevent other possible uses, but are not, in themselves, necessarily undesirable. If, however, they are uncontrolled in a *laissez-faire* multiple-use plan, they become single-use purposes by default.

Careful consideration, but not necessarily undue favoritism, must be given uses that are denied by any other use, and reasonable restraints should be placed on hazard-creating pre-emptive uses. Those areas that will not bear the gamut of use must be determined early in the planning process. If the supply of any class of distinctive areas is clearly limited, these should be retained in single-use status. If, on the other hand, some classes are in abundant supply, a portion can be returned to the multiple-use pot.

Land Acquisition

Meeting national needs for recreation and preservation of scenic beauty will require public acquisition or other public control of much acreage now in private hands. There will be problems of equity for three parties—the property owners who must lose their holdings for the greater public interest, the local authorities that depend on property-tax revenues, and the taxpayers who must foot the acquisition bill.

Extensive property acquisition for federal use often leads to difficulties for local taxing authorities. These difficulties have been largely ignored in the past. There has been an almost inviolate policy against making federal payments in lieu of local taxes. Recently, however, Congress authorized payments, based on a small percentage of land value, to local authorities for federal wildlife refuges. The Administration's proposal for a redwoods park includes economic adjustment payments over a limited period of time to local communities to counteract the initial loss of tax base and economic activity.

The rapidly escalating cost of property acquisition for recreational and scenic areas appears to many people to place a heavy burden on the general taxpayer even though the "real" cost, in terms of resource use, of land acquisition is much less than the money cost, because property owners by and large will save the greater portion of payments received for land taken by condemnation. Just as federal acquisition of property should involve neither niggardliness nor indifference to the problems of individual landowners and local taxing authorities, it should not be a source of reward for speculative dealing in land. But the present land-acquisition process unfortunately provides ample opportunities for inordinate price rises. These result from several factors. Among them are the long time-lapse between the area study and Congressional authorization for purchase; piecemeal and strung-out acquisition due to budgetary restraints; the availability of detailed information on specific acquisition proposals through the justification of budgetary requests; the unavoidable (but in many respects equitable) inclusion in appraisals of land in the vicinity of a proposed park of value elements created by the expectation of the park itself; and the difficulty of getting detached judgments of values by local juries when condemnation cases go to courts.

The problem of escalating prices must be ameliorated if an adequate public-acquisition program is to be carried through. Otherwise, land costs will rise beyond the capacity of any politically feasible commitment of public funds. New approaches, some of them radical, are called for. As a general principle, acquiring authorities should be empowered to use with great flexibility the widest variety of tools at hand. This means, *inter alia*, minimizing full acquisition by such devices as the purchase of easements and authority for option and lease-back arrangements.

A Federal Land Agency should be established with authority to acquire options or to purchase before specific park authorization. Financed with an initial capitalization to be used as a revolving fund and with authorization to borrow by issuing bonds, this agency would act as soon as plans indicated the desirability of beginning acquisition. It would pay local taxes on all its holdings. When a land-using agency obtained the necessary appropriations, it would reimburse the Federal Land Agency for its outlay, including accumulated interest and taxes.

The states should be encouraged to use property-tax assessments to measure the fair and true value of property. Where participation of the owner is required in determining his property's value ("self-assessment"), a record of owner-accepted valuation can be built up. Any sales income above this valuation can be taxed heavily. But one must ask whether the property owner who forfeits his land to condemnation should not share in, equally with neighboring owners whose land is not taken, the enhancement of values created by a public development.

Condemnation cases involving large estimated values—say $50,000 or more—should be adjudged by panels of disinterested experts under an administrative proceeding, with right of appeal to courts. Juries are often not sufficiently equipped to provide fair judgments in such cases.

Questions of Value and Cost

The creation of resources for public outdoor recreation sometimes requires only a kind of transfer payment. For example, establishment of a national seashore may chiefly involve acquisition of private property already being used for recreation. But in other cases, we must be concerned with the allocation of scarce resources among alternative uses: A flourishing sport fishery may call for severe restraints on commercial fishing; a national park may mean the cessation of lumbering or mining; land for a city recreational area could be used instead for offices or factories. Creation of the Indiana Dunes National Lakeshore was vigorously and successfully opposed for decades by local interests who believed that the area should be given over to industry. Recreation advocates must be able to convince a majority of their fellow citizens that the value of a recreational activity will be greater than the values it would displace, or else make such a nuisance of themselves that the line of least resistance for the majority is to placate them. In essence, the problem is to compare tangible market values with intangible "human" ones. This is a problem that can only be solved politically. Here, as in many other human affairs, passions spin the plot.

Economic estimates of recreation value are usually attempted in planning a multiple-use resource development, such as a dam and its accompanying reservoir. What total annual benefits, expressed in dollars, should be ascribed to the fishing, boating, swimming, water skiing, sightseeing, and other recreational activities that the lake will bring? In principle, these benefits, when added to those expected for flood control, water supply, hydropower, and other uses, will enable an estimate to be made of the total benefit-cost ratio of the project; this can then be compared with the net benefit that might be obtained from other uses of the same funds.

If the lake were to be privately owned and operated, its projected recreational value might be taken as equal to the entrance fees and net returns on rented boats and other equipment that could be expected from visitors. But the local motel keepers, restaurant managers, and service-station operators might well be willing to pay a larger sum, because the lake would increase both the numbers and the length of stay of future tourists. Oil companies, automobile and tire manufacturers, and makers of fishing tackle might offer to help pay for developing the lake on the basis of the increased sales it would generate. Local municipalities and the state government might chip in if their poorer citizens could swim in the lake without charge and if property values were fairly certain to go up because the lake would add beauty and interest to the local environment.

Even in such a simple case as this, the "economic" value of recreation and other intangibles is extremely difficult to assess. The irrational nature of recreation and the impact of natural beauty, and the uniqueness of many public sites compound the difficulty. No private entrepreneur can offer a Mount Rainier, a Grand Canyon, or a Crater Lake. Nor can the technique of cost effectiveness be used to balance public expenditures for recreation against alternative claims. The principle that human beings need and should have recreation for its own sake means that its benefits and therefore its cost effectiveness cannot be compared with the benefits of obtaining some other objective such as physical or mental health or the amelioration of social ills. The enormous diversity of interests among individuals makes comparison of the value of various kinds of recreational facilities not only invidious, but nearly impossible, except in the crudest fashion. An attempt should be made to meet the needs of large numbers of people before paying too much attention to small minorities, but the latter should not be totally neglected.

Diversity of interests and values among human beings is one of the most telling justifications for private philanthropy in our society, particularly where it can be combined with pioneering experimentation or with service to minorities. The far-sighted Rockefellers have demonstrated the possibilities for private provision of public recreation by creating with their own funds a national park in the Virgin Islands. In the future, as recreation increases in public virtue, we can expect both foundations and generous individuals to contribute to it as they now give to higher education.

The frugal, rational French have tried to give some index of value to natural beauties and wonders. Their three-star "curiosities" are worth a "voyage," those with two stars only a detour. A single star simply indicates that one should stop and look if he happens to be on the right road. But this system is tautological, because detours and "voyages" are themselves pleasurable and valuable. A great natural wonder justifies a trip, but the reverse is also true.

I have already suggested the use of fees to even out visitor loads and to reduce the pressures of crowds in the central areas of national parks. A more fundamental question remains: How much of the total cost of public outdoor recreation should be borne by the users and how much by the taxpayers? We have given an implicit partial answer to this question by stating that all citizens have a right to outdoor recreation, just as they have a right to health, education, and welfare. The taxpayers must bear enough of the cost to ensure that this right can be exercised by all who wish to do so. Fees should not be imposed when a charge might destroy or damage the social value of an outdoor recreation facility. To uplift the quality of life in an urban ghetto, it may be highly desirable to provide attractive free outdoor recreation, including free transportation to and fro.

One principle of value seems clear: Irreplaceable and unique resources should be preserved, even at considerable cost, for they are beyond price. The California redwoods are a prime example. These ancient trees have outlived civilizations and occur only in one relatively small area of the earth. They could not be replaced within any meaningful time-span. It would be the height of arrogance and selfishness for our generation to deny them to all future human beings.

REFERENCES

1. Lewis Mumford, "Technics and the Nature of Man," Speech at Smith-

sonian Institution Bicentennial Celebration Commemorating the Birth of James Smithson (September 16–18, 1965).

2. W. R. Revelle, personal communication. Mr. and Mrs. Revelle are Peace Corps Volunteers stationed in the village of Nanga Medamit in Northern Sarawak, where they both teach primary school.

3. Aristotle, *Politica,* Book 7, Section 15 (Oxford, 1908).

4. Quoted by Thomas Woody, "Leisure in the Light of History," *Annals of the American Academy of Political and Social Science,* Vol. 313 (September, 1957), pp. 4–10.

5. Quoted by Willard C. Sutherland, "A Philosophy of Leisure," *Annals of the American Academy of Political and Social Science,* Vol. 313 (September, 1957), pp. 1–3.

6. Aristotle's principle has been modified by John Kenneth Galbraith, who points out in his *Affluent Society* that "the case for more leisure is not stronger on prima facie grounds than the case for making labor time itself more agreeable." In *The New Industrial State* he adds, "There is no intrinsic reason why work must be more unpleasant than non-work. . . . Men will value leisure over work only as they find the uses of leisure more interesting or rewarding." It should be noted that Galbraith, like Aristotle before him, is a professor and consequently a member of a community which as he himself says has always insisted "on extensive exemption from formal commitment to toil."

7. Lynn White, "The Historical Roots of Our Ecological Crisis," *Science,* Vol. 155 (March, 1957), p. 1203.

8. Walt Whitman, *Leaves of Grass,* Preface and "Song of the Open Road."

9. Outdoor Recreation Resources Review Commission, "Outdoor Recreation for America" (Washington, D. C., 1962).

10. Karl Mannheim, *Man and Society in an Age of Reconstruction* (New York, 1944), p. 317.

11. Related to the question of neighborhood creation of recreation facilities is the problem of involving private citizens in the improvement of outdoor manners. Dan Ogden of the Department of the Interior has written in a personal letter to the editors of *Dædalus* that we need "to build into most of our citizens' attitudes and behavior, patterns which will sharply curtail vandalism, littering, dumping, polluting, discourtesy, carelessness with fire, and other antisocial acts which annually destroy an important part of our outdoor recreation investments. We also need efforts to train citizens in group-work and group-leadership techniques and to equip them with ideas and how-to-do-it skills so that citizens' committees for beautification and outdoor recreation can be established in every community in the land and in most neighborhoods in our large cities."

12. Quoted by Stewart Udall in *The Quiet Crisis* (New York, 1965), p. 112.

13. William Bartram, *Travels* (1791) quoted by Stewart Udall in *The Quiet Crisis,* p. 41.

THE ROLES OF EDUCATION

GEORGE J. MASLACH

The Reorganization of Educational Resources

THE PRESIDENT of the United States recently said that in "almost every field of concern, from economics to national security, the academic community has become a central instrument of public policy in the United States." Only by utilizing and modifying the full resources of the university could this degree of influence have been achieved. Recently the desire to serve three masters—the traditional roles of teaching, research, and public service—has imposed stresses on the structure of various educational institutions. Nathan Pusey, Clark Kerr, and others have observed the current struggle between these roles, as they have been shaped by the general education concepts of Cardinal Newman, the research orientation of Abraham Flexner, and the Land Grant Act of Justin P. Morrill, which provided the philosophy of public-service and professional schools. Educational institutions have always adjusted the relative effort devoted to these three demands, especially during periods of crisis. Thus, the problem posed by such new national concerns as natural resources, conservation, and recreation is not whether the university should recognize and act on these issues, but how it should reorganize its limited intellectual resources for new tasks while preserving or extending its major role of teaching.

An examination of current university catalogues usually reveals one large liberal arts college presided over by one dean and a dozen or so professional schools, each having its own hierarchy and academic territory. The liberal arts college with its five areas of study —the humanities, the fine arts, the physical, life, and social sciences —has always been looked upon as the basic source of the "general education" necessary to all students. Often, two thirds of a university's student body are enrolled in its liberal arts program.

Professional schools, formed to deal with specific problems of society, operate at the interface of science and society, exploiting a given body of knowledge for the benefit of mankind. The older schools of medicine, law, and agriculture are typical of the early needs of society, while more recent demands have produced schools of criminology, social welfare, and optometry. Each school tends to establish a strong and obvious liaison with its base of knowledge in the college of liberal arts: medicine with the life sciences, engineering with the physical sciences, mining with the earth sciences, and law with the social sciences.

In many instances, a problem area is recognized before a coherent body of knowledge necessary to its optimal treatment has been developed. If this is the case, an "interdisciplinary" nonteaching institute or center is formed. Such a decision can lead to problems of separate but equal research titles and the eventual pressure to form a new teaching unit. This latter form of accommodation probably would be chosen to treat current concerns in natural resources, conservation, and recreation, for, unlike the fields of the traditional professional schools, none of these topics is linked distinctly to a given body of scientific knowledge.

To complicate the situation, most universities hesitate to consider new independent problem-oriented areas, not so much because they fear further intellectual fractionalization, but because they wish to avoid expanding a fundamental conflict between the goals of government agencies and the goals of the university. This conflict is not the publicized, albeit nonexistent, one of teaching versus research, but the more alarming contest of teaching and research versus public service. The goals of a government agency include the need for an informed public awareness of current and potential problems in a given area such as conservation, research to increase the body of knowledge necessary to obtain optimal general solutions to these problems, and direct aid in the form of research funds applied to specific tasks. The university, on the other hand, while recognizing the public-service function such agencies have provided in the past, favors basic research efforts exemplified by faculty-aided graduate-student theses. Public awareness of national concerns could be obtained in a simple fashion through continuing-education programs, an extension of service increasingly provided by many universities. A pedestrian treatment of new national concerns could obviously be obtained within a university, but only at the cost of eroding the undergraduate teaching effort. To avoid this erosion, some way must be found to implant in our undergraduate effort the presentation of national problem-oriented concerns as a new form of "general education," involving the professional schools. Were the professional schools to display their involvement with "relevance" to the total student body, an integration of now isolated disciplines might be possible.

Fortunately, educational leaders have been aware of this approach and the educational challenge it poses. Some trends are already apparent, and Julius A. Stratton, former president of M.I.T., has clearly identified one of the questions that modern educational institutions must face.

What will be the impact of our growing sophistication of knowledge, which now requires that we deal with problems as complete or partial systems, uniting—for example—elements of pure science and engineering with historical, economic, and political considerations?

. . . I recognize the importance of each of our three traditional roles—of teaching, of research, and of service. . . . But in only one of these is the university unique, without counterpart—and that is in the preparation of young men and women for professional careers and for their responsibilities as citizens.

The Massachusetts Institute of Technology began as an institution directed toward engineering and architecture, issues then relevant to the demands of a growing industrial nation. Mr. Stratton notes that today this theme of relevance "has taken [M.I.T.] further afield," into the physical and biological sciences, management, economics, political science, and psychology—all of which "reflect the interlocking and coupling of science and technology with the whole range of human affairs." Mr. Stratton considers this progressive broadening "inescapable."

As a guideline, [the university] must always hold fast to the idea of relevance to the needs of contemporary society. . . . It seems to me that we have now rather staked out the principal boundaries of our academic territory and that we have come to a proper time for consolidation and deepening.

Nathan Pusey has written in a similar vein but from a liberal arts viewpoint. In a recent address at the American University of Beirut Centennial, he indicated that science and the professions in our time promise to carry forward "the ancient liberal idea of a mind trained and informed." The historical conflict between the humanities and scientific and professional training is being resolved, Mr. Pusey asserted, by new developments in the universities.

Liberal education for our time, and for the future, cannot be separated from professional education, because ours is no longer a world for amateurs, but a world peopled and moved by professionals.

Liberal education must be acquainted with and work through professional education if it is to understand the experience of men in our time and escape fatuity; it is no less true that professional education is beginning to be increasingly informed by liberal education, in the sense that it searches beneath immediate practical considerations for the theoretical understanding.

Two assumptions are fundamental to both positions: that the professional schools are an integral part of the university capable of making a unique contribution to "general education," and that these schools have developed a new "liberal science" form of education which is being utilized increasingly by national leaders. If such a "general education" contribution can be made, it would appear logical that the format of freshman and sophomore courses introduced at Harvard College years ago and labeled "humanities," "social science," and "natural science" should be expanded to include an offering where the focus is on a topic of widespread current concern—for example, pollution, recreation, transportation, or conservation. A team of faculty members from the professional schools and the liberal arts could teach such a course for a year or so. To insure timeliness and a broader spectrum of contributing faculty, emphasis could then be shifted to a new topic with a new team of instructors. Special interest could be generated by field observation in the many problem areas. Los Angeles smog, San Francisco Bay pollution, Boston and Cambridge freeway location, rapid-transit developments, and urban sprawl all testify to our propensity to apply yesterday's solutions to tomorrow's problems.

What would such a course accomplish? First, it would identify and define for a large segment of our young population the number and the magnitude of our society's growth problems. Second, it would demonstrate that the scientific attitude is little understood and inadequately applied to human problems. Third, it would disclose those areas where codified knowledge does not exist and, consequently, where a scientific methodology cannot be employed. Fourth, it would display the complex influences that shape the design of any chosen solution. Fifth, it would bring before the entire university many of the true activists of our society, the graduates and faculties of our professional schools. If they have truly forged a "central instrument of public policy," they should demonstrate the products of that effort and reveal the rationale of their thinking.

Sixth, through its participation, the liberal arts faculty could review critically the aesthetic, social, political, and economic implications of physical design. Finally, were it properly exploited, a course involving representatives of the life, physical, and social sciences, as well as the humanities and fine arts, would provide the appropriate educational feedback for the active professional, who would place his contribution before his colleagues in the university community. Only by a dramatic display of the professional decision process can young students appreciate the impact of higher education on the world today. Only through a presentation of plans with commentary, criticism, review, and defense will all segments of our society eventually become sensitive to the basic problems of our society, including those of natural resources, recreation, and conservation.

If the argument for a closer educational tie between the liberal arts form of higher education and the liberal sciences or professional type is valid, so also must be that for a closer collaboration among the many professional schools. On a single campus, there are often a dozen independent schools—all working for changes in society, all with fixed curricula prohibiting interaction with other groups, and all utilizing similar analytic tools. Proliferation and isolation occur in the liberal arts by the creation of departments; in the liberal sciences, by the formation of new colleges or schools.

Most professional schools establish close links with those liberal arts disciplines that provide the basic knowledge most useful to their purposes. This is true, for example, of the relationship of engineering to the physical sciences. Such a liaison can lead, predictably, to inbreeding and isolation from large segments of society. The individual member of a professional school located in an academic community naturally develops strong bonds with scientific colleagues located nearby. Moreover, each school inevitably creates its own storehouse of ideas and facts, all carefully labeled in a tyranny of compartmentalization. Under these circumstances, contact with society is limited, further confining the class and scale of problems that can be dealt with by adherents of one school.

Parkinson's Law usually takes over at this point, and there is a clamor for new professional schools to treat such problem areas as transportation, water resources, and air pollution. This pathological process cannot yield more than a short-term remedy for a specific problem. The status it renders to a given need of society is usually false. The damage this process inflicts on academic institutions is obvious: further compartmentalization, a breakdown in communication, an increase in theoretically oriented groupings removed from real problems, and the perpetuation of obsolete organizations no longer relevant to the needs of society and without healthy roots in the disciplines unique to those needs. One example of this process should suffice. Fifty years ago, schools of mining were numerous; today, no more than six exist in the entire United States.

Schools that have endured for a long period have formulated analytic concepts and application techniques with broad usefulness. They have maintained a sensitivity to the changing needs of society. If a meaningful collaboration between professional schools evolves, it will most likely be in the form of sharing specific concepts and techniques originally developed for single purposes. John C. Calhoon, Jr., has stated the case for engineering:

Engineering has evolved a set of concepts with wide applicability. Within the domain of engineering education, these concepts are named the engineering sciences. In content, they encompass the basic principles of transformation, of exchange, of transfer, of communication, and of distribution. Although these same processes may be present and recognized in other disciplines, they have not been reduced to the analytical rigor that has been possible in engineering systems. Engineers have had the advantage of working with systems wherein the variables can be controlled or dealt with separately. It has been possible, therefore, to achieve an analytical development of these elements of change and to generalize their study.

The processes of change and control which appear in engineering systems also appear in biological systems, social systems, political systems, and in other relationships between men. A basic question arises: Are the processes of interaction between physical entities so different from the processes of interaction between non-physical entities that one cannot expect to apply the same principle? If we believe in the basic unity of nature, and in the ultimate goal of scientific generalization, we should hold some hope for the possibility that the advances in the sciences of change, which we call the engineering sciences, can be extended to non-engineering areas of study. Engineering has an obligation to broaden these subjects and to make them available to the total academic community.

One problem is that the engineering education community has not itself recognized what it has conceived under the name of engineering sciences. I truly believe that these studies would be more aptly named the "sciences of change." The engineering sciences are applicable as scholarly subject matter or as cultural courses for many curricula of the university spectrum. For these purposes, the topics perhaps cannot be taught so rigorously as they are in engineering and perhaps the mathematical analysis may necessarily give way to a more general analytical approach. Nevertheless, if engineering has anything of a truly cultural or scholarly nature to offer the rest of the academic community, it lies in the area of engineering sciences.

Engineering education must also contribute its techniques—techniques that have been developed through engineering and for whose use engineering should take the leading role. Among these techniques are those applicable to computers and programming, to operations analysis, to communication, and to programmed learning, to mention just a few. The engineering approach is an orientation toward a job or goal. In executing this approach, the engineer has evolved a logical analysis and synthesis procedure which permits even those systems with numerous variables to be subjected to analytical study. These same techniques are applicable, at least in a modified way, to classical problems such as those in teaching and languages, or to newly developing programs and problems in the social sciences. Again, it is my opinion that the engineering educator must take the lead in initiating the use of these devices and concepts in other areas. With knowledge comes responsibility. The engineer holding this knowledge must take the responsibility to fashion its use for the needs of others.

This philosophy can be extended to the locally developed concepts and techniques of other professions. Engineers feel inadequate when confronted with the technical concepts and techniques of other fields—jurisprudence, regional planning, social welfare, and political structure, for example. There is a need to do more than learn the language.

The ideal collaboration between professional schools in an academic community can best be achieved by new combinations of sequential degrees where the Master's degree assumes a role of major importance. The combination of the degree of Master of Business Administration with an earlier Bachelor's degree in another field is an example with a long and felicitous history. The fields of city and regional planning, engineering, and public administration all appear to offer potential combined-degree benefits. A major deterrent is a department's demand that all course prerequisites be satisfied by the holder of a Bachelor's degree in another discipline. This provincial attitude must be opposed or circumvented even if new degrees must be constructed. A sequence of degrees is not intended to create the superprofessional, for no one man can accommodate all the necessary knowledge in sufficient depth. If, however, we are going to encourage an appreciation and an understanding of the proper use of tools developed by other disciplines, we must recognize the new expertise a professional can gain from a short graduate program in a discipline outside his field.

In relying heavily on the Doctor of Philosophy designation, we have encouraged the research orientation to the detriment of a professional or design orientation. If professional schools are an integral part of the university, a professional doctoral program can be constructed which would differ only in the content of the thesis. If the usual research doctoral thesis is oriented to the uncovering of new knowledge, the professional doctoral thesis should be concerned with the application of that knowledge to a problem whose solution is important to society.

The final teaching resource of the university, loosely identified as continuing education, is often administered as an independent extension service. As such, it is removed from the major faculty talent of the campus. In spite of this handicap, continuing education, as it is presently developing, can afford the best opportunity for the presentation and discussion of national concerns in today's university environment. It provides direct contact with and feedback from the entire community. With an increased number of campuses devoted to higher education, a constant shift toward urban living, and the emergence of television as a mass medium, continuing education has modified its offerings. Not only can television be used as a direct link with the community, but closed-circuit television with scrambled transmission and two-way audio channels permits specialized groups to be reached directly in hospitals and industries. Radio has also been utilized in a novel fashion to provide the listener, who pays, with audio linkage to the speaker, whom he can question.

The modern offerings of continuing education fall into two categories. The first is a well-developed series of sophisticated, high-cost short courses through which the practicing professional can learn the latest developments in his field. Many universities in the United States offer such courses in law, medicine, and engineering. The second category holds great promise for considering national concerns. Basically, it is an open-ended presentation and discussion by leading spokesmen of national stature. Presented directly to a critical and questioning audience, the entire program is transmitted to the surrounding community and is recorded for rebroadcast in other areas. Unfortunately, topics for both the professional-oriented short courses and the discussions of national concerns are chosen largely on the basis of financial supply and demand. Such programs must be self-supporting; thus, the "box office" dominates decisions about which areas to treat. In certain respects, however, the requirement of being financially independent does limit the amount of trivia that would otherwise be presented.

The next major change in extension or continuing-education services will be to incorporate this function into the regularly budgeted teaching activities on a given campus. The short courses oriented to the active professional are as much a function of higher education as the original degree programs. In many respects, they represent one way for the university professor to deal with the real problems of his profession. The consideration of national concerns before a campus audience and the television transmission of this debate to the surrounding community are similar to and an extension of the "general education" course mentioned earlier. If such a course brought outside practitioners to the campus, the entire program, if recorded, would benefit not only the student body but the general community.

The reorganization of academic resources proposed in this paper consists of several small incremental changes. They include modifying the concept of "general education" so that it includes the contributions of professional schools to the education of all students at the university; an increased collaboration among professional schools through the sharing of commonly used concepts and techniques and the application of those concepts and techniques to the real problems of society; and the greater use of professional and public offerings at the continuing-education level. By these changes the goals of government agencies—public awareness, basic research, and applied research—could be achieved. More important, however, would be the gains these changes would bring about as they influence the university. The concept of a new undergraduate general-education course devoted to national problems would provide the "relevance" often lacking in the first years of higher education. It would also afford the participating faculty an opportunity to acquaint young college students with the results of graduate research and professional activity.

Professional schools might begin to collaborate extensively with no prodding. The present lack of such co-operation is emphasized so that further fractionalization and proliferation by the construction of new schools can be avoided. In a positive sense, co-operative team-teaching among professional-school faculty could lead to responsible co-operative team effort in the field.

The presentation of issues of national concern through continuing-education programs promises to bring about the greatest change within the university. Through this effort, all elements of the university would become involved in the solution of community problems so that the university could, in fact, be a "central instrument of public policy in the United States." Already questions of national policy related to selective service, pollution, race relations, and the invasion of privacy are being debated, recorded, and transmitted through university channels. By simple extrapolation of the numbers and kinds of people increasingly involved in education, one can visualize the need to provide a forum for open public debate of problems of national concern and national goals. The university campus, by means of the mass media, could eventually become such a forum. In recent years, many of our present goals have been set without benefit of this debate—for example, the space program, activity in Viet-Nam, and the poverty program. What is going to provide the forum for debating such future issues as the limitation of automobiles for each family and the regulation of genetic control? In the early years of this country, such debate was carried out in Congress, for congressmen were then more directly responsible for the legislation proposed. Today, with the increased complexity of living and, in turn, of corresponding legislation, it is the responsibility of the true authors of that legislation to initiate and participate in public debate. As the academic community is deeply involved in the determination of public policy, it is logical for that debate to be carried out in a university environment.

ROBERT S. MORISON

Education for Environmental Concerns

To WRITE an essay on education for environmental management is to write an essay on the future of the university. Nothing is alien to our environment, and, thus, nothing can be alien to the environmental manager. Almost without exception, the separate parts of a modern American university's curriculum yield some angle of perspective on the environment. The university exists, in part, to train specialists for intensive study in the various branches of modern knowledge. At the same time, the university remains dedicated to the proposition that life is coherent and can be understood within a single frame. Both attitudes must be kept clearly in mind as we educate ourselves to be responsible stewards of our environment.

The management of the environment will require specialists of all kinds: the geologist to tell us about the nature of the earth and the derivation and future of its watercourses; the soil specialist to tell us about the thin layer of degraded rock and accumulated organic matter on which life depends; the biologist to describe living things and the means by which their variety is maintained in a dynamic, constantly changing state of equilibrium; the conservationist to maintain, restore, and alter the face of nature so that it can best minister to the complex fancies of man. Finally and perhaps most important, we need the anthropologist, the sociologist, the economist, and the philosopher to tell us about man and his ways, for it is man, the most "successful" of all the species, who occupies, exploits, and pollutes the largest number of ecological niches.

Supplying these specialists is, however, only the first and much the easiest part of the problem. It is becoming increasingly obvious that ordinary run-of-the-mill specialists by themselves are of limited value. The collaboration of several different technologies is required to solve all but the simplest of environmental problems, and most

285

of these problems are far more complex than they seem to be at first glance. As soon as we begin to analyze our purposes, we find that the goals that seemed obvious at first are not nearly so easy to define as we had thought. Moreover, once the possible goals are defined, it becomes painfully apparent that there is little unanimity about which goals to choose.

For purposes of analysis, let us consider the collaboration between specialists that is required to reach an already defined and chosen goal—cleaning up the river that runs through a town. The major source of contamination is domestic sewage. The standard objectives of sewage disposal involve the removal of solids, partly by physical settling and partly by conversion of organic matter with the help of bacterial fermentation. The professional sanitary engineer has long enjoyed some training in biology as well as civil engineering because biological methods are used in sewage disposal. Moreover, he is concerned with removing organisms dangerous to health. Nevertheless, no single profession can now be expected to command all the biology, the physics, and the chemistry, not to mention the economics and the sociology, necessary to cope with the many problems involved in the disposal of domestic sewage. The time-honored removal of solids and elimination of pathogenic bacteria, and the addition of sufficient oxygen to render the final effluent clear, odorless, and innocuous to health are increasingly found to be inadequate. The remaining inorganic materials—nitrogen, phosphate, potash, and certain as yet ill-identified trace elements—remain to feed a luxurient growth of algae and other aquatic weeds. Alive, these organisms render the water unattractive and make water sports dangerous; dead, they essentially replace the organic matter so laboriously removed from the original sewage. The decaying weeds release noxious gases that disturb the passer-by and rob the water of its oxygen so that it can no longer support animal life. For many practical purposes, the river so contaminated is as badly off as it would have been had we not tried to deal with the original sewage problem.

Although we now understand in broad outlines the events leading to the overgrowth of aquatic plants, the details of the process differ from place to place. The control of these plants requires the co-operation of biologists, chemists, and physicists, as well as sanitary engineers. Such collaboration presupposes that each specialist has had a certain degree of familiarity with the disciplines of the other specialists involved. Each must also develop a certain sympathy and understanding of the current weaknesses and inadequacies of his sister specialties. A successful collaborative friendship can be easily ruined if the chemist is obviously contemptuous of the biologist's inability to determine whether the overgrowth in a particular pond is primarily due to an excess of nitrogen, of phosphorous, or of some unexpected trace element. Some other quite different factor may be responsible: the unusually high temperature of the water, the speed with which the water circulates vertically, or the unusual distribution of light intensities. Conversely, the biologist should not be too obviously incredulous when he hears that the chemist has no feasible, cheap way of removing phosphate.

The requirements for breadth of understanding and sympathy become even greater when we come to the matter of goal selection. A thoughtful conservationist shows his sensitivity to this problem by beginning a recent article on education for conservation with the following anecdote:

The scene was rural, but only an hour's drive from an urban center. The attractive gray-haired lady from the city listened at length, and with some patience, to the "farm planner" as he expounded the merits of birdsfoot trefoil as a crop on the field from which he had just extracted his soil auger. "No, no, young man," she admonished as she led him to a spot where they could survey a neighbor's rocky pasture covered with Queen Anne's lace and chickory: "There! That's what I want. How do I get it?"[1]

This charming story is true not only for little old ladies but for almost everybody else. The industrialist who once looked upon the stream flowing by his factory as a source of power and, later on, as a drainage ditch is now beginning to wonder if the stream would not be more useful as a recreational area, which would also attract scarce personnel. Once restored to recreational quality, it could support a small fishing industry, which would incidentally delight the palates of the sophisticated with the shellfish that are now rapidly disappearing. Before we make such choices, however, we must know a great deal more than we do now about the differential benefits to be gained from the extraordinary costs that must be incurred.

Squarely in the center of our problem is the need to develop more sensible ways of thinking about and more persuasive ways of talking about value judgments. In the past, humanists and philosophers have tended to assert a more or less exclusive right to deal with problems of value. The rest of the scholarly world has been glad enough to acquiesce, since the relevance of theoretical studies of value to practical affairs is not always obvious. We must now realize that what we decide about value will determine to a very great measure what we do with our environment. If, for example, "one impulse from a vernal wood may teach you more of man, of moral evil and of good, than all the sages can," it becomes immediately more important to preserve green belts in the neighborhoods of cities than to increase the budget for the municipal university. How we can validate Wordsworth's statement is unclear, but we are going to have to try. Now that we have the power and the resources to abolish woods altogether, or to make new ones spring up where no tree has grown for a thousand years, we must be sure about why we like to walk in the woods and listen to vernal impulses. Conversely, we must become more explicitly aware of the motives of those who have cut down forests in the past and more vigorously analytical of the benefits as well as the costs of alternate uses of forest products.

As we begin to come to grips with some of our more obvious environmental problems, we discover how little thought we have given to the ultimate goals toward which we are racing with ever increasing speed. The United States and, in varying degrees, all the Western democracies have concentrated on means rather than ends. The general idea has been to develop those conditions under which each individual can pursue his particular happiness. Underlying this procedure is the assumption that each individual would have little difficulty selecting his own objectives and that it would be meddlesome of society to talk about such matters in public. This generally laudable respect for private purposes has provided an insecure philosophical basis from which to undertake common action for common purposes. At this point we may pause only to notice the embarrassment we feel when we try to explain to ourselves why we should try to reduce smog or why some of us do not like automobile graveyards. Nowhere is our awkwardness more apparent than in the discussion of standards.

Although one's instinctive personal reaction is that even one junk automobile in a neighbor's front yard or any noxious fumes in the air we breathe are bad and should be avoided, any sophisticated person knows that you cannot approach the problem in this way. This matter came into painfully sharp focus as the "zero tolerance" problem, after Congress passed a law stating, in effect, that foods should contain *no* substances capable of causing cancer. Scientists find it impossible to prove the absence of something. About the best they can do in regard to potential carcinogens in food is to say something like: "Contains no more than one part per million of any known substance which when given to rats at a concentration of one part per 10,000 for three months is followed by an increase in the incidence of malignant tumors of the liver of less than 1 per cent."

In attempting to control pollution, we must begin by recognizing that some pollution is inevitable. One automobile crossing the empty Dakota Bad Lands changes the composition of the air; one privy on an Appalachian hillside pollutes the Ohio River. The practical engineering question remains: "When does the pollution become intolerable?" This question in turn raises philosophical, ethical, and aesthetic questions of the greatest moment. But curiously we are so embarrassed discussing such matters in public that we quickly turn the problem into one of public health. As was pointed out at a recent meeting of environmental policy-makers, we do this for two reasons. The American people "have already been sold on health as a value and are prepared to pay a lot for it." Moreover, although it is at least theoretically possible to correlate so many parts per million of pollution with some measurable increase in morbidity or mortality, it is presumably less easy to measure how much the total sum of human welfare has been reduced merely because smog has obscured the view of the North River for one million office workers and caused their eyes to burn on the way home. Sooner or later, we may need to ask ourselves whether good health is an end in itself or a means to something else. Can we go on indefinitely equating the goodness of life only with its length?

We are now in a position to ask what kinds of educational arrangements are necessary to prepare us for dealing more consciously and more effectively with our environment. If our analysis of the problems to be solved is correct, the educational requirements are of two rather different kinds.

There is, first, a need to train substantial numbers of environmental specialists to develop and operate the technologies necessary for modifying, restoring, and maintaining the environment in accord with whatever goals we set. The second and more challenging task is to devise ways of educating and guiding the entire population to make informed and satisfying choices of goals.

The modern well-rounded university already provides adequate opportunities for mastering the basic knowledge necessary for managing the environment. Basic biology, physics, chemistry, economics, and sociology are all readily available. As one approaches the specific problems of the environment, existing knowledge appears to be less adequate. Thus, everyone is more or less aware of the rapid progress in basic genetics and the less spectacular but still steady advances in animal and plant nutrition and metabolism, including photosynthesis. Much less work has been done, however, on how these basic factors combine in a given lake or stream to determine the growth of a particular species of algae. This lag in application can be traced, in part, to the individual scientist's lack of motivation to enter the necessary "applied" fields. It also reflects the very real inability of modern scientific methodology to deal with what Warren Weaver has called "organized complexity." The two factors work together in a vicious circle (itself a primitive example of organized complexity). Young people are not attracted to complex problems because they recognize the lack of an adequate methodology, and the methodology remains inadequate because few first-rate people are motivated to improve it. The present state of affairs in ecology illustrates the nature of the difficulty and suggests a possible solution.

Although there is a great deal of talk about the importance of "ecosystems," no such system has been adequately described even in qualitative terms. Quantitative analysis of ecosystems is in its infancy. Some scholars are beginning to foresee dimly the outlines of how modern systems analysis and computer simulation may be applied to some of these problems. Challenging though these possibilities may be to a few experts, they have not reached the stage where they can be presented in an exciting and convincing way to students. The freshman or sophomore with a head for mathematics and a love of precise definitions is much more likely to go into molecular biology where provocative personalities have blazed a clear trail to the understanding of several interesting and very basic matters. The only discernible and not very satisfactory path to a more productive future for community biology may be through the encouragement and support of those few individuals who can develop effective methods of analysis and simulation, so that the secrets of community action become as accessible as those of the genetic code now are.

If difficulties are encountered in attracting sufficient student interest in ecology, those difficulties are only intensified as we reach the applied and professional levels. Here the purpose is not so much to understand the environment as to do something about it.

In view of the now obvious importance of maintaining the integrity of the environment, surprisingly few young people are stimulated to take up these vocations. It seems quite obvious to an urban planner that a mass transport system provides a more rapid and comfortable form of transportation to and from work than the individual automobile. Moreover, it would also stay the conversion of productive land into highways and reduce one of the primary sources of smog. To the average young engineer, however, designing anything as old hat as a subway train is an unexciting prospect. In addition, the solution to the problem involves a number of economic, social, and psychological variables—the kind of thing he went into engineering to avoid.

Unhappily, bright young men and women tend to select careers that seem exciting to them rather than those that are demonstrably needed by society. In this, they are only following their teachers, for scholars, scientists, and artists have all proclaimed that the best work is done when the inspired individual follows his curiosity and need for self-expression. Indeed, there is convincing evidence that knowledge advances according to the rules of some inner dynamic that interacts with the tastes and curiosities of the knowledge-seekers. A particularly fertile hypothesis or the development of a particularly powerful methodology determines where the progress will be; the demonstrated need for a new type of knowledge plays rather a small role in the process.

In recent years, however, public awareness of the importance of science to our civilization has resulted in efforts to harness the scientific process so that it can be driven toward foreseeable ends. Whatever can be done to modify the direction by providing money and facilities will probably be done and have some influence, but the over-all effect is likely to be limited. Money can hasten development of an existing idea or technique; its role in stimulating an original idea is less clear. The National Foundation for Poliomyelitis, with the large sums at its command, developed the Salk vaccine some years earlier than would have been possible without such aid. On the other hand, the key element was the invention of a method for growing the virus in tissue culture, and this came about largely through the efforts of an individual who was attracted to the investigation of viruses a decade before the foundation was established.

The proportions of students electing to enter a given branch of knowledge have remained remarkably constant even though financial support has increased sharply in some areas and not in others. In spite of the enormous publicity given to science since World War II and especially since the first Sputnik, the percentage of people going into the natural sciences after they are graduated from college has remained level. Indeed, a somewhat smaller percentage of students is taking high-school physics. Confronted by these unsettling facts, one can only point to the need for more people with better and more exciting ideas about environmental studies and hope that the ways to attract first-class students into the area will be found. A first step might be to free some of the rare leaders from the many committee meetings called to map out programs in environmental management, so that they may return to classroom and laboratory where they can develop their ideas and attract more students.

Finally, we must improve the status of the environmental professions. A rather musty civil-service atmosphere still clings to sanitary engineering, public health, toxicology, conservation, and even urban planning. Once a generation, perhaps only once a century, a Christopher Wren, a Baron Haussmann, or a Frederick Law Olmstead shows us that a genius can apply himself to the urban environment and incidentally satisfy a personal need for public recognition if not glamour. (*Si monumentum requiris; circumspice.*) More rarely, a man acquires immortality simply by cleaning up a city and making it more livable, as Sir Edwin Chadwick and John Snow did in the last century. Society seems even less prepared to recognize those who would preserve the natural rural environment, although one of the acknowledged merits of Theodore Roosevelt was his encouragement of Gifford Pinchot. Democracies have been slow in finding suitable incentives and rewards for those who would make the general conditions of living more healthful, comfortable, and beautiful for all.

Even when we succeed in encouraging prospective environmental managers to seek professional training, we quickly discover that the prestigious professional schools associated with most universities come out of ancient traditions. The universities of the Middle Ages had their schools of theology, law, and medicine, and these are still the principal professional schools operating at the graduate level. The newer professions have not succeeded in developing recognizable traditions and have, therefore, borrowed rather awkwardly from the tradition of the university in general. Nowhere is this more clear than in the tendency to turn the Ph.D.

into a kind of jack-of-all-trades. Not so long ago, one expected to find a person with a doctorate to be engaged in the traditional business of uncovering new knowledge and teaching it to students. Now perhaps as many as half of the holders of the degree are practicing other professions. The typical Ph.D. in the agricultural sciences, for example, is not so much a teacher and contributor to knowledge as he is a developer and promoter of new agricultural technology. A large, industrialized chicken farm may have several Ph.D.'s on its staff to guide the breeding program and to keep up with the ever advancing knowledge of nutrition. Such men do need to be trained well beyond the level available in an undergraduate agricultural college, so that they know how new knowledge is developed and how to evaluate the results of experimentation. It is less clear, however, that they need to spend much time in learning to do basic research. Much the same could be said for the large number of Ph.D.'s in engineering who are now being absorbed into the more progressive kinds of manufacturing. Perhaps even more analogous to the classical profession is the Doctor of Philosophy in psychology who spends his life practicing clinical psychology on a more or less individual basis.

The characteristics of professional, as opposed to strictly academic, education are the training to *do* as well as to think and a somewhat broader approach to the subject than is strictly necessary for most researchers and teachers. Conversely, professionals have somewhat less obligation than academics to contribute new knowledge of a theoretical sort or to qualify as teachers.

One of the difficulties in attracting young people into the newer professions arises because the prestige of professions varies almost directly with their age. Holders of degrees in law, medicine, and theology do not feel particularly inferior to holders of the Ph.D. Some of them may, in fact, feel a trifle superior. Nobody has succeeded in transferring this type of dignity and self-confidence to a degree that might be suitable for those practicing such professions as clinical psychology, advanced agricultural technology, engineering, or environmental management. The matter may be most acute as we begin to think seriously about preparing people to manage the environment. It is more unlikely that a Ph.D. in any of the recognized disciplines could provide adequate preparation for the people who must make the environment more suitable for human needs. The two existing professions that seem most likely—public health and civil engineering—are for various reasons not so promising as they look. Competitors like regional and urban planning are almost certainly too specialized.

We should probably be looking toward a six- or seven-year program leading to some definite graduate degree that would confer dignity and prestige, but not necessarily testify to the ability to make original contributions to knowledge. The curriculum should contain enough biology so that the candidate would emerge with some understanding of how biological systems work, enough engineering to give a sense of man's power to alter the physical environment in both adaptive and nonadaptive ways, and enough of the humanities and social sciences to give a feeling for what men think they want, what they really want, and how human institutions work to forward or frustrate human desires. This is a large but, perhaps, not impossible order; anything less is inadequate to the purpose. The engineer without familiarity with both biology and the humanities cannot go very far in meeting the need. The conventional engineer is too used to problems that are in a sense easy to solve because they are posed in a limited frame.

Modern engineering technology can make drastic changes in the environment before we have had time to assess their ultimate results. The topsoil it has taken centuries to accumulate can be removed in a few years. A marsh can be drained before anyone weighs the benefit of its increased agricultural production against its recreational value to bird-watchers, Sunday walkers, and October hunters who utilized it in its pristine state. On the other hand, left to himself, the biologist or ecologist is likely to become so bemused by the mystical beauty of the balance of nature that he underestimates the importance of human needs or the power of modern engineering technology to compensate for what may at first glance seem to be wanton destruction. The economist and the sociologist are likely to develop too abstract a picture of both man and nature in a pseudo-scientific search for order in human affairs. A more balanced view is needed that recognizes man as a part of nature—a somewhat peculiar part since he can modify the direction in which natural forces operate in order to reach objectives different from those which nature might produce if he were not there.

In the long run, changes in the environment will evolve from the conscious or unconscious choices of the majority of ordinary people. Ordinary people alter the environment directly by building houses, clipping hedges, and throwing beer cans out of cars, and indirectly by voting to build roads, sequester wildlife areas, or control smog.

The future of the environment will be largely what we choose it to be. These choices will, in turn, depend in large part on what we think life itself ought to be. In the past it has been customary to describe the American standard of living in terms of the amount of food, clothing, real estate, and chattels available to each individual. No longer, however, can this quantitative enumeration be directly equated with happiness or personal welfare. The cherished automobile loses much of its value if caught in a continuous traffic jam; the lovely cruiser or the beautifully designed fishing rod are left at the dock when rivers and lakes lose their oxygen and give off methane and hydrogen sulfide; even food loses some of its savor when its production entails the inadvertent poisoning of birds and fish.

John Kenneth Galbraith has described the many ways in which members of the affluent society have focused production on individual rather than community welfare. In spite of the clarity of his presentation, we have difficulty in adjusting ourselves to its implications largely because of the accounting problems involved. To a large extent, the shift from an individual-centered to a community-centered economy is a shift from a system of bookkeeping that easily adds innumerable objects like washing machines, to one which tries to give a value to the feelings of people about things they enjoy in common. Our thoughts and judgments must turn from the individual and the material to the moral and the aesthetic. The morality will doubtless remain basically utilitarian, but the perspective from which the utility is measured is likely to be broader and to involve more individuals. Most modern democracies have attempted to duck the moral and the aesthetic issues by concentrating on means while leaving value judgments to the individual.

Insofar as moral judgments are a matter of religion, the democratic state *must* abstain because of its dedication to religious toleration. As a practical matter, it has been *able* to abstain because in matters of individual morality, such as those covered by the Ten Commandments, most men hold astonishingly similar views, even though their religions may vary considerably. The ethical base of most democracies is, therefore, utilitarian rather than transcendental, and legislative bodies, as well as individuals, make most of their moral choices after a reasonably careful appraisal of the probable results of various courses of action.

This tradition seems to leave no alternative to assuming that an informed electorate will make the proper choices when exposed for a long enough time to the best evidence available. To become suitably informed on a modern program for the environment will require considerable sophistication in the weighing of scientific evidence, most of it presented in a statistical way. Few things of significance to the environment happen as the inevitable result of a single definable cause. Just as the smog in Los Angeles is the result of hundreds of thousands of motorists driving hundreds of thousands of cars, each with its own rate of emitting pollutants, and the weather conditions, a result of additional thousands of factors, so the effect of the smog on any given individual depends upon his basic constitution, health, the degree and duration of his exposure, and other unidentifiable factors. Weighing all these factors simply to make a prediction requires considerable training and experience in the natural sciences and in the use of statistics.

On various occasions, it has been recommended that the teaching of statistics and probability begin earlier and go on longer than has been usual in our educational system. Indeed, the argument for replacing the study of plane geometry in high school with a course in probability and statistics is a persuasive one. Today we have largely abandoned the thought that the right decision can be arrived at by a process of logical deduction topped off by a Q.E.D. Right action almost always depends on the weighing of probabilities. Even the most basic scientific generalizations are expressions of probability rather than inescapably logical conclusions. Nevertheless, a statement of probabilities is not yet wholly convincing, even to the most sophisticated. Relatively few people feel as safe in an airplane as they do in an automobile, even though the odds against accidents are far higher in the first case. We will not be modern men until we believe our statistics the way we now believe our eyes.

In addition, the average man must become aware of statistical realities in another, more subtle way. It is not enough to *know* what is going to happen to others as a result of an overt act of neglect; one must *care* about it as well. One must become statistically moral in the sense that one *cares* about what happens to numerous unseen people as much as one cares about the welfare of the few who are close enough to be seen and heard. Other people in other places and in future times will benefit most from our efforts to preserve the environment. Many of the benefits will be discouragingly intangible—a blue sky instead of a gray one, trees and green fields instead of barren hillsides, bird songs instead of a silent spring, clean streets, well-proportioned façades, and quiet walks instead of ugliness, traffic jams, and noise. The educational system for tomorrow must not only make it clear how these presumable goals can be achieved but why they are worth achieving.

Quite possibly, and perhaps quite shockingly to some, this increased concern for goals may mean that certain branches of knowledge will have to renounce a part of their highly cherished objectivity and return to an earlier interest in ends as well as means. In many instances, the answer to why a particular goal is selected will be found in personal taste and feeling. Formal education and scholarship once directed a substantial part of their efforts to cultivating "sensibility" and refining tastes. In recent years, the apparent success of objective or scientific methods has tended to erode the dignity of subjective approaches and to cast doubt on their effectiveness. Consequently, we are better prepared to describe and improve our means than to choose satisfactory ends. Much of recent literature concerns the individual's difficulty in discovering valid personal goals. The difficulty is many times greater when the goals of an entire group or society must be set. Trained as we are to doubt the validity of our own feelings, we can scarcely be blamed for not giving much weight to the feelings of others. Nevertheless, the collective feeling about the consequence or inconsequence of clean air, pure water, and graceful cities will decide the way in which we employ our energies in the future. If the educational system is to prepare the oncoming generations for collective aesthetic decision-making, it will have to develop more self-confidence in its ability to deal effectively with questions of taste and other nonquantitative matters. Above all, it must recognize that aesthetic choice can no longer be regarded entirely as an individual matter with consequences safely limited to inner experience.

The need for a reorientation toward a greater concern with the social consequences of aesthetic choice is probably strongest at the university level. The elementary and secondary schools, being less sophisticated about the epistemological problems involved and less squeamish about appearing to dictate in matters of taste, have always had far less trouble taking positions on the good, the true, and the beautiful. On occasion, they have even indulged in outright propaganda for conservation of natural areas and beautification of cities. The universities must, of course, continue to deal with such matters with considerably more circumspection and to give special attention to the difficulties involved in arriving at group decisions in matters of feeling. They must, nevertheless, leave their students with a conviction of the importance of these matters in everyday life.

The educational system of the future must ensure that the decision-makers—and in a democracy that includes almost everybody—know enough of science to understand the consequences and the costs of different courses of action and enough of philosophy, the humanities, and the arts to appreciate their value. Only the urgency of this plea for a unified or "general" education for the whole population is new. When society commands the means to do almost anything it wants, value judgments of ends are crucial.

It is not nearly so easy to explain why the study of philosophy, history, and literature prepares one for making discriminating judgments about the significance and beauty of life as it is to point out what physics and chemistry have to do with the practice of engineering. To an embarrassingly great extent, advocates of the liberal arts as a preparation for life in the real world find it hard to go much beyond Matthew Arnold's view that it is good to know the best that has been thought and said in the world and that somehow this will contribute to sweetness and light. In a rapidly industrializing society bent on supplying the means of subsistence and creature comforts for all and dominated by the austerities of a remnant puritanism, there often seems to be something a little irrelevant, if not actually frivolous, about a preoccupation with sweetness and light. In the crudest possible terms, "Who but a starry-eyed do-gooder would try to weight the integrity of the West Virginia landscape against the ten-foot seam of coal one could get by tearing it up?"

By an interesting paradox, the progress of science and technology has now demonstrated that it is not inevitable and certainly not desirable that we do everything we can do, that the choice of what to do is, in fact, our most important problem, and that the ultimate basis of choice is aesthetic. We must have faith that the soundest base for aesthetic judgment is the cultivation of the best that has been known and thought.

REFERENCES

1. Lawrence S. Hamilton, "Education for the Changing Field of Conservation," *Science Education*, Vol. 51, No. 2.

Notes on Contributors

DAVID ALLEE, born in 1931, is associate professor of resource economics at the New York State College of Agriculture at Cornell University. Mr. Allee is also associate director of the Cornell University Water Resources Center.

HELMUT K. BUECHNER, born in 1918, is head of the Office of Ecology at the Smithsonian Institution.

F. FRASER DARLING, born in 1903, is vice president of the Conservation Foundation. He is the author of *A Herd of Red Deer: A Study in Social Behaviour* (1937), *Bird Flocks and the Breeding Cycle* (1938), *West Highland Survey* (1955), *Wildlife in an African Territory* (1960), and *The Unity of Ecology* (1963).

JOSEPH L. FISHER, born in 1914, is president of Resources for the Future, Inc. He is co-author of *Resources in America's Future* (Baltimore, 1963) and *World Prospects for Natural Resources* (Baltimore, 1964).

HAROLD GILLIAM, born in 1931, is a staff member of *The San Francisco Chronicle*. Mr. Gilliam is the author of *San Francisco: City of the Golden Gate* (1959), *The Natural World of San Francisco* (1967), and *For Whom the Bay* (forthcoming).

FREDERICK GUTHEIM is a consultant on urban affairs in Washington, D.C. His review of European experience with new towns appeared in *Taming Megalopolis* (Garden City, 1967), ed. by H. Wentworth Eldredge. He has also contributed to *The Regional City* (London, 1966), ed. by Derek Senior, and to *Cities and Space* (Baltimore, 1963), ed. by Lowden Wingo, Jr.

JOHN V. KRUTILLA, born in 1922, is a senior staff member of Resources for the Future, Inc. His publications include *Multiple Purpose River Development: Studies in Applied Economic Analysis* (1958), *The Columbia Treaty: The Economics of an International River Basin Development* (1967), and *Unemployment, Idle Capacity, and Public Expenditure Criteria* (forthcoming).

Notes on Contributors

HANS H. LANDSBERG, born in 1913, is director of the resource appraisal program for Resources for the Future, Inc. Co-author of *Output, Employment, and Productivity 1899-1939* (1941) and *Resources for America's Future* (1963), he is the author of *Natural Resources for U. S. Growth* (1964).

R. BURTON LITTON, JR., born in 1918, is associate professor of landscape architecture at the University of California, Berkeley. During 1968 he was on a visiting scholar program at Resources for the Future concerning "Recognition, Definition and Use of Landscape Resources." He is the author of *Landscape Description and Inventories* (Berkeley, 1968).

GEORGE J. MASLACH, born in 1920, is dean of the College of Engineering of the University of California at Berkeley.

ROBERT S. MORISON, born in 1906, is director of the Division of Biological Sciences at Cornell University. He is the author of *Scientist* (1964) and the editor of *The Contemporary University: U.S.A.* (1966).

ALEXIS PAPAGEORGIOU, born in 1920, is an architect. He collaborated with D. Pikionis on the design of the contemporary park on the western slopes of the Acropolis.

ROBERT W. PATTERSON, born in 1905, is an architect and landscape architect. Mr. Patterson is a member of the President's Advisory Board on Water Pollution Control and director of the National Wildlife Federation.

ROGER REVELLE, born in 1909, is professor of population and director of the Center for Population Studies at Harvard University. Mr. Revelle was director of the Scripps Institution of Oceanography from 1951 to 1964.

S. DILLON RIPLEY, born in 1913, is secretary of the Smithsonian Institution. He is the author of *Trail of the Money Bird* (1942), *Search for the Spiny Babbler* (1952), *A Synopsis of the Birds of India and Pakistan* (1961), and *Land and Wildlife of Tropical Asia* (1964).

ATHELSTAN SPILHAUS, born in 1911, is professor of geophysics at the University of Minnesota. His publications include *Workbook on Meteorology* (1942), *Meteorological Instruments* (1953), *Weathercraft* (1951), *Satellite of the Sun* (1958), *Turn to the Sea* (1959), and *The Ocean Laboratory* (1967).

ANN LOUISE STRONG is professor of regional planning and director of the Institute for Environmental Studies at the University of Pennsylvania.

AZRIEL TELLER, born in 1941, is assistant professor of economics at the University of Illinois. Mr. Teller's dissertation, "Air Pollution Abate-

300

ment—An Economic Study Into the Cost of Control," is being prepared for publication.

AARON WILDAVSKY, born in 1930, is professor of political science and chairman of that department at the University of California at Berkeley. He is the author of *Dixon-Yates: A Study in Power Politics* (1962), *The Politics of the Budgetary Process* (1964), *Leadership in a Small Town* (1964), and co-author of *Presidential Election* (1964; revised edition in press).

NATHANIEL WOLLMAN, born in 1915, is professor of economics and chairman of that department at the University of New Mexico. His publications include *Water Supply and Demand* (1960), *Value of Water in Alternative Uses* (1962), and *Water Resources of Chile: An Economic Model* (in press).

INDEX

ACTION program, 195
Adirondack State Park, 235
Aerial surveys, 16
Aesthetic choice, 297–298
Aesthetic minority, 155–156
Aesthetic power, 147–160
Aesthetic quality, of landscape, 91–94
Aesthetics, economics and, 136
Affluence: agricultural changes and, 63; environmental decay and, xi, xx, 166, 295
Agricultural sciences, Ph.D. in, 293
Agriculture: alternate resource use in, 59–61; bushels-per-acre yield in, 113; economics of scale in, 84; fertilization problems in, 57–58, 62, 84; government support of, 64; land development and, 59, 62–63; national goals and, 63–66; pollution and, 57–61, 161–162; price manipulation in, 63–64; resource issues in, 56–66; technological change in, 56–57, 61–62; urban centers and, 60; world food supply and, 64–65
Air: as collective good, 40–41; market for, 41–42; as resource, 40
Air pollution: abatement level and economics of, 43–45; "alerts" in, 48–49; automobile exhaust and, xi, xxi, 48–49, 119; blight and, 133; bronchitis and, 46; build-up of, 51; cancer and, 40, 46; citizenship and, 40–41; city-wide emission standards in, 52; control of, xxi, 39–54; control equipment for, 50; cost of, 40, 53; criteria for, 50; cumulative effects of, 50; ecological balance and, 35; economic realities of, 49–54; effects of, 39, 40–50; emphysema and, 46–47; equiproportional abatement of, 51–52; federal respon-
sibility in, 54; harmful concentration standard for, 47; heart disease and, 47; industry-wide emission standards for, 52; lung cancer and, 46; Mayor's (N.Y.) Task Force in, 53–54; national bill for, 45; new economics and, 156; physical effects of, xxi, 40–50; selective abatement of, 52; sources of, 52–53; warning system for, 47; see also Environment; Environment decay
Airsheds, jurisdiction over, xxvii
Alaska, ecology of, 11–12
Algae, biology of, xxx, 286, 290
Allee, David, xxxvi, 56–66, 301
American Cancer Society, 40
American University, 277
Ancient buildings, preservation of, 248
Animal ecology, beginnings of, 3; see also Ecology; Ecosystems
Animals, destruction of, ix–x; see also Wildlife
Appalachian Mts., wildlife in, 163–165
Aquatic plants, control of, 286–287
Architectural Forum, 75
Architecture: in Experimental City, 228; free-time pursuits and, 237; in natural setting, 237; for outdoor recreation areas, 235–250; parks and, 237–238; psychology and, 91–92
Aristotle, 254–255
Arizona, University of, 4
Armistead, Booth, 198
Arnold, Matthew, 298
Atomic Energy Commission, 69
Automation, xxxv; see also Computer technology
Automobile engine, new types of, xxii
Automobile exhaust, measurement of, xxi

Index

Automobile graveyards, 162
Automobiles: in national parks, 264; pollution from, xi, xxi, 48–49, 119, 222
Avian economics, ecology and, 7

Bacterial cultures, waste in, 219
Bacterial fermentation, training in, 286
Baker v. *Carr*, 90
Barnett, Harold J., 110, 112
Bartram, William, 263
Bates, Marston, 9
Bathhouse architecture, 239
Beer cans, pollution by, xxix, xxxvii, 294
Bellow, Saul, 151
Bennett, William, 69
Bentham, Jeremy, 134
Bio-degradable materials, xxix–xxx
Biological integration, levels of, 20
Biological systems, engineering and, 280
Biology: community, 290; ecology and, 4; in environmental education, 286–287
Biome, concept of, 7
Biopolitics, concept of, 10
Bird populations, depredations in, 164
Birds of prey, disappearance of, 164
Birth rate: environment and, 179; *see also* Population
Black communities, new towns for, 207, 209
Blight, pollution and, 133
Blumenfeld, Hans, 212
Bodega Head environmental planning, 68–69, 80
Bodenheimer, F. S., 16
Botany, ecology and, 3
Boulding, Kenneth, 6
Boston, rivers in, 258
Brandywine, Pa., land ethic problem in, 87–90
Bridge Canyon Dam, 170
British Broadcasting Corporation Third Programme, 155
Bronchitis, air pollution and, 46
Buckingham, James Silk, 213
Buechner, Helmut K., xxxvi, 20–27, 301
Bureau of Outdoor Recreation, 238, 256
Burgard, Ralph, 229

Cain, Stanley, 9

Caldwell, Lynton K., 10–12, 18
Calhoon, John C., Jr., 280
California: new communities in, 191; population growth in, xix; single-purpose planning in, 67–82; smog and, xix, 278, 296
California Planning and Conservation League, 78
California sardines, declining harvest of, xxi
California State Division of Highways, 75, 78–79
California State Park Commission, 70
Canada, new towns in, 203
Cancer, air pollution and, 46
Carbon dioxide, as pollutant, xxi, 20
Carson, Rachel, xxxiii, 17, 24
Carver, Humphrey, 203
Central Arizona project, 34, 38
Chadwick, Sir Edwin, 292
Cheek, Leslie, 198
Chemicals, in agriculture, 57–58
Chemistry, in environmental education, 287, 298
Chester County, Pa., land use in, 88–89
Chicago, rivers as recreation areas in, 258
Chlorinated hydrocarbons, xxii, xxxiii
Cigarette smoking, as air pollution, 46, 120, 127
Cities: air pollution in, 39; blight of, 133; experimental, xxxvii, 219–231; farm decline and, 60–61; of future, xxxv; as gathering places, 225; growth of, 220, 224–225; our love-hate relationship with, xxxiv; megalopolis as poisoner of, 84–85; migration to, xx; open spaces in, 257–258; optimum size of, 223; rebuilding of, xxxv; rivers as recreation sites in, 258; as vital threat, 220; *see also* Megalopolis; New towns; Urbanization
Citizen government, air pollution and, 143
"City of Man," New York, 209
City parks, 258, 262; *see also* National parks; Parks
City planning, in Experimental City, 225–226
Civil War, resource industries following, 109
Clean air: benefit of, to society, 44; cost of, 40–45; demand for, 42; *see also* Air; Air pollution

Coal: consumption of, 1945–65, xiv–xv, 108; conservation of, 107; liquefaction and gasification of, 108; new technology for, 115; pollution from, xii, xxiv, xxix, 133
Coal mines, abandoned, 163
Coal resources, estimates of, 107–108
Coastal waters, as recreation areas, 265–266
College education, 275; *see also* University
Colonies, American, population forecast for, ix
Colorado River, diversion of, 34, 38
Columbia, Md., "new town" at, 191–193, 195–196, 198–204, 211
Commodities and services, use of, 1940–65, xiv–xvi
Communication, waste in, 225–226
Communities, stress in, 12; *see also* New towns
Community planning, 202
Commuting, waste in, 225, 229
Computer technology, in new economics, 158–159
Concentration, pollution and, 223
Connecticut General Insurance Company, 193
Conservation: breadth of, 18; concept of, 9; ecology and, 12; economic progress and, 181; education for, 186, 287–288, 292; environmental decay and, 17, 177–178; leadership and planning in, 184; politics and, 176, 181–182; public support for, 157, 187; recreation areas and, 181; school education on, 186; as social problem, 174; tax deductions and, 182–183, 185
Conservation Foundation, 186
Conservationists: business motives of, 183; defined, 174; goals of, 181–182, 185; Internal Revenue Code and, 182, 185; national organization of, 186–187
Conservation Movement, 107, 108, 148, 181–185
Consumer, cost control by, 144
Cooley, Richard, 11, 18
Coolidge, Calvin, 254
Copper, shortage of, 111
Corps of Engineers, U.S., 33, 73, 78, 174, 194, 207
Cost-benefit estimates, in environment control, 33–35, 148

Craik, Kenneth, 92
Crisis mentality, environment decay and, 83–90

Dakota Bad Lands, 289
Dams and reservoirs, water development and, 33
Dansereau, Pierre, 3, 12
Darling, F. Fraser, xxxvi, 3–18, 301
Dasmann, Raymond, 9, 12, 91
Davis Dam, 33
DDT, xxxiii, 23; *see also* Pesticides
Deer, adjustment of, to environment, 164–165
Deevey, Edward, 7
Delaware River Basin Commission, xxviii
Detergents, bio-degradable, xxix–xxx
Diablo Canyon area, planning in, 71, 80
Diet changes, agriculture and, 64–65
Disposal plants, xxx–xxxii, 175–177
Don Mills Valley, Toronto, 203
Dostoevski, Feodor, 159

Ecological balance, engineering and, 35
Ecological reconnaissance, 15
Ecology: aerial surveys and, 16; community and, 14; concepts in, 20; conservation and, 3–18; defined, 3; and economic development, 35; humanist view of, 24; landscape architecture and, 14; Law of the Inoptimum and, 3; mathematics and, 16; natural areas in, 9; natural beauty and, 36–37; pesticide problems in, 17; politics and, 10; public policy and, 11; regional dimension in, 36; scientific principles of, 5; social involvement and, 15; specialization in, 6; *see also* Ecosystems
Economic analysis, political action and, xxii–xxix
Economic decisions, utility values and, 136
Economic development: environmental effects of, 161–172; unique commodity in, 167
Economics: new, *see* New economics; population increase and, xvii, xix; recycling and, 222; of resources, 131–135; usefulness of, 136
Economic theory, aesthetics and, 136
Economic value, social value and, xxiii

Index

Ecosystems: complexity of, 24; concept of, 7, 15; defined, 21; education and, 25, 290; human society as, 24; irreversible effects in, 166–168; model of, 21; recreation and, 162, 236; as synthesis, 20–27

Education: on conservation, 186, 287–288, 292; degree programs in, 281–283; for environmental concerns, 285–298; "general" vs. "liberal science," 278; in new economics, 152; Ph.D. degree in, 282, 293; in pollution control, xxxii, 25, 285–298; university and college, 275

Educational feedback, 25, 279

Educational resources: bachelor's and advanced degrees in, 281–282; reorganization of, 275–284; see also Education

Egler, Frank E., 20, 22

Eichler, Edward P., 191, 196

Eisenhower, Dwight D., 208, 256

Electric power generation, regulation of, xxvi, 122

Electric utilities: coal and oil consumption by, xiv–xv; pollution by, xii

Ellemberg, H., 7

Elton, Charles, 3, 5, 8

Emphysema, air pollution and, xxi, 46–47

Energy, demand for, 115

Engineering: environment changes and, 294; water conservation and, 32–33

Engineering education, 281

Engineering sciences, concepts in, 280

Environment: ecology and, 14; future of, 295; irreproducible factor in, 168; low regard for, in past, 133; monetary quantification concept in, 125; "priceless" elements in, xxv; psychology of, 91–92; psychosomatic diseases and, 13; quality of life and, 179–180; sociology of, 91–92; as subject for new economics, 131; technology and, 171, 274; as unique commodity, 167; see also Air pollution; Environment decay; Environment quality; Pollution; Pollution control

Environment changes: difficulties in, 124; gains and losses in, 128; measurement of, xxi

Environment control: budget for, 140; collective action in, 129; common theories in, xxxvi–xxxvii; cost of, xxiv–xxv, 128, 142, 175; cost-benefit ratio in, 127–128; education in, 25, 285–298; four areas of action in, xxxiii–xxxvi; government support of, 26, 124–126; minority rights and, 178; multipurpose agencies in, 158; personnel selection in, 139; prediction in, xxii; productivity and, 136; roles in, xxi–xxxiii; satisfaction from, 138; science in, xxi–xxiii; standard-setting in, 129; technology and, 129, 171, 274; university support of, 26; zoning and restrictions in, xxvi–xxvii, 72, 183–184; see also Pollution control

Environment decay: affluence and, 166; agricultural causes of, 57–61; American culture and, 161; crisis mentality in, 83–90; as disease, 222; education and, 285–298; educational feedback in, 25, 279; industrial production and, 172; information lack in, 159; irreversible effect in, 166–168; money economy and, 132; new economics and, 147; philosophical view of, 288; red tape in, 174–175; social change and, 174–175; population control and, 178; public attitudes toward, 295; technology and, 129, 166, 171, 274

Environment needs, satisfaction of, 143

Environment problems: crisis in, 143; public awareness of, 291; university programs in, 285–286, 294; value judgments in, 287

Environment quality: concept of, 124; cost of, 128, 140–142, 175; education and, xxxii, 285–298; government agencies for, xxx; measurement of, 137; new economics and, 131; new problems in, x–xx; ombudsman for, xxix; present value of, xxv–xxvi; public action and, xxvi; social value and, xxiii; threats to, 142

Everglades, Florida, wildlife in, 164

Experimental City, 219–231; architecture in, 228; fume sewers in, 227; funds for research in, 230–231; as laboratory, 224; location of, 229; optimum environment in, 228; people factor in, 224; planning in, 225–226; population size in, 219; public utilities in, 227; waste control in, 220

Factory wastes, fishing and, 169
Fairfax County, Va., "new town" in, 197–200
Farmers, displacement of, 61–62
Farming: in Experimental City, 229–230; land value and, 60; output per farm, 61; productivity in, 56–66; technology and, 112–113; unemployment and, 62; *see also* Agriculture
Farm land, as resource, 112
Farm problem, as national problem, 63
Farmsteads, deterioration of, xx, 162–163
Federal government: financial support from, 176–177; and national parks program, 262–264; new towns and, 191–192
Federal Housing Authority, 194
Federal Interstate Highway Act, 74
Federal Land Agency, 268
Federal Power Commission, 122
Federal system, in new economics, 153; *see also* under U.S.
Feedback system, 21; in land-grant colleges, 25; and pollution control, 279
Fertilizer: from garbage disposal, 220; pollution from, 57–58, 84; productivity and, 62; *see also* Nitrogen fertilizers
"Finagle factor," in new economics, 148–150
Fisher, Joseph L., xxv–xxvi, 31–38, 301
Fishing, factory wastes and, 169
Flexner, Abraham, 275
Flood control dams, xxi, 74, 81
Food and Agriculture Organization, 15
Food production, resource depletion in, 112; technology and, 64–65
Ford Foundation, 197
Forest growth: as long-range resource, 113; rate of, 109–110
Forest land: amount devoted as, 114–115; in Experimental City, 229
Forest products, demand for, 110
Forests, despoiling of, 162–163
Fosberg, Ray, 14, 18
Fossil fuel, reserves of, 109; *see also* Coal
Fourier, Charles, 213–214

Freeways, environment decay and, xix, 75
Fuel oil, pollution from, xii
Full-employment economy, 141
Fuller, R. Buckminster, 219
Fume sewers, in Experimental City, 227

Galbraith, John Kenneth, 144, 295
Garbage disposal, fertilizer from, 220; *see also* Disposal plants
Garbage dumps, San Francisco, 77
Gas chromatography, 17
Gasoline consumption, 1940–65, xiv–xv
Gause, G. F., 10, 134–135
General education, modifying of concepts in, 283; *see also* Education
General Electric Company, 196, 211
Ghettos: civil disorders in, 210; community planning and, 202; dirt and despair in, xx; quality of life in, 271
Gilliam, Harold, xxvii–xxix, xxxvi, 67–82, 301
Glass bottles, pollution by, xxix
Golden Gate Park, 68, 78, 80
Government programs, attitudes toward, 154; *see also* Federal; U.S. (adj.)
Grand Canyon National Park, 170–171, 179, 246
Greenbelt Towns, 207, 213
Greenhouse effect, 20
Griffin, C. W., Jr., 45
Gross National Product: atmosphere pollution and, 137; commodity use and, xvi–xvii; consumption pattern and, xvii; education and, 141; environmental improvement costs and, 140; leisure and, 255; natural resources and, 149; paper industry and, xxiii; physical environment and, 140; pollution and, xi, 140–145; population and, xiii, xviii–xix; resources and, 136
Growth, available space and, 180; *see also* Population; Population growth
Gulf Oil Company, 193, 199
Gutheim, Frederick, xxxvi, 191–214, 301

Habitat, conservation and, 8
Hackensack Meadows (N.J.) development, 208
Hahn, Marshall, 198

Index

Hammond, E. Cuyler, 40, 51

Hansen, Alvin, xvii

Harvard Graduate School of Design, 186

Haussmann, Baron Georges Eugène, 292

Hayes, Rutherford B., 110

Health, pollution control and, xxiv–xxv, 13, 222

Heart disease, air pollution and, 47

Heckscher, August, 198

Helicopter-lift hospital units, 226

Herbicides, poisonous, xxxi

High-density living, pollution from, 223

Highway engineering, as single-purpose planning, 75–76

Highways, land depletion through, 114, 162

Hill, Whytham, 4

Hippies, 255

Historic buildings, preservation of, 247

Historic Center, concept of, 249

Historic sites, as recreation areas, 246

Hobby farms, 229–230

Holgate, Martin, 16

Homeostasis, in ecosystem, 21

Hoover Dam, 33

Housing and Home Finance Agency, 191

Housing developments, 193–194; new towns and, 212

Howard, Ebenezer, 213

Hudson Institute, 15

Human society: individual qualities in, 23–24; level of biological integration in, 21–23; points-of-view approach to, 23

Hume, David, 134

Huxley, Julian, 3–4

Hydrocarbons, from automobile engines, xxii, xxxiii

Hydrogen sulphide, 295

Hydro-power production, recreation and, 170

Ibans, of Sarawak, 254

Imperial Dam, 33

Income tax, new economics and, 157; see also Internal Revenue Service

Indian Dunes National Lakeshore, 269

Indian tribal lands, new towns and, 207

Industrial economy, resource allocation in, 171

Industrial production, environment decay and, 172

Information: university courses and, 278–279; utility of, in Experimental City, 225–227

Insect control, xxxi

Institutions, modifying or internalizing of, 128

Insulating belt, for Experimental City, 229

Interfaith Housing Corporation, 200

Internal Revenue Service, urban environment and, 182, 226

International Biological Program, 7

International Telegraph and Telephone Corp., 202

International Union for Conservation of Nature and Natural Resources, 9

Irrigation: environment decay and, 34, 59; water resources and, 116

Janss Corporation, 194

Jefferson, Thomas, xxxiv

Jet plane, and supersonic jet, 112

Jevons, William Stanley, 134

John Hancock Life Insurance Company, 193

Kaplan, Marshall, 191, 194, 196

Kennedy, John F., 206

Kerner Commission report on violence, 210

Kerr, Clark, 275

Kitimat, British Columbia, 203

Klutznick, Philip, 194

Kneese, Allen, 141

Krutilla, John, ix, xxxvi, 161–172, 301

Labor-saving devices, 255

Lakes, restoration of, xxx

Land; classification system for, 245–249; damage to, 5; as ecological community, 5; farm value of, 5; leasing of, in Experimental City, 228–229; paving over of, 70, 114; public good and, xxxiv; recreational use of, 37, 113–114, 263, 267–269; for tree raising, 114–115; urban and rural ethics of, 83–85; urban development and, 60; as wealth symbol, 83

Land drainage, wildlife and, 59

Land ethics: Brandywine experience in, 87–90; urban and rural, 83–85

Land Grant Act, 275

Land-grant colleges, feedback in, 25
Landowner: megalopolitan, 86–88; mentality of, 83–84
Landsberg, Hans H., ix–xxxvii, 107–129, 302
Landscape, degradation of, 161
Landscaping and landscape design: aesthetic quality in, 91–94, 166; American vs. European, 162; architecture and, 244–245; in California, 79; conservation and, 186; diversity in, 93–94; psychology and sociology of, 92
Land use: as aesthetic problem, 91; California standards of, 79; government regulation of, 90; planning agencies for, xxix; self-determination in, 88
Land-Use Review Commission, California, 78
Lehrer, Tom, 119
Leisure, need for, 254–255; *see also* Recreation
Leopold, Aldo, 4, 6, 10, 91
Leslie, T. E., 16
Levels of integration, concept of, 20–22
Levitt, William J., 194
Levitt and Sons, Inc., 202
Levittown, Pa., as industrial town, 211
Liberal arts colleges, 275
Liberal sciences, university programs in, 277–279
Life, quality of, 179–180, 271
Linn, Karl, 260
Litchfield Park, Ariz., 204
Littering, 162
Little, Arthur D., Inc., 197
Litton, R. Burton, Jr., xxvi, 91–94, 302
Locke, John, 134
Lodge, James, 219
Logging activities, 161–163
London County Council, 203
Los Angeles, smog in, 222, 278, 296
Lotka, Alfred J., 16
Lowenthal, David, 139
Lubin, Carol, 197
Lumber industry: growth of, 110; quality in, 121
Lung cancer, air pollution and, 46

McAteer, Eugene, 77
McDermott, Walsh, 226
McHarg, Ian, 14

McKissick, Floyd B., 207, 209
McLuhan, Marshall, 31, 205
Maine: pollution control in, 177; wildlife in, 163
Malthus, Thomas Robert, ix
Mannheim, Karl, 256
Manufacturing, recycling in, 221–222
Manure, as soil additive, 58
Marble Canyon Dam, 170
Marbut, C. F., 4
Marshall, Alfred, 145
Maryland, University of, 195
Maslach, George J., xxxii, xxxvi, 275–284, 302
Massachusetts Institute of Technology, 277
Massasoit State Park, 246
Mass production, recycling and, 221
Mather, Stephen, 245
Megalopolis: landowner ethics in, 86–87; as poisoner of cities, 84–85
Metals: quality in, 121; resources and stockpiles of, 115–116
Michigan Survey Research Center, 154
Mill, John Stuart, 134
Milliman, J. W., 127
Mill villages, 213
Minerals, shortage of, 110–111
Mining towns, 36, 213
Minnesota, University of, 230
Minority: good vs. bad, 147; triumph of, over masses, 147–160
Minority rights, in environment control, 178–179
Model cities programs, 202–203, 219
Monetary quantification, in environment quality, 125
Morison, Robert S., xxxii, xxxiv, xxxvi, 285–298, 302
Morrill, Justin P., 275
Morris, William, 248
Morse, Chandler, 110, 112
Mueller, Eva, 154
Muir, John, 262–263
Multiple-use plan, in outdoor recreation programs, 266–267
Multipurpose analysis, 81
Multipurpose planning, 68
Mumford, Lewis, 67, 133, 237, 253

Napa River, feasibility study of, 80
Napa Valley (Calif.) environment policy, 68, 73–74
National Advisory Commission on Civil Disorders, 210

Index

National Conference on Outdoor Recreation, 254
National Environmental Research Council, 9
National Foundation for Poliomyelitis, 291
National Institutes of Health, 226
National parks: attitude toward, 154–155; crowding in, 180, 235, 262; daily visitors, 1940–65, xiv–xv; development of, 37; outdoor recreation in, 262–263; per capita visit increase in, xii; user charge in, 144
National Parks Association, 14
National Recreation Survey, 236
Natural beauty, ingredients of, 36
Natural gas, as boiler fuel, 122
Natural resources, as unique commodity, 167; see also Resources
Natural selection, 10
Natural world, transformation of, ix
Nature, expanded contact with, 138–139
Nature Conservancy program, Great Britain, 8–9
Neutra, Richard, 140
New cities: development and planning of, 210–211; population of, 209; see also New towns
New economics: cost-benefit analysis in, 148; educational level and, 152; mission of, 153–154; of natural resources, 147–160; as politics, 147; urbanization and, 149
New England, mill villages in, 213
Newman, John Henry, Cardinal, 275
New rivers, as recreation areas, 266
Newton, Sir Isaac, 134
New towns, 191–214; activities by states in, 208; European, 212–213; geographical factors in, 208; housing in, 212; innovation in, 204–205; legislative management of, 193–194; parochialism in, 203; population of, 209; potential of, 204; representative list of, 192; risk and labor in, 195; transportation in, 206–207; see also Experimental City; New cities
New York City, Mayor's Task Force in, 53–54
New York–New Jersey Co-Operative Commission on Interstate Air Pollution, 47–49
New York State Urban Development Corporation, 208

Niche, Elton's concept of, 8, 10
Nicholson, E. M., 16
Nielson, C. Overgaard, 7
Nitrogen fertilizers: pollution by, xii, xvii; use of, 1940–65, xiv–xv; see also Fertilizer
Nitrogen oxides, from automobile exhaust, xxii
Noise pollution, 222–223
Nonfuel minerals, shortage of, 110
Nonmarketed goods, importance of, 114
North Atlantic Regional Water Resources Study, 144
Northrop, F. S. C., 134
Nuclear power plant, Bodega Head Area, Calif., 69–70
Nuclear reactors, contamination by, xxxi, 20, 23, 166

Oakland, Calif., city planning in, 208–209
Oakland East (Calif.), community project, 203, 208–210
Odum, Eugene P. and Howard T., 7
Ogden, Dan, 253 n
Ohio River, pollution of, 289
Ohio River Sanitary Commission, xxviii
Oliver, Richard A., 74
Olmstead, Frederick Law, 258, 292
Ombudsman, for environment control, xxix
Ore, quality of, 121
Osborn, Fairfield, 9
Outdoor recreation: balance in, 261–262; in cities, 257–258; diversification in, 264–265; economics of, 269–271; in hyper-productive society, 263–271; land acquisition in, 267–269; multiple-use factor in, 266–267; need for, 253, 255; shoreline and coastal waters for, 265–266; in suburbs and countryside, 260–261; value and cost of, 269–271; variety in, 259–260; see also Recreation
Outdoor Recreation Resources Review Commission, 238, 245, 256
Outdoor shelter, architecture for, 239
Ovington, Derrick, 7
Owen, Robert, 213–214
Ozone, xxxiii

Pacific Gas & Electric Co., 69–71, 81
Paley Commission, 110–111

Panofsky, Erwin, 248
Papageorgiou, Alexis, xxxvi, 235–250, 302
Paper consumption, pollution through, xii, 128, 132; quantities, 1940–65, xiv–xv
Paper industry, Gross National Product and, xxii–xxiii
Parker Dam, 33
Parking lots, 114
Parkinson's Law, 279
Park Movement, 245
Parks: architecture of, 237–238; in cities, 258, 262; visual problem of, 239; *see also* National parks
Patterson, Robert W., xxvii, xxxvi, 174–187, 302
Pennsylvania, University of, 14
Pesonen, David, 70
Pesticides: concentration of, in man and animals, xxxiv; ecological research and, 17; gains vs. losses from, 125; poisoning and pollution from, xxxi–xxxiii, 58, 125
Phalansteries, 214
Ph.D. degree, application of, 282, 293
Physical nature, man in theory of, 134
Pinchot, Gifford, ix–x, 4, 91, 107, 292
Planning, single-purpose, *see* Single-purpose planning
Plastics: forest products and, 110; pollution through, xii; production of, 1940–65, xiv
Platt, John R., 112
Playgrounds, in cities, 260
Points of view, concept of, 20–22
Political action, economic analysis and, xxii–xxix
Political problems, environment control and, xxvi–xxvii
Politics: conservation and, 176, 181–182; ecology and, 10; new economics as, 147; urban dispersal and, 224
Polluting materials, use of, xii
Pollution: affluence and, xi, xx, 166, 295; in agriculture, 57–61; air, *see* Air pollution; before World War II, x; benefit of, to polluter, xxiv; causes of, xi; concentration as cause of, 223; cost of, xxiv, 124, 143, 175–177; as disease, 222; ecological balance and, 35; knowledge and information of, 278; political boundaries and, xxvi; population and, xi, 17, 178; quantum jump in, x; tech-nological fix for, xxix; university courses in, 277–278; water, *see* Water pollution; *see also* Environment; Environment decay; Pollution control
Pollution control: cost of, xxiv, 124, 143, 176–177; in Experimental City, 227; new technology for, xxxi-xxxii; quantification and standards in, 126; regressive program in, 142–143; regulation in, 158; *see also* Environment control
Population: ecology and, 7; environment decay and, xi, 17, 178; of Experimental City, 219; future increase in, xx; Gross National Product and, xiii, xviii-xix; human society as, 21–22; land use and, 114; level of integration in, 21; model of, 21; pollution and, xi, 17, 178; rural-urban distribution of, 84; urbanism and, 12; wastes of, 219–220
Population density: changes in, xix; land use and, 114; recreation and, 239
Population growth: economic growth and, xvii–xix; and Gross National Product, xviii–xix; pollution and, xi, 17, 178; resource use and, 111
Porterfield, Robert, 198
Poverty, environment control and, 142
Powell, John Wesley, ix
Prairie chicken, disappearance of, 164
Predator animals, disappearance of, 163–164
Prediction, in environment control, xxii
President's Recreation Advisory Council, 79
Production: meaningful activity in, 138; pollution from, 172
Professional schools: modified concepts in, 280–283; traditions in, 292–293
Prosperity, consumption patterns and, xvii; *see also* Affluence
Protestant ethic, 254
Psychosomatic diseases, environment and, 13
Psychologist, and landscape design, 92
Public health, in Experimental City, 226
Pusey, Nathan, 275, 277

Radioactive fallout, xxxi, 20, 23, 166

Index

Rampart Dam, Yukon River, 14
Reconnaissance, ecological, 15–16
Recreation: architecture for, 235–250; in cities, 257–258; ecosystem and, 162; federal policy in, 254; hydro power and, 170; land as, 113–114; national parks and, 180; need for, 137–138; outdoor, *see* Outdoor recreation; planning for, 236; pollution and, 178; population and, 236; public attitude toward, 179; resources and, 113–114, 271
Recreation areas: conservation and, 181; land classification for, 245–249
Recreation facilities: attitude toward, 154–155; Gross National Product and, 137
Recreation systems, development of, 37
Recycling, in manufacturing processes, 221–222
Redwoods, preservation of, 159, 271
Resources: conservation of, 122, 184; Conservation Movement and, 148; disaggregation of, 108–109; economic assignment of, 171; educational, *see* Educational resources; evaluation of, 107; of future, 112; imports and, 118; monopoly and oligopoly in, 145; new economics of, 131–145, 147–160; political considerations in, 127; population growth and, 111; quantity and quality of, 107–129; recreational, 113–114, 271; re-evaluation of, 149; side-effect syndrome in, 123; technology and, 110–112, 119–121; upgrading of, 109
Resource industries, labor and, 109
Resources for the Future, 112–114, 186
Resource use, quantum jump in, 112
Reston, Va., "new town" at, 191–193, 197, 200–204, 211
Reston Foundation for Community Progress, 198
Revelle, Roger, ix–xxxvii, 253–271, 302
Riney, Thane, 15
Ripley, S. Dillon, xxxvi, 20–26, 302
River Basin Commissions, xxviii
Rivers: damming of, xxi; pollution of, 162, 169, 289; as recreation areas, 266
Roadside businesses, environment decay and, xix

Roosevelt, Theodore, 292
Rouse, James W., 194, 196, 198–199, 205
Rubber tires, deterioration of, xxiv
Rudd, Robert, 17
Ruhr River Associations, Germany, xxvii–xxviii
Rural land ethic, 84–85
Rural landscape, culture and, 161
Rural-urban population distribution, 84

San Andreas Fault, utility company excavations near, 70
San Francisco: freeway controversy in, 75–76; planning in, 68
San Francisco Bay, filling of, 76–78
San Francisco Bay Conservation and Development Commission, 81
San Juan River, N.M., 34
Satellite technology, resource use and, 112
Satterthwaite, Ann, 253 n
Sauer, Carl, 6
Save San Francisco Bay Association, 77
Scheffey, Andrew, 253 n
Schurz, Carl, 14, 110
Scientific Age, 108
Scitovsky, Tibor, 132
Sears, Paul, 9
Sewage treatment: education in, 286; in Experimental City, 227–228
Sewage treatment plants: cost of, 175; federal funds for, 176–177; nutrients for, xxx; technology and, 141
Schantz, Homer, 4, 6
Shelford, Victor, 4
Shopping centers, in Experimental City, 226
Side-effect syndrome, in resource conservation, 123
Sierra Club, 14
Silent Spring (Carson), xxxiii
Simmel, Georg, 132
Simon, Robert E., Jr., 193–194, 196–197, 199, 205–207
Single-purpose planning: defined, 67–68; fallacy of, 67–82
Slobodkin, Larry, 7
Slum clearance, 195; vs. urban dispersal, 223–224
Smithsonian Institution, 26
Smog, Los Angeles, xix, 278, 296

Smoking: and air pollution, 46; response to warnings on, 120
Smokestacks, fly ash from, 220
Snow, John, 292
Social change, conservation and, 174
Social values, measurement of, xxiii
Sociologist, in landscape design, 92–93
Solomon, M. E., 16
Soot removal, xxiv
"Soul City," 207, 209
Space, protection of, 179–180
Spilhaus, Athelstan, xxxi, xxxvi, 147, 204, 219–231, 302
Spurr, S. H., 14
Standard of living, environment and, 295
State Park Commission, Calif., 69
State park systems, 37, 261–262
Steady-state system, 21
Steam power plants, 122
Stein, Clarence S., 197
Steward Air Force Base, 207
Straight, Michael, 198
Stratton, Julius A., 277
Stress, ecology and, 12
Strong, Ann Louise, xxvii, xxxvi, 83–90
Suburbs, recreation in, 260–261
Sulphur: from coal, xxiv, xxix; from paper mills, 132
Sulphur dioxide, control of, 220–221; from electric power plants, xii, xvii
Summerson, John, 248–249
Sunset International Petroleum Corp., 194
Supersonic transport plane, 112
Supreme Court, U.S., 122

Teachers Insurance and Annuity Association, 193
Technological "fix," pollution control through, xxix
Technology: economic rootlessness and, 141; education and, 277; environment control and, 129; environment quality and, x–xx, xxxi, 166, 171, 294; mechanical slaves and, 219; pollution and, 17, 166; resources and, 110–112, 119–121; in Scientific Age, 108; water pollution and, 119
Teeters, Robert, 253 n
Television, in Experimental City, 220, 225

Teller, Azriel, xxiii–xxiv, xxxvi, 39–54, 302
Tilden, Freeman, 245
Timber resources, 110; see also Forest(s)
Tourists, national park crowding and, 180, 235–236, 262
Towns, new, see New towns
Train, Russell, 12
Transportation: in Experimental City, 227; new towns and, 206–207
Trash piles, xx, xxix, 162
Trees, land devoted to raising of, 114–115; see also Forest(s)
Trobriand Islanders, work and play of, 254
Truman, Harry S, 110

Udall, Stewart L., 67, 199, 207
UNESCO, 14
United States Army Corps of Engineers, 33, 73, 78, 174, 194, 207
United States Atomic Energy Commission
U.S. Bureau of the Census, 226
U.S. Bureau of Reclamation, 207
U.S. Geological Survey, 205
U.S. Department of Health, Education, and Welfare, 176
U.S. Department of Housing and Urban Development, 191, 202, 206–209
U.S. Department of the Interior, 8, 108
U.S. Fish and Wildlife Service, 165
U.S. Forest Service, 4
U.S. Public Health Service, xxviii
U.S. Supreme Court, 122
Universities: curricula in, 275–276; environmental programs in, 285–298; support from, 26; teaching resources of, 281–282
Uranium resources, 115
Urban America, Inc., 195
Urban dispersal, need for, 223
Urbanization: ancient buildings and, 248–249; land use in, 114; new economics and, 149–150; new towns and, 191–214; population and, 12; resources and, 149; see also Cities
Urban land ethic, 83
Urban renewal, 249
Urban Ventures, 207
User charge, in national parks, 144

Index

Utilitarian economics, 135
Utility, concept of, 135

Vacations, pollution from, xii
Vogt, William, 7

Warning system, for air pollution control, 47
Washington, D.C., recreation facilities in, 259
Washington-Baltimore area megalopolis, 200
Washington-Boston metropolitan area, 191
Washington Center for Metropolitan Studies, 197
Waste: computer model of, 223; control of, at source, 220–221
Waste disposal, new technology and, xxxi–xxxii; see also Sewage disposal
Waste heat, xxxi
Water: contexts of, 31–38; deteriorating quality of, 117–118; for drinking, 119; engineering efficiency and, 32; quantity-quality relationship in, 122; regional differences in supply of, 117
Water conservation, matrix of, 31–32
Water development, cost-benefit ratio in, 33
Water pollution: cost of, 150, 176; cost-benefit analysis in, 150; new economics and, 147; public attitude toward, 155; recycling and, 221; technology and, 119
Water resources, use and, 31–32, 116–117
Watersheds, jurisdiction over, xxvii
Water supply: differences in, by regions, 117; in Experimental City, 227–228

Water treatment, costs in, 126, 150, 176
Weaver, Robert C., 206
Weber, Max, 254
Wheat, in food aid programs, 65–66
White, Gilbert F., 139
White House Conference on Natural Beauty, 74
Wild animals, destruction of, ix–x, xxxiii, 164–165; see also Wildlife
Wildavsky, Aaron, xxvii, xxix, xxxvi, 147–159, 303
Wilderness, in American culture, 161
Wilderness Society, 14
Wildlife: destruction of, ix–x, 164–165; land drainage and, 59; in pre-Civil War era, 163; reproduction of, 163
Wildlife management, beginnings of, 4
Wildlife refuges, 8, 155, 163, 264, 294
Wirth, Conrad L., 235
Wollman, Nathaniel, xxiii, xxxvi, 131–145, 147, 253 n
Woodlands, recycling in, 7
Woods Hole Oceanographic Institute, 253 n
Wordsworth, William, 288
Work: defined, 137–138; play and, 254–275
WPA County Guides, 261
Wren, Christopher, 292
Wright, Henry, 197

Yellowstone National Park, 235, 246
Ylvisaker, Paul, 209
Yosemite National Park, 262–263
Yukon River, damming of, 14

Zoning: and conservation, 183–184; on regional or state level, 72

314